Renal Function

Renal Function

Mechanisms Preserving Fluid and Solute Balance in Health

■   ■   ■   ■   ■

Third Edition

Heinz Valtin, M.D.
**Andrew C. Vail Professor Emeritus and
Constantine and Joyce Hampers Professor of
Physiology, Dartmouth Medical School,
Hanover, New Hampshire**

James A. Schafer, Ph.D.
**Professor of Physiology and Biophysics, and
Medicine, University of Alabama School
of Medicine, Birmingham, Alabama**

Little, Brown and Company
Boston/New York/Toronto/London

Library of Congress Cataloging-in-Publication Data

Valtin, Heinz.
    Renal function / Heinz Valtin, James A. Schafer. — 3rd ed.
        p. cm.
    Rev. ed. of: Renal function, mechanisms preserving fluid and solute balance in health / Heinz Valtin. 2nd ed. c1983.
    Includes bibliographical references and index.
    ISBN 0-316-89560-1
    1. Kidneys—Physiology. I. Schafer, J. A. (James A.), 1941-   . II. Valtin, Heinz, 1926. Renal function, mechanisms preserving fluid and solute balance in health. III. Title.
    [DNLM: 1. Kidney—physiology. 2. Water-Electrolyte Balance. WJ 300 V215r 1994]
QP249.V34 1994
612.4'63—dc20
DNLM/DLC
for Library of Congress   94-13503
                                                    CIP

Printed in the United States of America
SEM

Second Printing

Editorial: Evan R. Schnittman, Kristin Odmark
Production Editor: Karen Feeney
Copyeditor: David Bemelmans
Cover Designer: L. D. Willis & P. Newbery

To

Nancy, Tom, Alison & Steve

and to

Margy, Jimmy, Kirsti

Contents

■   ■   ■   ■   ■

Preface

■   ■   ■   ■   ■

After 20 years of gratifying success, it was time to render this book suitable for biomedical education in the next century. The book therefore has a coauthor, a new trim size, color illustrations, major concepts emphasized in boxes that appear in the margins, clinical vignettes, and shorter lists of references at the end of each chapter. More extensive lists have been placed in an electronic repository (directions on how to access that repository are given at the end of Chapter 1, under Suggested Readings). Major topics that have been added or given new emphasis include: epithelial transport, including channels and carriers and their molecular structure and function; cellular biology and signal transduction; the functional meaning of nephron heterogeneity and of anatomical relationships; endothelial factors; and the multifaceted regulation of sodium balance on the one hand and of water balance on the other. While all topics have been brought up to date, most changes have involved refinements rather than new concepts.

As was the case with the second edition, it has been our aim to shorten the book rather than lengthen it, and for everything that we have added we have tried to delete something of equal length. Throughout, we have made every effort to restrict ourselves to the general principles that underlie scientific clinical practice. Popular features of past editions, such as problems and detailed answers, have been retained, as has an extensive list of normal values, which can be found in the appendix at the end of the book. Once more, we have tried to place all information in its functional context. Thus, instead of a separate chapter devoted to hormones, we have described renin-angiotensin-aldosterone with renal hemodynamics and sodium balance, the antidiuretic hormone with water balance, and so forth.

Request for critique: Suggestions from students and teachers for improving this text have been both welcome and helpful. We renew the invitation for this, the third edition.

Finally, the senior author (H.V.) expresses his heartfelt thanks to a loyal readership!

H.V.
J.A.S.

Acknowledgments

■　　　■　　　　　■　　　　　■　　　　■

If this text is largely free of error, it is because we have been able to call on colleagues for advice. That advice has come in two forms: Some friends and colleagues, like L. Gabriel Navar and F. John Gennari, checked entire chapters; others were called on for quick, on-the-spot consultations. Among the latter, we express our gratitude to Jill W. Verlander, S. Marsh Tenney, C. Craig Tisher, Edwin A. Rutsky, Eugene E. Nattie, Mark A. Knepper, Robert D. Harris, Brian R. Edwards, Kirk P. Conrad, Malcolm B. Brown, and Donald Bartlett, Jr. In listing names, one always lives in fear of having forgotten someone; if that has happened, we apologize to that person(s) and ask that they please call the omission to our attention.

Because most illustrations in the original literature are designed for a research-oriented readership and therefore are often not suitable for an introductory text, we have redesigned or modified all line drawings save two (Fig. 3-5 and Fig. 7-2D). Our drawings were rendered in final form by *Art & Science*, by Reed Detar at Dartmouth, and by the Production Department at Little, Brown and Company. We thank several friends and colleagues for contributing original photographs and electron micrographs; their names are given in the legends to the figures.

We are grateful to David Bemelmans for sensitive and economical copyediting. Kristin Odmark and Evan Schnittman coordinated the entire project, and Karen Feeney skillfully shepherded the book through production.

Renal Function

Components of Renal Function

1

■   ■   ■   ■   ■

The lay view of renal function is that the kidneys remove waste liquids and potentially harmful end products of metabolism, such as urea, uric acid, sulfates, and phosphates. While this is true, it should be emphasized that an equally important function is the conservation of substances that are essential to life. Such substances include water, sugars, amino acids, and electrolytes such as sodium, potassium, bicarbonate, and chloride. Therefore, the kidneys should be viewed as regulatory organs that selectively excrete and conserve water and numerous chemical compounds and thereby help to preserve the constancy of the internal environment.

A castaway at sea may survive for three weeks without drinking water, and a man lost in the desert may survive from two to four days without water or salt. Conversely, a healthy individual frequently tolerates dietary excesses of fluid and salt. The reason that such extreme conditions can be endured lies primarily in the renal control of salt and water excretion and conservation. The renal adjustments must be relatively rapid if they are to preserve life. In fact they are brought into play within minutes or at most a few hours after an individual has been subjected to an environmental challenge.

ANATOMY

The major gross anatomical features of the mammalian kidney are illustrated in Figure 1-1. The kidney consists of a *cortex* surrounding a central region, the *medulla,* and a *pelvis* that connects with the *ureter.* The medulla is divided into an outer and an inner portion (Fig. 1-2), the latter, or *inner medulla,* having one or more *papillae* (tips), depending on the species. Each papilla empties into an open-ended pouch, the *minor calyx,* which, in turn, connects with a *major calyx.* The calyces are extensions of the ureter; they conduct tubular fluid from the collecting ducts into the ureter and thence into the bladder. The *outer medulla* is further subdivided into an *outer stripe* and an *inner stripe* (Fig. 1-2). The *renal artery* enters the kidney alongside the ureter, branching to become progressively the *interlobar artery,* the *arcuate artery,* the *cortical radial artery,* and then the *afferent arteriole* that leads to the *glomerular capillary network.* The venous system has subdivisions with similar designations, terminating in the *renal vein,* which also courses beside the ureter.

The renal blood flow is unique in that it traverses two capillary networks in series: (1) the *glomerular capillary network,* and (2)

■ **Blood Supply** ■
to Kidneys

Renal Blood Flow (RBF)
~1,300 mL/min
(~25% of cardiac output)

Renal Plasma Flow (RPF)
~715 mL/min
(when hematocrit = 45%)

Unique Feature
Two capillary networks in series
   glomerular capillary
   network
   peritubular capillary
   network

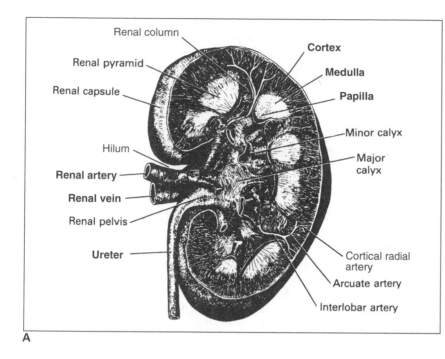

Renal column
Renal pyramid
Renal capsule
Hilum
Renal artery
Renal vein
Renal pelvis
Ureter

Cortex
Medulla
Papilla
Minor calyx
Major calyx
Cortical radial artery
Arcuate artery
Interlobar artery

A

Figure 1-1. A. Sagittal section of a human kidney, showing the major gross anatomical features. The renal columns are extensions of cortical tissue between the medullary areas. Not shown is the adrenergic nerve supply, not only to the large renal vessels but also to the vascular and tubular components of the nephron. Redrawn and very slightly modified from Braus, H. *Anatomie des Menschen,* Vol. 2. Berlin: Springer, 1924.

B. Vasculature of the kidney from a desert rodent (*Meriones*), showing: the cortex with numerous glomeruli; the outer medulla, containing capillary networks, and vascular bundles with vasa recta; and the inner medulla, containing vasa recta. (For further orientation, see Fig. 1-2B.) The vessels were filled with silicone rubber (Microfil) by arterial injection. Courtesy of L. Bankir.

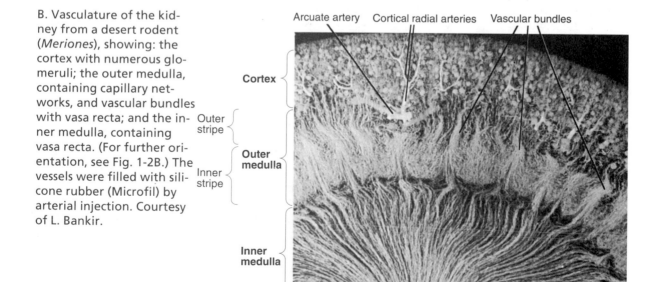

Arcuate artery   Cortical radial arteries   Vascular bundles

Cortex
Outer stripe
Outer medulla
Inner stripe
Inner medulla

B

the *peritubular capillary network.* The first, which together with Bowman's capsule forms the *renal corpuscle,* lies between the afferent and efferent arterioles. The second lies distal to the efferent arteriole and surrounds the tubules. Because the blood pressure is dropped not only by resistance in the afferent arteriole, but then further by resistance in the efferent arteriole (see Fig. 6-1), hydrostatic pressure in the peritubular capillary network is less than that in the glomerular capillary network.

The term *renal blood flow* (RBF) refers to the total amount of blood flowing into the kidney via the renal artery. The blood flow out of the kidney via the renal vein is very slightly less than the arterial inflow; the difference between the two flows is the urine flow, which is negligibly small compared to the total blood flow. In adult humans about 1,300 mL of blood (i.e., about 25% of the cardiac output) flows through the two kidneys each minute, even though, together, they constitute less than 0.5% of the total body weight. About 1,299 mL of blood leaves through the renal veins each minute, so a normal urine flow is about 1 mL per minute. *Renal plasma flow* (RPF) refers to the amount of plasma that traverses either the renal artery or the renal vein per unit time. Obviously, if the hematocrit (Hct) is 45%, RPF constitutes 55% of RBF.

The Nephron

The nephron, or functional unit of the kidney, consists of a glomerular capillary network that is surrounded by Bowman's capsule, a proximal tubule, a loop of Henle, a distal tubule, and a collecting duct (Fig. 1-2A). Each of the tubular parts can be subdivided as shown in Figure 1-2A and as summarized in the adjacent box. Together, the adult human kidneys comprise roughly two million such functional units, which provide tremendous reserve. At rest, one can survive on about one-tenth this amount of functioning renal tissue, and one can lead an active life even though about 75% of the tissue has been destroyed.

Superficial and Juxtamedullary Nephrons

There are two major types of nephron (Fig. 1-2A and B). The superficial nephron arises in the outer parts of the cortex, it has a short loop of Henle that reaches varying distances into the outer medulla, and its efferent arteriole branches into the peritubular capillary network that surrounds the tubular segments belonging to its own and other nephrons. This capillary network nourishes the tubular cells, picks up substances that have been reabsorbed from the tubules, and brings substances to the tubules for secretion.

■ **Major Parts of** ■
the Nephron

Renal Corpuscle
Glomerulus (glomerular capillaries)
Bowman's capsule

Proximal Tubule
Proximal convoluted tubule
Proximal straight tubule

Loop of Henle
Thin descending limb
Thin ascending limb
Thick ascending limb

Juxtaglomerular Apparatus (JGA)
Macula densa cells
Granular endothelial cells

Distal Convoluted Tubule
Collecting Duct
Cortical collecting duct
Outer medullary collecting duct
Inner medullary collecting duct

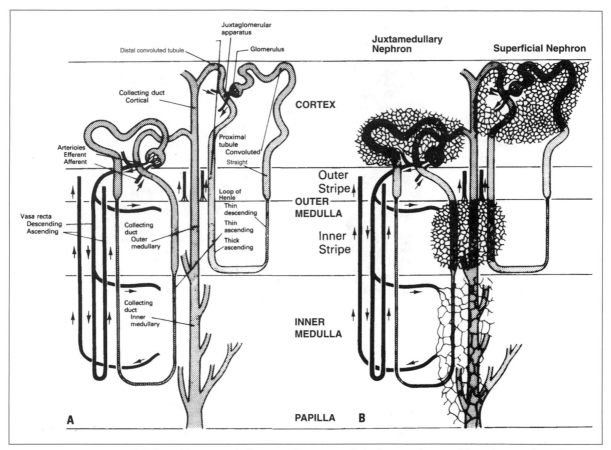

Figure 1-2. A. Superficial and juxtamedullary nephrons, and their vasculature. The glomerulus plus the surrounding Bowman's capsule are known as the *renal corpuscle.* The beginning of the proximal tubule—called the *urinary pole*—lies opposite the vascular pole, where the afferent and efferent arterioles enter and leave the glomerulus. The early distal tubule is always apposed to the vascular pole belonging to the same nephron; the juxtaglomerular apparatus is located at the point of contact (see also Fig. 1-3).

B. Capillary networks have been superimposed on the nephrons illustrated in (A). Both diagrams are highly schematic (for a more accurate portrayal, see Beeuwkes, R., III, and Bonventre, J. V. *Am. J. Physiol.* 229:695, 1975), and they do not accurately reflect some relationships that probably have functional meanings. In the rat, for example, long thin descending limbs of Henle are located next to collecting ducts, and short thin descending limbs are closely associated with the vascular bundles made up of descending and ascending vasa recta in the outer medulla. The drawings are based on Kriz, W., and Bankir, L. A standard nomenclature for structures of the kidney. *Am. J. Physiol.* 254 (Renal Fluid Electrolyte Physiol. 23): F1, 1988.

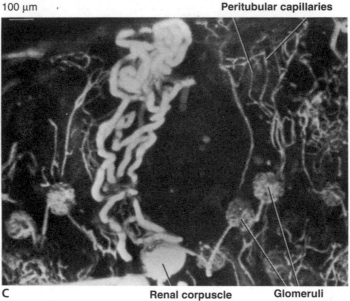

C

Figure 1-2 Continued.   C. The cortex of a dog kidney (photomicrograph) illustrating the highly convoluted course of the proximal tubule. A micropipet (white streak at the lower left) was inserted into Bowman's space, and the convolutions were filled with a silicone rubber compound (Microfil). Other glomeruli, as well as peritubular capillaries, were partially filled with Microfil through an intra-arterial injection. Photograph courtesy of R. Beeuwkes and A. C. Barger.

■ **Two Major Types** ■
of Nephron

Superficial
Renal corpuscle lies in outer cortex
Lower filtration rate
Short loops of Henle
Peritubular capillary network without vasa recta

Juxtamedullary
Renal corpuscle lies deep in cortex, next to medulla
Higher filtration rate
Long loops of Henle
Vasa recta as well as peritubular capillary network

The juxtamedullary nephron arises from the deep cortical regions, i.e., near or 'next to' the medulla, as its name implies. Its glomerulus is larger than that of a superficial nephron, and its loop of Henle extends varying distances into the inner medulla, sometimes all the way to the papilla. Its efferent arteriole continues not only as a peritubular capillary network but also as a series of vascular loops called the vasa recta. The vasa recta descend in bundles to varying depths in the inner medulla. There they break up into capillary networks that surround the collecting ducts and the loops of Henle. The blood then returns to the cortex in ascending vasa recta that run within the vascular bundles. The ratio of outer cortical to juxtamedullary nephrons varies with the species of mammal. In humans, about seven-eighths of all nephrons are superficial and one-eighth are juxtamedullary.

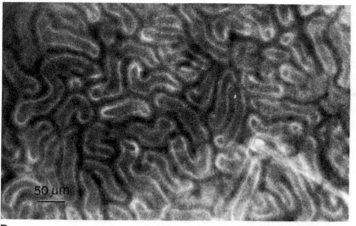

D

Figure 1-2 Continued.   D. The surface of a rat kidney as seen during micropuncture. The so-called bag of worms consists mainly of segments of proximal convolutions as they repeatedly rise to the surface. A few segments of distal convolutions are also visible, but glomeruli are not usually found at the surface of a mammalian kidney. Each tubular segment is surrounded by peritubular capillaries. The light, linear streak in the lower right is a micropipet that has been inserted into a tubular segment. The pipet is out of focus because its shaft lies above the renal surface. Photograph courtesy of J. Schnermann.

Heterogeneity of Nephrons

Initially, those who studied the kidney considered all nephrons to be identical. Then, with an increase in our ability to dissect the nephron, both anatomically and functionally, we have witnessed a progression from recognition of a single nephron to several major types; of four main tubular parts (proximal tubule, loop of Henle, distal tubule, and collecting duct), to several subdivisions of those parts (Fig. 1-2A and B, and box in margin on p. 4); and of homogeneity of cells within a given part to identification of several types of cells within a part or subdivision. Such anatomical and functional differences are referred to as *heterogeneity*. It is likely that the biological reason for heterogeneity is the necessity for the kidney to preserve constancy of the internal environment, and therefore to regulate balance for water and numerous solutes independently of one another (see below, under *Evolution*).

Ultrastructural Differences

Epithelial cells lining the various nephron segments differ in many respects, such as size, number and length of microvilli at the apical (mucosal or luminal) surface (see Fig. 4-1), number of mitochondria, number and extent of basal infoldings, and others. Some of the major differences are shown in Figure 1-3; many fruitful correlations between structure and function have been drawn, and these will be referred to when appropriate.

Juxtaglomerular Apparatus (JGA)

This structure (Fig. 1-3) consists of specialized epithelial cells in the thick ascending limb (the *macula densa cells*), of lacis cells, and of specialized secretory or granular cells at the vascular pole where the afferent and efferent arterioles enter and leave the glomerulus. The JGA thus is a combination of specialized tubular and vascular cells. During embryonic development the distal tubule forms in the area of its own glomerulus so that the macula densa cells come into contact with the lacis cells as well as with the granular cells of the afferent and efferent arterioles belonging to the same nephron. The JGA secretes renin, which is involved in the formation of angiotensin and ultimately in the secretion of aldosterone. It has been postulated that the JGA may be part of a feedback system that helps to regulate the glomerular filtration rate and the renal blood flow, a topic that is considered further in Chapter 6.

PROCESSES INVOLVED IN THE FORMATION OF URINE

The anatomical arrangement of the nephron permits several theories of function; these were hotly debated until the true picture emerged about 70 years ago. In 1842, William Bowman proposed that the glomerular capillaries secrete water, which flushes out solutes secreted by the renal tubules, a view elaborated about 40 years later by Heidenhain. In 1844, Carl Ludwig stated that urine is formed by ultrafiltration of plasma at the glomerulus, and that it merely passes down the nephron without further alteration save for concentration of its solutes by passive reabsorption of water. In 1917, Arthur Cushny modified Ludwig's view by proposing that not only water but also solutes are reabsorbed by the tubules, in "proportions, which are determined by their normal values in the plasma." Cushny denied the possibility of selective tubular secre-

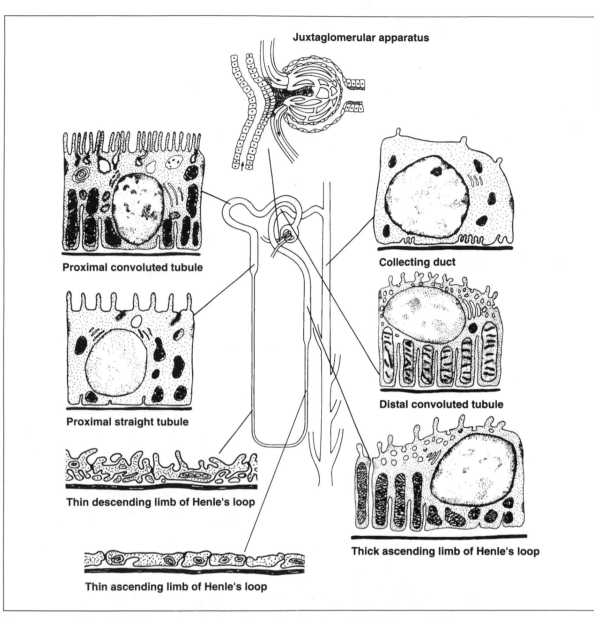

Juxtaglomerular apparatus

Proximal convoluted tubule

Proximal straight tubule

Thin descending limb of Henle's loop

Thin ascending limb of Henle's loop

Collecting duct

Distal convoluted tubule

Thick ascending limb of Henle's loop

Figure 1-3. Diagrams illustrating some of the ultrastructural differences of the major parts of the nephron. Each part can be subdivided into segments, on the basis of ultrastructural and functional features. Also shown is the juxtaglomerular apparatus, which lies at the point of contact between the early distal tubule and the vascular pole of its own glomerulus. Not indicated here is *heterogeneity* of nephrons—i.e., the fact that the anatomical (and functional) features of analogous parts of a nephron (say, the descending limb of Henle's loop) may differ in a superficial nephron from those in a juxtamedullary nephron, or that the features may differ within a given component of a nephron, such as the proximal or distal tubule.

tion because he thought it was a process that would require vitalistic discrimination. It was not until 1923 that E. K. Marshall, Jr., proved that tubular secretion occurs.

We now know that the formation of urine involves a combination of ultrafiltration at the glomerulus, followed by selective tubular reabsorption of water and solutes, and selective tubular secretion of solutes. The subject of renal physiology deals primarily with defining what substances are filtered, reabsorbed, and secreted, in what amounts, in which parts of the nephron and by which cells, by what mechanisms, and to what purpose. Most important is the consideration of how these processes are finely regulated so as to maintain a constant and optimal amount of each solute and of water in the body.

MAGNITUDE OF RENAL FUNCTION

The tremendous amounts of water and of certain solutes that are handled by the kidneys every day are illustrated in Table 1-1. The quantities that are filtered become even more astonishing when one considers that the total amount of water in an adult human is about 42 liters, and the pool of readily exchangeable sodium is about 3,000 mmol. This disparity between total availability of essential substances and the rates at which they are filtered points up the necessity for their conservation through reabsorption. Since the examples listed in Table 1-1, as well as many others, are critical components of the internal environment, it is

Table 1-1. Daily renal turnover of H_2O, Na^+, HCO_3^-, and Cl^- in an adult human.

		Filtered	Excreted	Reabsorbed	Proportion of filtered load that is reabsorbed (%)
H_2O	L/day	180	1.5	178.5	99.2
Na^+	mmol/day	25,000	150	24,850	99.4
HCO_3^-	mmol/day	4,500	2	4,498	99.9+
Cl^-	mmol/day	18,000	150	17,850	99.2
Glucose	mmol/day	800	≈0.5	799.5	99.9+

not surprising that they are reabsorbed so avidly. What may be surprising is that the kidneys should operate in such a seemingly inefficient manner as to filter the substances in the first place. The answer to this apparent paradox probably lies in the evolution of renal function.

Evolution

One possible scheme for the evolution of the kidney is depicted in Figure 1-4. The prochordate ancestor of the vertebrates, such as the acorn worm, may have evolved in the Cambrian Sea about 550 million years ago. These animals drank the sea water, bathed their tissues in it, and then expelled the residue through a simple ciliated conduit, which may be the forerunner of the kidney. The Cambrian Sea probably had a NaCl concentration near to that of present-day mammalian extracellular fluid (Fig. 2-2). As protovertebrates migrated into fresh water, they retained an internal environment of high salinity, and thus their body fluids had a higher osmolality than the freshwater surroundings. The consequent osmotic flow of water into these animals (now freshwater fish) could have resulted in fatal swelling unless an organ capable of high rates of water excretion had evolved through natural selection. This organ was the glomerulus, promoting the ultrafiltration of large amounts of plasma, about 93% of which is water. The ultrafiltrate of plasma, however, also contained essential small solutes (often referred to as crystalloids), such as sodium, chloride, bicarbonate, sugars, and amino acids. These essentials were reabsorbed in the proximal tubules, along with osmotically obligated water. The need to expel water may have been so great that a new structure evolved, namely, the distal tubule, in which the small molecules could be reabsorbed to the virtual exclusion of water.

When the vertebrates migrated onto land, they faced the opposite problem of the freshwater fish: desiccation. The consequent need to conserve water was apparently solved in two ways: In reptiles, the process of filtration was reduced through evolutionary degeneration of the glomerulus, and uric acid became the excretory end product of protein catabolism. In contrast to urea, which is the main nitrogenous end product of mammals, uric acid can exist in highly supersaturated solutions and can thus be excreted with minimal amounts of water. In mammals, on the other hand, glomeruli of high filtering capacity were retained, as was the ability to recover essential small molecules mainly in the proximal tubules. In addition, selective forces apparently led to the development of loops of Henle, which promote the avid conservation of wa-

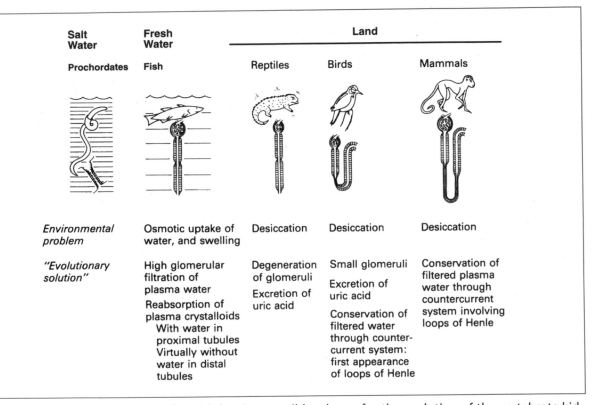

	Salt Water	Fresh Water	Land		
	Prochordates	Fish	Reptiles	Birds	Mammals
Environmental problem		Osmotic uptake of water, and swelling	Desiccation	Desiccation	Desiccation
"Evolutionary solution"		High glomerular filtration of plasma water. Reabsorption of plasma crystalloids With water in proximal tubules Virtually without water in distal tubules	Degeneration of glomeruli Excretion of uric acid	Small glomeruli Excretion of uric acid Conservation of filtered water through counter-current system: first appearance of loops of Henle	Conservation of filtered plasma water through countercurrent system involving loops of Henle

Figure 1-4.   One possible scheme for the evolution of the vertebrate kidney. Modified from Pitts, R. F. *Physiology of the Kidney and Body Fluids* (3rd ed.). Chicago: Year Book, 1974; and Smith, H. W. *The Evolution of the Kidney.* Porter Lectures, Series IX, Lawrence: University of Kansas Press, 1943, pp. 1–23. It should be noted that J. D. Robertson, among others, does not agree with this scheme. He has proposed that glomerular kidneys may have existed in marine protovertebrates, and that they thus may have been a useful preadaptation for life in fresh water. Evidence is in fact accumulating that the original habitat of fish was in the sea, and their origin probably goes farther back (by some 40 million years) than is depicted here.

ter through the countercurrent system (see Chap. 8). It is of considerable interest that birds exhibit both solutions, excreting uric acid and also having some nephrons without loops of Henle and some nephrons with such loops.

Not all experts agree with this scheme. An alternative view is mentioned in the legend to Figure 1-4.

SUMMARY

The kidneys are regulatory organs that help to maintain constancy of the internal environment in regard to both its volume and composition. They accomplish this purpose through ultrafiltration of plasma at the glomerulus, selective reabsorption of water and solutes, and selective tubular secretion of solutes. The objective of renal physiology is to understand the mechanisms, both within and outside of the kidneys, by which the renal regulation of fluid and solute balance is accomplished. Many special features of renal function, such as the very high rate of blood flow in relation to the size of the kidneys, the difference in both structure and function of the nephron depending on its location within the kidney (heterogeneity), and the apparent inefficiency of concurrent, high rates of filtration and reabsorption, may be understood through the evolutionary forces that selected for ability to preserve water and solute balance.

PROBLEM 1-1

Note: The answers to this and subsequent problems are given in a special section at the end of the text.

Given the following additional data, show how the values for Na^+ listed in Table 1-1 were obtained: plasma concentration of Na^+ (P_{Na^+}) = 139 mmol/L; urine flow ($\dot{V}$) = 1.1 mL/min; urinary concentration of Na^+ (U_{Na^+}) = 95 mmol/L (see Table 11-A in the Answers section). Some of the numerical values will be slightly different from those listed in Table 1-1 because the latter were rounded off.

PROBLEM 1-2

A solution of 0.9% NaCl is commonly used in clinical practice. How many equivalents of Na^+ does 1 liter of this solution contain? How many equivalents of Cl^- does 1 liter contain? What is the osmolality (mOsmol/kg) of this solution? What is the osmolality of a solution of 0.9% NaCl if 5 g of glucose is added to each 100 mL? How many milliequivalents of calcium and how many milliequivalents of chloride are contained in 1 mmol of $CaCl_2$? How many milliosmols are contributed by 1 mmol of $CaCl_2$?

APPENDIX

Normal Values

There are a number of normal values that one should have readily at hand, especially for calculating problems. These are given in the Appendix at the end of the book.

SUGGESTED READINGS

Note: Whereas the first two editions of this text contained long bibliographies, we have adopted a new policy in this third edition: Each chapter will be followed by a short list of general, mostly very inclusive articles, which describe a subject in detail and which cite specific further readings. For the reader interested in a longer list of references, we have filed extensive, annotated bibliographies for each chapter on Internet. These bibliographies can be retrieved via anonymous FTP by connecting to 'ftp.dartmouth.edu'. In the /pub directory there is a subdirectory named 'Renal-Function' containing the bibliographies in a file named 'Valtin3.ref'. This file, which is 150 to 200 kB in size (about 70 printed pages), should be retrieved by FTP to your own computer.

Current, Regular Reviews

For this first chapter only, we list, in addition to the references described above, a number of periodicals that regularly publish reviews on specific aspects of renal physiology and renal pathophysiology:

New England Journal of Medicine
Especially the sections entitled 'Mechanisms of Disease' and 'Seminars in Medicine'.

Hospital Practice
Superbly illustrated, succinct reviews that apply the basic sciences to clinical problems.

News in Physiological Sciences (NIPS)
Published jointly by the American Physiological Society and the International Union of Physiological Sciences. Short review articles, often with summary illustrations, as well as pithy tidbits of the 'latest'.

American Journal of Physiology

This journal is published in several sections, of which the following are particularly applicable to this textbook: *Renal, Fluid and Electrolyte Physiology; Cell Physiology;* and *Regulatory, Integrative and Comparative Physiology.* Many issues begin with a very useful invited review.

Kidney International

Editorial reviews are a regular feature, as is *Nephrology Forum,* where disease processes are explained through basic science principles.

Journal of the American Society of Nephrology (JASN)

Annual Review of Physiology

Each volume is organized by the major subdisciplines of physiology, and a circumscribed topic of each subdiscipline is reviewed briefly.

Physiological Reviews

Each issue covers several specific topics in great detail.

Seminars in Nephrology

Sometimes, an entire issue is devoted to a topic in basic science.

General

There are a number of comprehensive works that cover the field of nephrology all the way from the basic sciences to specific diseases. Most of them are updated regularly and frequently. A look at any one of them is likely to get the reader started on a given topic.

Brenner, B. M., and Rector, F. C., Jr. (Eds.). *The Kidney* (4th ed.). Philadelphia: Saunders, 1991.

Narins, R. G. (Ed.). *Maxwell & Kleeman's Clinical Disorders of Fluid and Electrolyte Metabolism* (5th ed.). New York: McGraw-Hill, 1994.

Rose, B. D. *Clinical Physiology of Acid-Base and Electrolyte Disorders* (4th ed.). New York: McGraw-Hill, 1994.

Schrier, R. W., and Gottschalk, C. W. (Eds.). *Diseases of the Kidney* (5th ed.). Boston: Little, Brown, 1992.

Seldin, D. W., and Giebisch, G. (Eds.). *The Kidney. Physiology and Pathophysiology* (2nd ed.). New York: Raven, 1992.

Windhager, E. E. (Ed.). *Handbook of Physiology; Renal Physiology.* New York: Oxford University Press, 1992.

Historical, Classics, Basics

Bowman, W. On the structure and use of the malpighian bodies of the kidney, with observations on the circulation through that gland. *Philos. Trans. R. Soc. Lond.* 132:57, 1842.

Gottschalk, C. W., Berliner, R. W., and Giebisch, G. H. *Renal Physiology. People and Ideas.* Bethesda: American Physiological Society, 1987.
Critically reviews the chronological development of major areas in renal physiology.

Kriz, W., and Bankir, L. (Co-Chairs). A standard nomenclature for structures of the kidney. *Am. J. Physiol.* 254 (Renal Fluid Electrolyte Physiol. 23):F1, 1988.
This nomenclature, prepared at the request of the Renal Commission of the International Union of Physiological Sciences, was published simultaneously in: Kidney Int. 33:1, 1988; Pflügers Archiv Europ. J. Physiol. 411:113, 1988.

Marshall, E. K., Jr., and Vickers, J. L. The mechanism of the elimination of phenolsulphonphthalein by the kidney—proof of secretion by the convoluted tubules. *Johns Hopkins Bull.* 34:1, 1923.

Oliver, J. *Nephrons and Kidneys: A Quantitative Study of Developmental and Evolutionary Mammalian Architectonics.* New York: Harper & Row, 1968.

Peter, K. *Untersuchungen über Bau und Entwickelung der Niere.* Jena: Fischer, 1909.
Described by Jean Oliver as a "truly monumental contribution."

Pitts, R. F. *Physiology of the Kidney and Body Fluids* (3rd ed.). Chicago: Year Book, 1974.

Schmidt-Nielsen, K. *Animal Physiology: Adaptation and Environment* (3rd ed.). Cambridge: Cambridge University Press, 1983.

Smith, H. W. *From Fish to Philosopher.* Boston: Little, Brown, 1953.

Smith, H. W. *The Kidney. Structure and Function in Health and Disease.* New York: Oxford University Press, 1951.

Smith, H. W. *Lectures on the Kidney.* Lawrence: University of Kansas Press, 1943.

Sperber, I. Studies on the mammalian kidney. *Zool. Bid. Fran. Uppsala* 22:249, 1944.

The Body Fluid Compartments

2

The internal environment that is regulated by the kidneys is a fluid medium, which is distributed in a number of discernible compartments. In this chapter, we shall consider both the size and the distinctive composition of these compartments, as well as some of the factors that maintain these characteristic differences.

SIZE OF THE COMPARTMENTS

Approximate sizes of the major fluid compartments of an adult human are shown in Figure 2-1, where the dimensions have been expressed both as absolute values and as a proportion of the body weight. The latter is important because it is one basis for estimating fluid volumes, both in experimental animals and in patients. It

Figure 2-1. Approximate sizes of the major body fluid compartments, expressed both as percentage of body weight and in mean absolute values for an adult human being who weighs 70 kg (154 lb). The ranges of normal among individuals are considerable, and thus no one value should be taken too rigidly; a good rule of thumb is '20, 40, 60', referring to the percentage of the body weight that is constituted by extracellular (ECW), intracellular (ICW), and total body water (TBW), respectively (*see* Table A-3 in the Appendix). The plasma has a very slightly higher osmolality than the intracellular and interstitial compartments; this small difference can be ignored when dealing with problems of fluid balance.

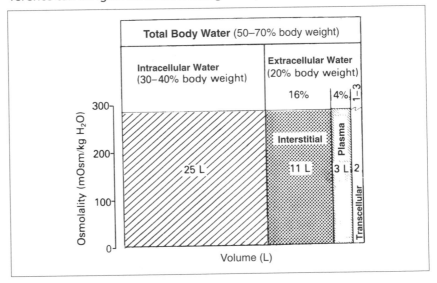

should be emphasized that all percentages refer to the proportion of *body weight,* not of total body water.

About 50 to 70% of the body is composed of water. The main factor that determines whether the lower or higher figure applies is the amount of fatty tissue, which has a low water content compared to other tissues (*see* Table A-3). Accordingly, women tend to have a lower percent of their body weight as water because they have a relatively higher percentage of fat than men, and obese individuals are at the extreme low end of the range.

The total body water (TBW) is distributed between two major compartments, the intracellular (ICW) and the extracellular (ECW). Of these, ICW is the larger, comprising nearly two-thirds of the TBW. The ECW has two further major subdivisions, the plasma and the interstitial, comprising about 4% and 16% of the body weight, respectively. Lymph, constituting 2 to 3% of the body weight, is included in the interstitial volume. Claude Bernard first pointed out that of all the body fluid compartments, the interstitial is probably the true internal environment, since it is the fluid medium that bathes all cells. A more recent point of view, adopted by some, is that intracellular fluid may be the true internal environment since it is within cells that major processes, such as enzymatic reactions, occur.

The transcellular compartment is a minor subdivision of ECW. It comprises a number of small volumes, such as cerebrospinal, intraocular, pleural, peritoneal, and synovial fluids, and the digestive secretions. Unlike interstitial fluid, the transcellular spaces are separated from the blood not only by capillary endothelium but also by epithelium. Except in special circumstances, such as loss of gastrointestinal fluid or the development of ascites in the abdominal cavity, the transcellular compartment may be neglected in experimental and clinical problems of fluid balance; the same holds true for the water that is contained in bone (3% of body weight) and in dense connective tissue (4% of body weight).

> ■ **The '20, 40, 60'** ■
> **Rule**
>
> ~*20% of body weight* = volume of extracellular fluid (ECF)
>
> ~*40% of body weight* = volume of intracellular fluid (ICF)
>
> ~*60% of body weight* = volume of total body water (TBW)

Relationship of Tissue Water to Tissue Volume

When referring to body fluid compartments the terms *volume, fluid, and water* are often used interchangeably; thus, extracellular volume, extracellular fluid, or extracellular water. Although this usage is not accurate, in most instances it is permissible for practical purposes, since the vast proportion of each compartment is water. Water constitutes about 93% of the plasma compartment, while for most intracellular spaces the value is 75 to 80%.

Measuring the Size of Compartments

These measurements involve the principle of dye dilution, which is based on the important relationship:

$$\text{Concentration} = \frac{\text{Amount}}{\text{Volume}} \tag{2-1}$$

The following is a simple example. We have a large beaker filled with water, and we want to know how much water is in the beaker. Obviously, the simplest way to obtain the answer is to pour the water into a graduated cylinder and read the meniscus. But for the purpose of illustrating the dye dilution principle, we add 1.5 g of a dye to the water. After mixing thoroughly so that the dye is distributed evenly throughout the water, we take an aliquot and measure the concentration of the dye in it; it is found to be 1.5 mg/mL. Rearranging Equation 2-1 and substituting, we have:

$$\text{Volume of water in beaker} = \frac{\text{Amount of dye added}}{\text{Concentration of dye}}$$

$$\text{Volume of water in beaker} = \frac{1,500 \text{ mg}}{1} \times \frac{\text{mL}}{1.5 \text{ mg}} = 1,000 \text{ mL}$$

■ Dye-Dilution Technique ■

1. Add an exactly known amount of marker substance
2. Allow time for the marker to be dispersed evenly in its volume of distribution
3. Subtract amount of marker lost from body
4. Measure concentration of marker
5. Apply Equation 2-2

Volume of Distribution

The above example illustrates the concept of *volume of distribution,* which is defined as the volume of liquid in which a given substance is distributed homogeneously. This is a general concept, which is not limited to the dye dilution technique. We can speak of the volume of distribution for virtually any substance, and we do so especially when considering the metabolism of drugs. Often, a volume of distribution does not coincide with one of the recognized anatomical volumes, such as the plasma or extracellular or intracellular volumes (Fig. 2-1). In such instances, we often refer to an *apparent volume of distribution.* Bicarbonate, for example, has an apparent volume of distribution equal to 50% of body weight, even though HCO_3^- is confined largely to the extracellular space (Fig. 2-2). The reason is that when HCO_3^- is given to correct a metabolic acidosis, it buffers not only extracellular, but also intracellular, H^+ (discussed in Chap. 9).

Total Body Water

This volume can be estimated with a drug, antipyrine, which distributes itself quickly throughout all the major fluid compartments, as do heavy water (D_2O) and tritiated water (HTO), which are used sometimes for the same purpose as antipyrine. The following is an illustration using tritiated water.

2. The Body Fluid Compartments

An adult woman who weighs 60 kg is given exactly 1 millicurie (mCi) of HTO intravenously. On the basis of prior experiments in humans, it is known that within 2 hours after the injection, this labeled water will have come into equilibrium with interstitial and intracellular water, and that by this time about 0.4% of the administered dose will have been lost from the body, mainly via the urine. At this time, therefore, a plasma sample is withdrawn and its radioactivity measured by liquid scintillation; it is found to be 0.031 mCi per liter of plasma water. From the relationship shown in Equation 2-1, and knowing that the concentration of HTO in the major compartments will be the same as in plasma, the TBW therefore will be:

$$\frac{0.031 \text{ mCi}}{1{,}000 \text{ mL plasma water}} = \frac{1 \text{ mCi} - (1 \times 0.004)}{\text{TBW}}$$

TBW = 32,129 mL, or approximately 32 liters.

Note that, in contrast to the example with the beaker, we now had to take account of the portion of the marker substance (in this case, THO), which was lost from the volume of distribution. Had we failed to make this correction, the result would have been an overestimate. Thus, the general equation for measuring a volume by the dilution principle is:

$$\text{Volume of compartment} = \frac{\begin{array}{c}\text{Amount of substance X given } \textit{minus}\\ \text{Amount of X lost from compartment}\end{array}}{\text{Concentration of X in the compartment}} \quad (2\text{-}2)$$

The final volume has been deliberately stated as 'approximately' 32 liters because the method may yield an estimate that is high by perhaps 1 liter. The discrepancy arises mainly from exchange of the isotope with hydrogen atoms of organic molecules.

Extracellular Water

The substances and equations used to measure the size of the various compartments are summarized in Table 2-1. There is no ideal test substance for estimating ECW because all substances that diffuse freely from the vascular into the interstitial compartment also in small part penetrate cells; for example, chloride ions enter erythrocytes and they are secreted as gastric juice, two losses that are difficult to quantify.

Plasma

This compartment is measured by the dilution of substances that distribute themselves almost exclusively within the plasma. Radioiodinated serum albumin falls short of the ideal for such a

Table 2-1.   Substances and equations used to
measure the size of the major body fluid compartments.

Compartment	Substance	Equation
TBW	Antipyrine D_2O HTO	2-2
ECW	Inulin Raffinose Sucrose Mannitol Thiosulfate $^{35}SO_4^{2-}$ $^{35}S^-$cyanate $^{36}Cl^-$ $^{22}Na^+$ or $^{24}Na^+$ $^{86}Br^-$	2-2
Plasma	^{131}I-albumin Evans blue, or T-1824 ^{51}Cr-erythrocytes	2-2
Interstitial	Not measured directly	Interstitial = ECW − Plasma
ICW	Not measured directly	ICW = TBW − ECW

substance in that some albumin crosses the capillary endothelium
into the interstitial space. The same shortcoming applies to the
dye known as Evans blue (T-1824), which is bound to serum albumin and thus has the same volume of distribution as the protein.
Radioactively labeled erythrocytes (such as ^{51}Cr) yield a slightly
inaccurate result because erythrocytes do not distribute themselves evenly throughout the plasma; the hematocrit (i.e., the ratio
of the volume of blood cells to that of whole blood) is less in fine, peripheral vessels than it is in large, major vessels.

Interstitial and Intracellular Water

These volumes are not measured directly because there are no
known substances that distribute themselves exclusively within
these compartments. They are thus calculated as the difference between two compartments that were measured by the dilution technique. The formulas are given in Table 2-1; their derivation is self-
evident, or can be deduced from Figure 2-1.

Body Weight

Although the data illustrated in Figure 2-1 were obtained by the dilution technique, this method is seldom employed to measure body fluid volumes. Rather, the body weight is used commonly for this purpose. In many circumstances, changes in body weight provide the most accurate estimate of a change in TBW. As has been mentioned, the measurement of TBW by the dilution technique involves an error of about 1,000 mL in an adult human. The body weight can be determined much more accurately, simply, and cheaply. And in an experimental animal or patient who is eating adequately, an acute (up to 72 hours) change in body weight will be due almost solely to a change in TBW. Of course, this measurement cannot tell us which of the body fluid compartments has lost or gained water, but this additional information can often be surmised from the history of an illness or experimental situation.

The usefulness of measuring body weight in the field of fluid and solute balance cannot be overemphasized. Too many physicians tend to forget that this simple measure frequently yields more accurate and immediate information than does the cumbersome practice of recording the daily intake and output of fluid by a patient.

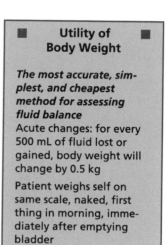

Utility of Body Weight

The most accurate, simplest, and cheapest method for assessing fluid balance
Acute changes: for every 500 mL of fluid lost or gained, body weight will change by 0.5 kg

Patient weighs self on same scale, naked, first thing in morning, immediately after emptying bladder

COMPOSITION OF THE COMPARTMENTS

The main solute constituents of the major body fluid compartments are shown in Figure 2-2. Note that these compartments are made up primarily of electrolytes. Although the conveyance by these fluids of nutrients and waste products such as glucose, amino acids, and urea is very important, the nonelectrolytes constitute only a small portion of the total solute.

The concentrations have been expressed as chemical equivalents. Although there is an electrical potential difference (P.D.) at the interface between the compartments (see Gibbs-Donnan Equilibrium, below), the separation of charges is confined to the immediate area of the interface and involves only a minute fraction of the total number of ions. Hence, the bulk of the fluid within a compartment is electrically neutral. The total number of equivalents varies, however, from one compartment to another. As Figure 2-2 shows, this difference is due to the variation in the concentration of proteins. At the pH of body fluids, proteins have multiple negative charges per molecule. Hence intracellular fluid, being relatively rich in proteins, has more total charges than does extracellular fluid. The same explanation applies to the greater total equivalents in plasma as opposed to interstitial fluid.

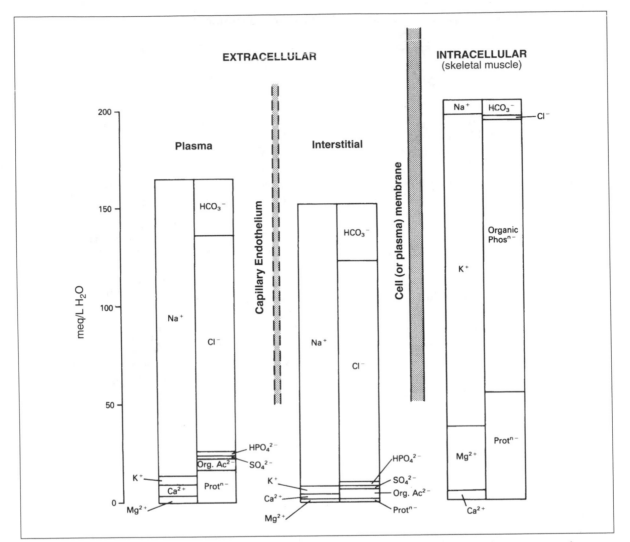

Figure 2-2. The main solute constituents of the major body fluid compartments. The concentrations are expressed as chemical equivalents to emphasize that the compartments are made up mainly of electrolytes, and that within any one space the total number of negative charges is neutralized by an equal number of positive charges.

The values depicted for intracellular fluid are rough approximations at best. They reflect current estimates for skeletal muscle, but because many cell types have unique compositions, these estimates are not precisely representative of all intracellular fluid. Furthermore, the composition may vary among subcellular compartments, such as the mitochondria, the nucleus, and the cytoplasm. The extent to which some intracellular ions are bound or ionized is not known, so that the equivalents for such ions, as well as for organic phosphates and proteins, are also approximations. Despite these limitations, the diagram serves to emphasize important and typical differences between intracellular and extracellular fluid. Organic phosphates include AMP, ADP, and ATP, glycerophosphate, and creatine phosphate. Slightly modified from Gamble, J. L. *Chemical Anatomy, Physiology and Pathology of Extracellular Fluid* (6th ed.). Cambridge: Harvard University Press, 1954.

Sodium is by far the most abundant cation of vertebrate extracellular fluid, and chloride and bicarbonate are the most abundant anions. In contrast, potassium is the most plentiful intracellular cation, and organic phosphates and proteins are the major anions. The similarity in composition between plasma and interstitial fluid is striking, and is explained by the fact that these two compartments are separated by a membrane, the capillary endothelium, which allows free diffusion of solutes of low molecular weight (often referred to as *crystalloids*) but which is relatively impermeable to the large plasma proteins, such as albumin and the globulins.

Explanation for Differences in Composition

The main difference between plasma and interstitial fluid is in the concentration of these proteins, which, as stated in the preceding paragraph, are largely excluded from the interstitial compartment by the capillary endothelium. In conformity with the Gibbs-Donnan relationship (see below), there is a difference of about 5% in the concentrations of diffusible ions between the two compartments. The concentrations of cations are slightly greater in plasma than they are in the interstitial fluid; the concentrations of diffusible anions are slightly smaller in plasma than they are in the interstitial fluid. Thus, the differences in composition between plasma and interstitial fluid can be accounted for almost entirely by the unequal distribution of proteins and the resultant Gibbs-Donnan equilibrium. Binding of certain cations, such as calcium and magnesium, to proteins makes a further, small contribution to the differences.

The intracellular compartment is separated from the interstitial fluid by the cell (or plasma) membrane (Fig. 2-2). The lipid bilayer of this membrane, unlike the capillary endothelium, exhibits very low permeabilities for almost all solutes except those that are either extremely small, such as water and urea, or that are nonpolar (not charged) and therefore able to enter the lipid matrix of the membrane. For this reason, solutes that are exchanged between the intracellular and interstitial fluid compartments must cross the plasma membrane by transporters, which are specialized proteins produced by the cell and inserted into cell membranes. There are numerous transporters and they vary among cell types; generally, they are grouped into three classes: *pores, channels, and carriers.* (Specific examples of transporters are described further in Chap. 4.)

- *Pores* are like holes in the membrane that allow any solute of sufficiently small size to cross the membrane.
- *Channels* are like pores except that they transport only ions or water, and are highly selective for the substances that they accommodate.
- *Carriers* can transport nonelectrolytes as well as ions. They are also highly selective. There are many kinds of carriers, and some transport two or more solutes simultaneously, in the same or opposite directions.

Some carriers involve *active transport,* that is, transport requiring an input of energy. All cells possess an active transporter that is often called the sodium-potassium 'pump'. This carrier, which is more formally referred to as *Na-K-ATPase,* hydrolyzes adenosine triphosphate (ATP) and uses the resulting energy to actively transport Na^+ out of cells and K^+ into them. Therefore, when this pump is inhibited—for example, when the energy supply is interrupted during anoxia or hypothermia—cells gain Na^+ and lose K^+ (Fig. 2-6). In addition to the pump mechanism, many ions cross cell membranes, not actively but rather passively (i.e., down their electrochemical potential gradients; explained further below). Such passive transport can occur either through ion-specific channels or by means of carriers that do not require a direct input of energy. But even though some charged particles enter cells, most of the negative charges within cells come from proteins and organic phosphate compounds that are synthesized by cells and to which the plasma membrane is virtually impermeable. Because of the intracellular location of these impermeable anions and because intracellular fluid has a negative voltage in comparison with the extracellular fluid (which fact repels negatively charged species from the cell interior), the two major extracellular anions (HCO_3^- and Cl^-; Fig. 2-2) by and large do not enter cells; hence, their intracellular concentrations are quite low (Fig. 2-2). Finally, many ions are bound to proteins and organic phosphates within the cell.

Thus, the striking compositional differences between extracellular and intracellular fluids (Fig. 2-2) result from the combined effects of: (a) selective permeabilities of the membrane separating these compartments, (b) the voltage across this membrane, (c) active transport, and (d) intracellular binding of ions.

Osmolality in the Major Compartments

It has been shown by a number of experimental techniques that the osmolality of interstitial fluid is equal to that of intracellular fluid (Fig. 2-1). It should be noted that this fact is not in conflict

---

■   **Body Fluid**   ■
Compartments

Extracellular: high Na^+
Intracellular: high K^+
Maintained by
Na-K-ATPase

All Compartments in
Osmotic Equilibrium
Osmolality slightly higher in plasma than interstitium: counteracted by systemic blood pressure

Osmolality slightly higher within cells than in interstitium: counteracted by Na-K-ATPase

with the differences in total equivalents depicted in Figure 2-2. Osmolality is a function of the *number* of discrete particles in solution (Chap. 7). Thus, a single atom of sodium contributes as much to the osmolality of a solution as does a single molecule of protein, even though the latter weighs perhaps 3,000 times more than the former. But at the pH of body fluids, each molecule of protein contributes several charges to the total equivalents of anions, whereas each atom of sodium contributes only one cationic charge.

The osmolality of the plasma is very slightly higher than that of interstitial and intracellular fluid (Fig. 2-1). This difference has not been demonstrated directly, since neither interstitial nor intracellular fluid can be sampled for measurement; however, because the plasma contains proteins with multiple negative charges whereas the interstitial fluid contains negligible concentrations of proteins (Fig. 2-2), the resulting Gibbs-Donnan equilibrium requires that a difference in osmolality must exist (explained below). That difference is due not only to the disparity in the protein concentration across the capillary endothelium, but also to the unequal distribution of ions imposed by the Gibbs-Donnan relationship (see below). The osmolality difference amounts to 1 to 2 milliosmol per kg H_2O (mOsm/kg; equivalent to ~20 to 30 mm Hg hydrostatic pressure); it is responsible for the *colloid osmotic pressure* (COP), alternatively referred to as the *oncotic pressure,* of the plasma.

Gibbs-Donnan Equilibrium

This equilibrium explains the unequal distribution of diffusible ions on the two sides of a membrane if one side contains a nondiffusible ion or if it contains a higher concentration of a poorly diffusible ion. First consider the initial situation illustrated in Figure 2-3, in which compartments 1 and 2 are separated by a rigid membrane that is freely permeable to Na^+ and Cl^- but impermeable to protein, Pr^-. The rate at which either diffusible (i.e., permeant) ion moves across the membrane will depend on three factors: (1) the *concentration difference* for that ion between the two compartments, (2) the *permeability* of the membrane for that ion, and (3) the *voltage* across the membrane. Initially, because no difference in electrical potential (i.e., voltage) is present and because the difference in concentration is greater for Cl^- (10 mmol/L) than for Na^+ (5 mmol/L), the rate of net Cl^- movement from compartment 2 to compartment 1 will exceed that of Na^+. And because the movement of Cl^- momentarily precedes that of Na^+, a negative charge will build up on the membrane facing side 1. The resulting separation of electrostatic charge produces a voltage across the membrane,

■ **Definitions** ■

Transmembrane Voltage
A difference in electrical potential across a membrane, often referred to as *Potential Difference* (P.D.)
Colloid Osmotic Pressure (or Oncotic Pressure)
The difference in osmolality that is due to the unequal distribution of proteins and the resulting *Gibbs-Donnan* effect

Figure 2-3. The attainment of a Gibbs-Donnan equilibrium. The schema assumes that the volumes of compartments 1 and 2 remain constant. This example does not represent any body fluid compartment, but is for illustrative purposes only. Modified from Pitts, R. F. *Physiology of the Kidney and Body Fluids* (3rd ed.). Chicago: Year Book, 1974.

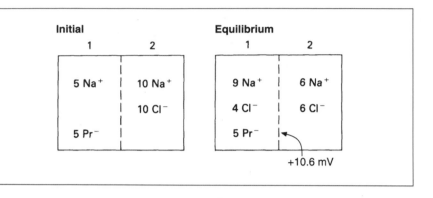

with side 1 negative compared to side 2. This voltage provides an increased driving force for the diffusion of Na^+ from side 2 to side 1, so that the rates of Na^+ and Cl^- diffusion become equal almost instantaneously. Furthermore, the presence of the voltage permits the buildup of Na^+ in compartment 1 against its concentration gradient. The combination of a difference in chemical potential (concentration difference) and in electrical potential (transmembrane voltage) as the driving forces for the diffusion of any ion is called the *electrochemical potential difference;* it is calculated according to Equation 2-3:

$$\Delta\tilde{\mu}_X = 2.3\ R\ T \log \frac{[X]_2}{[X]_1} + z\ F\ \Delta\Psi \tag{2-3}$$

where:

$\Delta\tilde{\mu}_X$ = the difference in electrochemical potential for the ion X, side 2 compared to side 1
R = the universal gas constant
T = temperature in K
$[X]_1$ and $[X]_2$ = concentrations of any ion on sides 1 and 2, respectively
F = the Faraday constant (96,500 coulombs per equivalent)
z = the valence of the ion X
$\Delta\Psi$ = the transmembrane voltage (side 2 compared to side 1)

Therefore, the equations for the electrochemical potential differences of Na^+ and Cl^- are, respectively:

$$\Delta\tilde{\mu}_{Na} = 2.3\ R\ T \log \frac{[Na^+]_2}{[Na^+]_1} + F\ \Delta\Psi \tag{2-4}$$

$$\Delta \tilde{\mu}_{Cl} = 2.3 \ R \ T \ \log \ \frac{[Cl^-]_2}{[Cl^-]_1} - F \ \Delta \Psi \qquad (2\text{-}5)$$

At equilibrium all of the permeant ions are distributed so that their electrochemical potential differences ($\Delta \tilde{\mu}$) become zero and their *net* diffusion ceases. Since this condition holds for both Na^+ and Cl^-, Equations 2-4 and 2-5 will be equal to each other. If one reduces this equality, the resultant is referred to as the *Gibbs-Donnan Equation*. In the case of Na^+ and Cl^- the equation is:

$$\frac{[Na^+]_2}{[Na^+]_1} = \frac{[Cl^-]_1}{[Cl^-]_2} \ \text{or} \ [Na^+]_1 \times [Cl^-]_1 = [Na^+]_2 \times [Cl^-]_2 \qquad (2\text{-}6)$$

The equilibrium conditions of the Gibbs-Donnan effect can now be understood, and they are illustrated by the example in Figure 2-3:

- The product of the concentrations of diffusible ions in one compartment will equal the product of the same ions in the other compartment (9×4 in compartment 1, and 6×6 in compartment 2).
- Within each compartment, the total cationic charges must equal the total anionic charges (9 of each in compartment 1; 6 of each in compartment 2); that is, there must be electroneutrality.
- The concentration of diffusible cations will be greater in the compartment containing the nondiffusible, negatively charged protein than in the other compartment, and the diffusible anions will be oppositely distributed.
- The osmolality will be greater in the compartment containing the protein (18 particles) than in the other compartment (12 particles per equal volume).
- The voltage across the membrane at equilibrium can be calculated from either Equation 2-4 or 2-5 by setting $\Delta \tilde{\mu} = 0$ (the condition of equilibrium). The equation then becomes the *Nernst Equation*. After converting units, the Nernst Equation for Na^+ is:

$$\Delta \Psi = -60 \ mV \times \log \frac{[Na^+]_2}{[Na^+]_1} = +10.6 \ mV \qquad (2\text{-}7)$$

(side 2 positive compared to 1)

The requirement for electroneutrality of each compartment is not in conflict with the existence of a small voltage across the membrane, because that voltage is produced by the separation of an insignificant fraction of oppositely charged ions by the membrane, much like charging a small capacitor. The higher osmolality of the compartment containing the protein is due not only to the protein concentration but also to the fact that the sum of the diffusible ions

■ Gibbs-Donnan ■ Equilibrium
1. A consequence of unequal concentrations of a poorly permeant ion on either side of a membrane
2. Product of diffusible ions in one compartment equals product of same ions in the other compartment
3. Each compartment is electrically neutral
4. Concentration of any diffusible ion is different in the two compartments
5. Osmolality is greater in the compartment containing the nondiffusible ion
6. Voltage develops across membrane, the side containing the impermeant ion having the same sign as that ion

on the side containing the protein (9 + 4) is greater than the sum of these ions on the other side (6 + 6). As explained above, the total difference in osmotic pressure that is due to the Gibbs-Donnan effect is known as the *oncotic pressure*.

These conditions hold also for the body fluid compartments, and apply to each of the diffusible ions within them. For example, each compartment is electrically neutral, and diffusible cations such as Na^+ are slightly more concentrated in plasma than in interstitial fluid, whereas the opposite is true of diffusible anions, such as Cl^- (Fig. 2-2). A Gibbs-Donnan distribution of ions *would* occur also across the cell membrane were it not for active transporters that keep some of the ions distributed away from equilibrium. The impermeant anions within cells (proteins and organic phosphates; Fig. 2-2) *would* cause the osmolality of the cell to exceed that of the extracellular fluid, and the cells would swell irreversibly due to osmotic water flow, if Na^+ were not pumped actively out of cells. Thus, despite a Gibbs-Donnan effect (but not an equilibrium) the osmolality of the cell is kept equal to that of the interstitial fluid by Na-K-ATPase.

MAINTENANCE OF COMPARTMENT SIZE

Importance of Total Solute Content

It follows from Equation 2-1 that for any given solute concentration, the volume or size of a compartment will be a direct function of the total amount of solute within it. The volumes of the main extracellular compartments, plasma and interstitium, depend primarily on the amount of Na^+ and its attendant anions (mainly Cl^- and HCO_3^-) in the body, since these constitute 90 to 95% of the total osmotically active particles in extracellular fluid. Although the plasma proteins are a major component of plasma by *weight*— about 70 g per liter—they contribute less than 1% to the total osmolality of plasma.

The effect of adding 'isosmotic' NaCl to the body is shown in Figure 2-4. Depicted at the top is the distribution of total body water in a healthy adult human, as it was summarized in Figure 2-1. Two liters containing 0.9 g of NaCl per 100 mL of solution is then infused intravenously, i.e., into the plasma compartment. This solution has an osmolality of nearly 290 mOsm/kg (see Answer to Problem 1-2). Since the capillary endothelium is highly permeable to Na^+, Cl^-, and H_2O, the infused solution is quickly distributed not only throughout the plasma, but also throughout the interstitial fluid. Although Na^+ will transiently enter the intracellular space, it will be quickly 'pumped out'. Thus, there will be no gain or loss of Na^+ from the intracellular space, and since Cl^- follows Na^+, there will be no net change in Cl^-; that is, the solute and hence the H_2O that were added intravenously will be excluded from the intracellular space and will be distributed evenly throughout the extracellular compartment. Accordingly, to the extent that none of the added NaCl solution is lost from the body, the extracellular compartment will be expanded by 2 liters, and the infused solution will be distributed between plasma and interstitial fluid in proportion to their sizes prior to the infusion. Since the infused solution had about the same osmolality as the body fluids, there will be virtually no change in the total solute concentration of extracellular fluid and hence no osmotic flow of water in or out of the intracellular compartment.

Maintenance of Plasma and Interstitial Volumes
Starling Forces

Because of the Gibbs-Donnan effect, the plasma has a slightly higher osmolality than does the interstitial fluid. Nevertheless, in

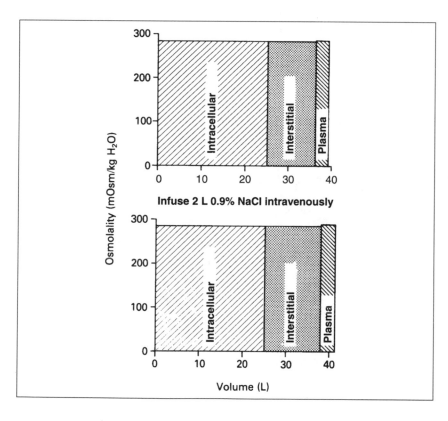

Figure 2-4. The effect of an intravenous infusion of 2 liters of NaCl having an osmolality about equal to that of plasma (called *isotonic saline*), on the volume and osmolal concentration of the body fluids. Note that there was no change in the osmolality of any compartment, and that therefore the increase in volume involved only the plasma and interstitial compartments.

■   **Starling Forces**   ■

***Promoting Filtration out
of Capillary***
1. hydrostatic pressure
   within capillary
2. oncotic pressure within
   interstitium
***Opposing Filtration out of
Capillary***
3. oncotic pressure within
   capillary
4. hydrostatic pressure
   within interstitium

***Net Fluid Flow in or out of
Capillary***
Determined by the alge-
braic sum of the Starling
forces, and by the filtration coefficient, K_f

the steady state, the size of each compartment is stable. This is be-cause the movement of water between the two compartments is governed not solely by osmotic differences but by a balance of all pressures, i.e., of the oncotic and hydrostatic pressures in both compartments.

The forces that determine fluid exchange across the capillary en-dothelium were outlined by Ernest Starling in 1896. This formula-tion, known as the Starling hypothesis, is illustrated in Figure 2-5. The major force promoting filtration of fluid out of the capillary into the interstitium is the hydrostatic pressure within the capil-laries. This pressure declines along the course of the capillary. A small amount of protein leaks out of the capillaries. Although most of this is returned to the systemic circulation via the lymph chan-nels, some remains, giving rise to a small interstitial oncotic pres-sure of perhaps 5 mm Hg, which also promotes filtration out of the capillary. These two forces are opposed mainly by the plasma on-cotic pressure and by a small hydrostatic pressure within the tis-sue referred to as the *turgor pressure*. The balance of these forces is such that there is net filtration of fluid out of the capillary along slightly more than one-half of the length of the capillary, and net reabsorption of fluid into the capillary as it approaches the venule.

Figure 2-5.   The Starling hypothesis of fluid exchange between plasma and intersti-tium. The four factors that determine this exchange are known as *Starling forces.*

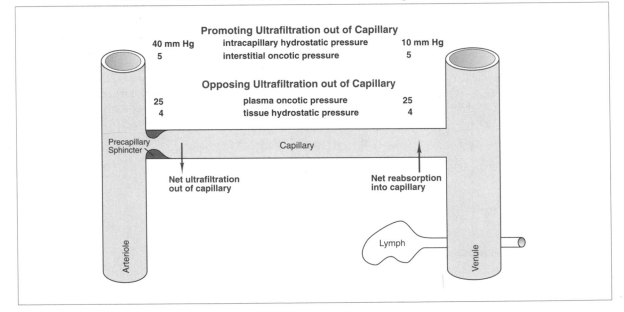

The slight excess of fluid that is filtered into the interstitium is returned to the systemic plasma by the lymph channels, so that in the steady state the volumes of the two compartments, plasma and interstitium, remain constant.

Although the principle of opposing forces outlined in Figure 2-5 is correct, it is possible that the main mechanism that ordinarily alters intracapillary hydrostatic pressure is not the resistance along the length of the capillary but rather the activity of the precapillary sphincters. When these relax, hydrostatic pressure throughout the capillary may be sufficiently high to promote net outward filtration along its entire length; when they contract, hydrostatic pressure may be so low that only reabsorption of fluid into the capillary occurs. Furthermore, the rate of fluid flow, J_V, across the capillary endothelium is a function not only of the Starling forces, but also of a filtration coefficient, K_f. Equation 2-8 expresses the total relationship:

$$J_V = K_f [(P_c - P_t) - (\pi_c - \pi_t)] \qquad (2-8)$$

where:

J_V = the flux of fluid across the capillary wall (e.g., in mL/min), with a positive value indicating flow out of the capillary
K_f = the filtration coefficient
P_c = hydrostatic pressure within the capillary
P_t = the hydrostatic pressure within the interstitium (often called tissue turgor pressure)
π_c = the oncotic pressure within the capillary (i.e., plasma oncotic pressure)
π_t = the oncotic pressure within the interstitium

The filtration coefficient is proportional to the total surface area of capillaries, as well as to capillary permeability per unit of surface area. When precapillary sphincters contract, many capillaries are shut off from the arterial circulation, so that total capillary surface area is reduced. Relaxation of the sphincters during the vasodilator phase has the opposite effect. Thus, activity of the precapillary sphincters, so-called vasomotion, governs fluid flow across the capillary endothelium (Eq. 2-8) by its effect both on the intracapillary hydrostatic pressure, P_c, and on the filtration coefficient, K_f. The balance between the vasodilator and vasoconstrictor phases is such that the net return of fluid to plasma equals its net egress from this compartment (the return via the lymphatics making a very minor contribution).

The above description applies mainly to H_2O, which moves from capillary into interstitium by so-called bulk flow. Small ions and nonelectrolytes, such as glucose and amino acids, move through the capillary endothelium by two means: by simple *diffusion* through aqueous pores, and by *solvent drag.* In the latter process, the solutes become entrained in the water. Large molecules, however, in particular plasma proteins, cannot easily cross the endothelium. Therefore, when water flows out of the capillary, plasma proteins are left behind—a process referred to as *ultrafiltration.* Lipid-soluble substances, such as O_2 and CO_2, can diffuse across the entire capillary wall, which is made up overwhelmingly of lipids.

Edema

Abnormal expansion of the interstitial fluid compartment, known as *edema,* is one of the most common findings in clinical medicine. It is divided into two forms: *localized* and *generalized.* Localized edema can be explained by changes in one or more variables of Equation 2-8, that lead to an increase in J_V. Examples include:

- Inflammation, because an increased vasodilator phase raises both P_c and K_f
- Lymphatic obstruction, because plasma proteins that get into the interstitium are not returned to the systemic circulation, resulting in an increase in π_t and a fall in π_c
- Venous obstruction, because P_c rises

Generalized edema, which is seen commonly in cardiac, hepatic, and renal failure, has a more complicated pathogenesis. It involves decreased urinary excretion of Na^+, retention of this ion, and expansion of the entire extracellular fluid volume, as follows (at a constant plasma Na^+ concentration) from Equation 2-1 (see also Fig. 2-4).

Maintenance of Intracellular Volume

Why do cells that have a high oncotic pressure and are freely permeable to water not swell and burst? As noted earlier, the reason is that the distribution of Na^+ between the intracellular and interstitial compartments is not governed only by the Gibbs-Donnan forces; in addition, Na^+ is pumped out of cells. That this process requires metabolic energy is shown in Figure 2-6. When cells are deprived of energy, as by exposing them to cold, or hypoxia, or metabolic inhibitors, they gain Na^+ and Cl^-, and with these solutes, water. That is, when the higher oncotic pressure of intracellular fluid is not opposed by the additional force of active Na^+ movement into the interstitium, cells do in fact swell and they may burst. The fact that intracellular K^+ decreases when the cell is deprived of energy constitutes part of the evidence that the relatively high intra-

---

■	**Edema**	■

Definition
Expansion of interstitial space
Localized
Due to changes in Starling forces and/or filtration coefficient
Generalized
Due to renal retention of Na^+

cellular concentration of K^+ in control conditions is to a large degree maintained by an active pump.

More than one-third of the metabolic energy of most cells is expended in transporting Na^+, thereby maintaining cellular volume. The question might well be asked why such an inefficient system is present when the simpler expedient of a rigid, thick cellular membrane that excludes Na^+ from the cell interior might solve the problem. As was the case for general renal function (Chap. 1), so once again the answer probably lies in evolutionary selection, in this instance for a system that allows great mobility, and that therefore requires pliable cells with a large surface area to permit rapid diffusion of metabolic substrates.

Figure 2-6. Effect of depriving cells of metabolic energy, on their content of Na^+, Cl^-, K^+, and H_2O. The heavy intracellular solutes (i.e., proteins) did not change in this experiment. Hence, expressing the data per unit of dry weight makes it possible to interpret the results as content of the measured substances per approximately equal number of cells. Note that during metabolic inhibition, the loss of K^+ is less than the gains in Na^+ and Cl^-; this net entry of solute is followed by movement of H_2O into cells. The example is from cells of the renal cortex, which do not have the extremely low Na^+ and Cl^- concentrations and the high K^+ concentrations that skeletal muscle cells have (see Fig. 2-2). But even in renal cortical cells, the concentrations of these ions differ greatly from those in extracellular fluid. Data from Leaf, A. *Am. J. Med.* 49:291, 1970.

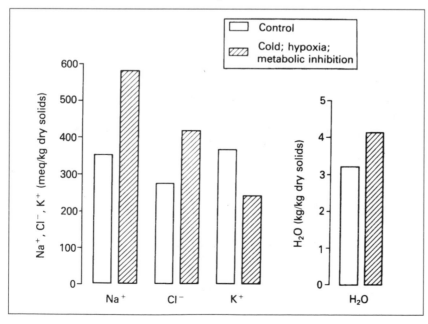

SUMMARY

Total body water, which comprises from 50 to 70% of the body weight, is distributed among three major compartments: (a) intracellular, (b) plasma, and (c) interstitial. The last two are the major subdivisions of extracellular fluid. Each compartment has a characteristic and stable size and composition. Sodium and its attendant anions are the major solutes in extracellular fluid. The main difference between plasma and interstitial fluid is the higher protein content in the former. The relative impermeability of the capillary endothelium to protein sets up a Gibbs-Donnan effect, which accounts for the slight differences in distribution of diffusible ions between plasma and interstitial fluid.

Organic phosphates and proteins are the major anions in most cells, and potassium is the main intracellular cation. The characteristic composition of intracellular fluid results from selective impermeabilities mainly for organic phosphates and proteins, the resulting Gibbs-Donnan equilibrium, the transmembrane voltage, binding to nondiffusible compounds, and active transport of sodium out of cells and potassium into them.

The volume of each compartment is fixed by the total solute within it. The steady size of the plasma and interstitial compartments is determined by the balance of Starling forces: (a) intracapillary hydrostatic pressure and (b) interstitial oncotic pressure favoring fluid movement out of the capillary, and (c) plasma oncotic pressure and (d) hydrostatic pressure within the interstitium favoring movement of fluid in the opposite direction.

Active 'pumping' of sodium out of cells offsets the oncotic pressure of nondiffusible organic phosphates and proteins, and thereby ordinarily prevents swelling and bursting of cells.

Practically speaking, the major fluid compartments have the same osmolality. Water moves freely and rapidly among the compartments, mainly in response to differences in osmotic pressure, until osmotic equilibrium is attained. During the steady state, there is no *net* shift of water from one compartment to another.

PROBLEM 2-1

A woman weighing 60 kg is given 10 mg of T-1824 dye (Evans blue) intravenously. Ten minutes later, a blood sample is obtained from another vein, and colorimetric analysis of the plasma shows the presence of 0.4 mg of T-1824 per 100 mL of plasma.

Assume that the administered dye was evenly distributed throughout the plasma compartment by the end of the 10 minutes, and that no dye was lost from the plasma during this interval. Then calculate the woman's plasma volume.

If the blood corpuscles, mainly erythrocytes, constituted 45% of whole blood—i.e., if the woman's hematocrit ratio is 0.45—what is her total blood volume?

PROBLEM 2-2

Figure 2-7 is an adaptation of Figure 2-1 in that it combines the plasma and interstitial space into a single extracellular compartment. Given the fact that water moves freely among the body fluid compartments and that, at equilibrium, the compartments are in osmotic equilibrium, predict the changes in both the volume and osmolality of the intracellular compartment (ICW) and the extracellular compartment (ECW) that would occur with the following perturbations once a new steady state had been established:

1. A loss of isosmotic fluid, as might occur in very severe diarrhea
2. A loss of 'pure' H_2O (i.e., of H_2O without solute), as might occur in a person lost in the desert who is not sweating
3. A loss of NaCl without a net loss of H_2O, as might occur in a patient with adrenal insufficiency
4. A gain of isosmotic fluid, as in generalized edema
5. A gain of NaCl without a net gain of H_2O, as in a person who suddenly goes on a very high salt diet

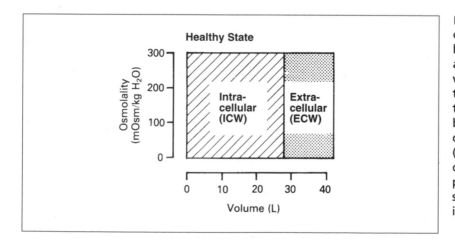

Figure 2-7. Volume and osmolality of the major body fluid compartments in an adult human who weighs 70 kg. In this figure, the plasma and the interstitial space have been combined into the single extracellular compartment (ECW). This simplification is often employed in the experimental or clinical analysis of fluid balance. ICW = intracellular compartment.

6. A gain of pure H_2O, as in the syndrome of inappropriate ADH secretion (SIADH).

(*Hint:* For an approach to this problem, see the analysis of Fig. 2-4.)

PROBLEM 2-3

A person who weighs 72 kg has a plasma Na^+ concentration of 125 mmol/L (i.e., abnormally low—see Table A-1 in the Appendix).

What, approximately, are the volumes of the major body fluid compartments in this person?

If one wished to raise the plasma Na^+ concentration in this person toward the normal value, say, to 135 mmol/L, how many mmol of Na^+ would have to be given?

SUGGESTED READINGS

Bernard, C. *Leçons sur les Phénomènes de la Vie Communs aux Animaux et aux Végétaux,* vol. 1. Paris: Baillière, 1878.

Brenner, B. M., and Stein, J. H. (Eds.). *Body Fluid Homeostasis.* New York: Churchill Livingstone, 1987.
This is Volume 16 in a series entitled 'Contemporary Issues in Nephrology'. The series covers both basic science and clinical topics.

Byrne, J. H., and Schultz, S. G. (Eds.). *An Introduction to Membrane Transport and Bioelectricity* (2nd ed.). New York: Raven, 1994.
A very well-written handbook for students beginning their study of membranes and transport. It omits only the electrochemical potential difference in its coverage of the subjects.

Fanestil, D. D. Compartmentation of Body Water. In R. G. Narins (Ed.), *Maxwell & Kleeman's Clinical Disorders of Fluid and Electrolyte Metabolism* (5th ed.). New York: McGraw-Hill, 1994. Chap. 1.

Guyton, A. C., Granger, H. J., and Taylor, A. E. Interstitial fluid pressure. *Physiol. Rev.* 51:527, 1971.

Macknight, A. D. C., and Leaf, A. Regulation of cellular volume. *Physiol. Rev.* 57:510, 1977.

Michel, C. C. Capillary Exchange. In D. W. Seldin and G. Giebisch (Eds.), *The Kidney. Physiology and Pathophysiology* (2nd ed.). New York: Raven, 1992. Chap. 3.

Rose, B. D. *Clinical Physiology of Acid-Base and Electrolyte Disorders* (4th ed.). New York: McGraw-Hill, 1994.

Schmidt-Nielsen, K. *Desert Animals: Physiological Problems of Heat and Water.* London: Oxford University Press, 1964.

Schultz, S. G. *Basic Principles of Membrane Transport.* Cambridge: Cambridge Univ. Press, 1980.
A more detailed coverage of membrane transport and bioelectricity than Byrne and Schultz (above), including the concept of the electrochemical potential.

Spring, K. R., and Hoffmann, E. K. Cellular Volume Control. In D. W. Seldin and G. Giebisch (Eds.), *The Kidney. Physiology and Pathophysiology* (2nd ed.). New York: Raven, 1992. Chap. 6.

Starling, E. H. On the absorption of fluids from the connective tissue spaces. *J. Physiol.* (Lond.) 19:312, 1896.

Zweifach, B. W., and Silberberg, A. The interstitial-lymphatic flow system. *Int. Rev. Physiol.* 18:215, 1979.

Glomerular Filtration

3

ULTRAFILTRATION

The formation of urine begins with the filtration of plasma water and its nonprotein constituents (called *crystalloids*) from the glomerular capillaries into Bowman's space (Fig. 1-2). This operation, called ultrafiltration (see Chap. 2, p. 34), leaves blood cells and protein macromolecules (the *colloids*) in the blood because they cannot pass through the permselective walls of the glomerular capillaries. The process is thus qualitatively the same as that occurring in systemic capillaries, although, as we shall see, the two are quantitatively different.

Proof for ultrafiltration by glomeruli was first obtained in 1921 by J. T. Wearn and A. N. Richards through the technique of micropuncture. They succeeded in collecting fluid from Bowman's space by means of tiny micropipets having a tip diameter of 7 to 15 μm. The collected fluid contained no protein as measured by methods then available (actually, very small amounts of protein are filtered and then reabsorbed), and it had approximately the same composition as plasma in respect to osmolality, electrical conductivity (i.e., total concentration of electrolytes), glucose and other solutes, and pH. Furthermore, the distribution of diffusible electrolytes between glomerular capillary plasma and fluid in Bowman's space conformed to the Gibbs-Donnan relationship. The early results were obtained in amphibians (frog and *Necturus*), and they have since been confirmed in rodents, dogs, primates, and other species.

FORCES INVOLVED IN GLOMERULAR ULTRAFILTRATION

These are the Starling forces, which were reviewed for systemic capillaries in conjunction with Figure 2-5. Those pertaining to mammalian glomeruli are shown in Figure 3-1. There are several differences between the systemic and glomerular systems: (1) Hydrostatic pressure is higher and remains relatively constant in glomerular capillaries, whereas it declines markedly along the length of extrarenal capillaries. (2) Glomerular capillaries are less permeable to proteins than systemic capillaries. Hence, the oncotic pressure in Bowman's space is lower than interstitial oncotic pressure. (3) In contrast to the plasma oncotic pressure in

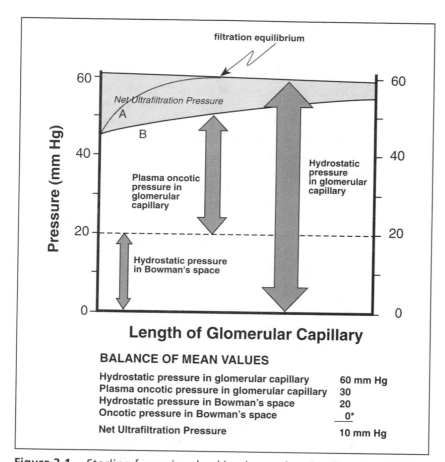

Figure 3-1. Starling forces involved in glomerular ultrafiltration. Note that ultrafiltration pressure declines in glomerular capillaries mainly because plasma oncotic pressure rises, not because of a decrease in intracapillary hydrostatic pressure, as is the case in systemic capillaries (Fig. 2-5). The point at which the sum of the hydrostatic pressure in Bowman's space plus the plasma oncotic pressure equals the hydrostatic pressure in the glomerular capillary is known as *filtration equilibrium*. This point is reached in some species (e.g., rats—Curve *A*) but not in others (e.g., dogs and humans—Curve *B*). An increase in the rate at which plasma enters the glomerular capillary will lead to a shift from Curve *A* to Curve *B*, and hence to a rise in the mean net ultrafiltration pressure and an increase in the glomerular filtration rate. Data from Navar, L. G., Carmines, P. K., and Paul, R. V. In S. G. Massry and R. J. Glassock (Eds.), *Textbook of Nephrology* (2nd ed.). Baltimore: Williams & Wilkins, 1989. Chap. 2.

*The concentration of protein in Bowman's space fluid is negligibly small; the estimated oncotic pressure is perhaps 0.3 mm Hg.

systemic capillaries, which stays relatively constant, that in glomerular capillaries rises along the length of the capillary. (4) The hydrostatic pressure in Bowman's space is considerably higher than its systemic analogue, the tissue hydrostatic pressure. Nevertheless, the balance of the Starling forces is such that the mean net ultrafiltration pressure is only slightly higher in glomerular capillaries (Fig. 3-1) than in extrarenal capillaries (Fig. 2-5). In the latter, net ultrafiltration pressure declines because capillary hydrostatic pressure decreases, whereas in glomerular capillaries, net ultrafiltration pressure declines mainly because plasma oncotic pressure increases. Furthermore, in glomerular capillaries, net movement of fluid is primarily or solely out of the capillaries, whereas in systemic capillaries net movement out of the vessels is nearly balanced by net return of fluid into the vessels.

Even though the mean net ultrafiltration pressure is similar in glomerular and extrarenal capillaries, the transmural movement of fluid out of glomerular capillaries, called the glomerular filtration rate (GFR), far exceeds the analogous flow, J_V of Equation 2-8, in extrarenal capillaries. Hence K_f, the filtration coefficient, must be much larger for glomerular capillaries. As defined in Chapter 2, K_f is a function of total capillary surface area as well as of the permeability per unit of surface area. Both factors are probably involved in raising the K_f of glomerular capillaries. Total glomerular capillary area has been estimated to be from 5,000 to 15,000 cm^2 per 100 g of renal tissue. In contrast, this area is perhaps 7,000 cm^2 per 100 g of skeletal muscle. In addition, per unit of surface area, glomerular capillaries may be at least 100 times more permeable to water and crystalloids than muscle capillaries.

There is one other determinant of glomerular ultrafiltration, at least in some species, and that is the rate at which plasma flows through the capillaries. Other things being equal, the greater the rate at which plasma enters the glomerular capillaries, the greater will be the rate at which it is filtered into Bowman's space. The reason is that, under these circumstances, the plasma oncotic pressure rises more slowly (as in a shift from *curve A* to *curve B* in Fig. 3-1), so that the shaded area, which represents the net ultrafiltration pressure, increases. By this means, the net ultrafiltration pressure can vary from 4 mm Hg to 12 mm Hg. In most instances, however, the Starling forces, not the rate of glomerular plasma flow, are quantitatively the most important determinants of glomerular ultrafiltration.

■ **Ultrafiltration: Glomerular vs. other Capillaries** ■

The glomerular system has:

Higher hydrostatic pressure in capillary and little decrease in this pressure along the capillary

Higher hydrostatic pressure in Bowman's space

Lower oncotic pressure in Bowman's space

Rise in plasma oncotic pressure

Higher K_f

CHARACTERISTICS OF THE
GLOMERULAR CAPILLARY

The fact that K_f is much greater in glomerular than in systemic capillaries suggests that the glomerular capillary differs from other capillaries, such as those of skeletal muscle. Both glomerular and extrarenal capillaries permit free passage of small molecules such as water [0.2 nanometer (nm) diameter], urea (0.32 nm diameter), sodium (0.4 nm diameter), chloride (0.35 nm diameter), and glucose (0.7 nm diameter); but they do not permit free passage of larger particles such as erythrocytes (8,000 nm diameter) or large plasma proteins. The limits of glomerular capillary permeability are suggested by the fact that hemoglobin (6.5 nm diameter), as well as smaller plasma proteins such as albumin (3.6 by 15 nm), are not freely filtered but do get through the membrane in small amounts. In other words, the glomerular capillary behaves as if it were a filtering membrane containing aqueous 'pores' with a diameter of 7.5 to 10 nm. These pores are not specialized membrane proteins like those described in Chapter 2 (under Explanation for Differences in Composition); rather, they are aqueous channels between the cells and in the basement membrane of the glomerular capillary wall (described next).

Given these functional characteristics, anatomists have examined the wall of the glomerular capillary, to see if it contained a structure with fenestrations of the required dimensions. The wall (Fig. 3-2C) consists of three layers: (a) endothelium, (b) basement membrane, and (c) epithelium (podocytes with foot processes). The endothelium appears to contain openings with a diameter of 70 to 100 nm. Although these apertures may be bridged by thin diaphragms, the endothelium appears to be freely permeable even to large molecules. It does, however, exclude blood cells from Bowman's space. The basement membrane consists of three filamentous layers (lamina rara interna, lamina densa, and lamina rara externa); the first and third of these layers are fused with the endothelium and epithelium, respectively. Many workers consider the basement membrane to be the most important restrictive layer, often referred to as the *filtration barrier*. The epithelium consists of highly specialized cells called *podocytes*, which are attached to the basement membrane by *foot processes* known as pedicels. Adjacent pedicels are separated by *filtration slits* measuring about 25 to 60 nm in width, and the slits are bridged by thin diaphragms, which appear to have small interstices, perhaps 7 by

■ **The Glomerular** ■
Filtration Barrier

Endothelium—a gross filter

Excludes cells

Basement membrane—the main barrier

Excludes most of the plasma proteins

Epithelium—possibly additional barrier

Specialized extension of Bowman's capsule Phagocytizes macromolecules

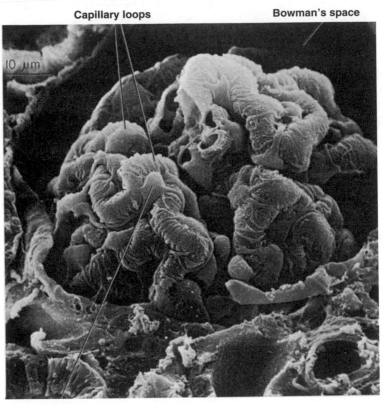

Capillary loops   **Bowman's space**

10 μm

Podocyte

A

Figure 3-2. Scanning electron micrographs of (A) a glomerulus, magnified about 1,440 times, and (B) a loop of a glomerular capillary, magnified about 5,900 times. A transmission electron micrograph (×36,000) of a glomerular capillary, viewed in longitudinal section, is shown in (C); the portion on the left indicates the distribution of negative charges in the glomerular capillary wall.

14 nm in dimension. Thus, the epithelium may constitute an important filtration barrier in addition to the basement membrane, and some investigators favor this view.

The above deductions are based simply on the size of apertures, which is not the only factor that limits passage of compounds through the glomerular capillary wall. The shape of a molecule (not just its diameter), its flexibility and deformability, and perhaps especially its charge also play important roles. The effect of the last is shown in Figure 3-3. Dextrans are polysaccharides that can be produced in a range of molecular weights and hence sizes,

Podocyte

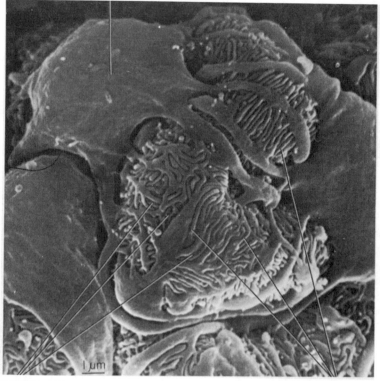

1 μm

Filtration slits

B

Foot processes

0.3 μm

Bowman's space   Foot processes

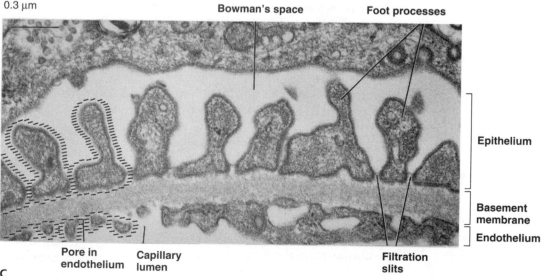

Epithelium

Basement membrane

Endothelium

Pore in endothelium   Capillary lumen

Filtration slits

C

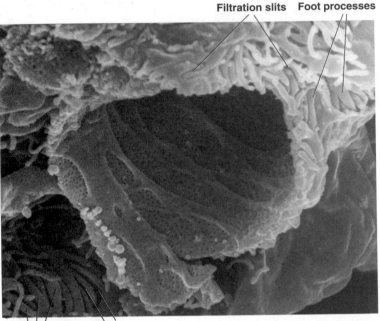

Filtration slits   Foot processes

Foot processes   Filtration slits   1 micron
D

Figure 3-2 Continued.   Shown in (D) is a scanning electron micrograph of a sectioned capillary loop (magnified approximately 10,000 times); it depicts the entire glomerular capillary wall, with openings (arrows) in the endothelium, and interdigitating foot processes that form filtration slits, on the exterior of the vessel. The basement membrane lies between the endothelium and the epithelium (podocytes). Photomicrographs (A) and (B) from Spinelli, F., Wirz, H., and Brücher, C. *Fine Structure of the Kidney Revealed by Scanning Electron-Microscopy.* Basel: Ciba-Geigy, 1972. Illustrations (C) and (D) were kindly supplied by C. C. Tisher and J. W. Verlander, respectively.

as well as in an electrically neutral form or with net negative charges (polyanionic dextrans) or net positive charges (polycationic dextrans). At any given effective molecular radius, the dextrans with positive charges pass more readily through the glomerular filter than do neutral dextrans; and negatively charged dextrans encounter even greater hindrance than do neutral dextrans (Fig. 3-3). This selective filterability is explained by the presence of negatively charged glycoproteins (called *glycosialoproteins*) on the surface of all components of the glomerular capillary wall (see left portion of Fig. 3-2C), especially on the endothelium, the lamina rara interna and lamina rara externa of the basement membrane, and the podocytes and foot processes, including the di-

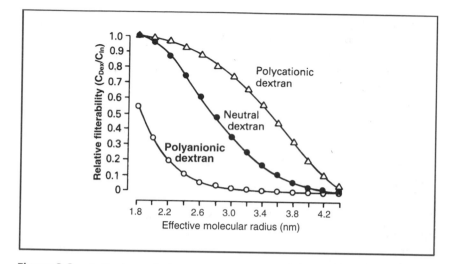

Figure 3-3. Influence of electrical charge of a molecule on the filterability of that molecule through the glomerular capillary wall of rats. At any given molecular size, negatively charged dextrans traverse the filtration barrier less readily than do neutral dextrans or, in turn, than do positively charged dextrans. Plasma proteins have multiple negative charges at physiological pH; therefore, the curve for polyanionic dextrans resembles the behavior of plasma proteins. Slightly modified from Bohrer, M. P., et al. *J. Clin. Invest.* 61:72, 1978.

aphragms in the filtration slits. In other words, the glomerular capillary wall, in addition to discriminating on the basis of size, also acts as an electrostatic barrier.

Although there is not yet consensus on all aspects of the nature of the glomerular filtration barrier, the following is a working model that many workers favor. The endothelium acts as a gross filter that screens out cells and controls access to the main filter, which may be the basement membrane. The epithelium may provide an additional, important barrier, and it can phagocytize macromolecules that have leaked through the basement membrane. There are also mesangial cells, which abut the capillary loops and which are thought to recondition and unclog the filter. By virtue of their contractile properties, mesangial cells probably influence the rate of plasma flow through glomerular capillaries and thereby the glomerular filtration rate.

Finally, the concept of anatomical pores as such may be naive. The functional characteristics of glomerular capillaries could be accounted for as well if the restrictive barrier were a hydrated gel, with the interstices between glycosialoprotein polymers constituting the channels through which water and crystalloids flow. Whatever the true picture, it does seem clear that the higher trans-mural filtration rate of glomerular as opposed to extrarenal capil-laries is due to a combination of a much greater permeability for water and crystalloids per unit of surface area, a larger capillary surface area per unit of tissue, and a slightly higher mean net ul-trafiltration pressure.

MEASUREMENT OF GLOMERULAR FILTRATION RATE (GFR)

The quantity of plasma filtered by the glomeruli can be deter-mined by the clearance of inulin, a starch-like polymer of fructose having a molecular weight of about 5,000 daltons (see Table A-5). It is a foreign substance that must be infused intravenously during the clearance test. Since it is not bound to plasma proteins, has a diameter of about 3 nm, and is not charged, it passes readily through the glomerular capillary membrane. In addition, it is not reabsorbed, secreted, or metabolized by renal tubules.

The principles involved in the measurement of the GFR by the inulin clearance are shown in Figure 3-4, where the values are those for human kidneys; the method entails the following steps:

1. Measure the rate of urine flow, $\dot{V}$; $\dot{V} = 1.1$ mL/min.
2. Measure the concentration of inulin in the urine, U_{In}; $U_{In} = 60$ mg/mL.
3. Calculate the amount of inulin excreted in the urine per min-ute.

$$U_{In} \times \dot{V} = \frac{60 \text{ mg}}{\text{mL}} \times \frac{1.1 \text{ mL}}{\text{min}} = 66 \text{ mg/min}$$

4. Now, if:
   (a) all inulin reaching the urine got there by filtration, and
   (b) inulin was not reabsorbed from the tubular lumen, and
   (c) inulin was not secreted into the tubular lumen, and
   (d) inulin was not metabolized by the kidneys, and
   (e) the plasma concentration of inulin, P_{In}, was 0.5 mg/mL; i.e., if each milliliter of plasma contained 0.5 mg of inulin, how many milliliters of plasma must have been filtered in order to excrete 66 mg of inulin?

$$66 \text{ mg} \div \frac{0.5 \text{ mg}}{\text{mL}} = 132 \text{ mL}$$

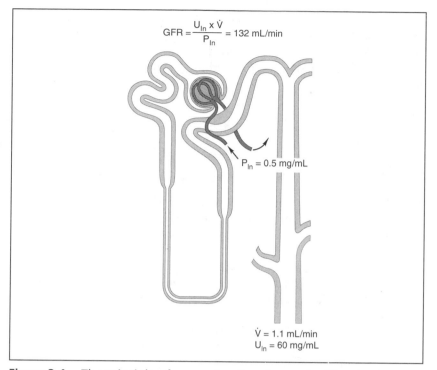

Figure 3-4. The principle of measuring the glomerular filtration rate (GFR) by means of the inulin clearance. In this figure, the single nephron represents all nephrons from both kidneys of an adult human.

5. Since 66 mg of inulin was excreted per minute, 132 mL of plasma must have been filtered each minute.

$$\frac{66\ \text{mg}}{\text{min}} \div \frac{0.5\ \text{mg}}{\text{mL}} = \frac{66\ \text{mg}}{\text{min}} \times \frac{\text{mL}}{0.5\ \text{mg}} = 132\ \text{mL/min}$$

Thus, during each minute, 132 mL of plasma and its contained small solutes were separated by ultrafiltration from the blood and its larger protein molecules flowing through the glomerular capillaries. This measurement of the GFR is called the *inulin clearance*, C_{In}, for which the formula is $U_{In} \times \dot{V}/P_{In}$. It is defined as the volume of plasma from which, in 1 minute's time, the kidneys remove all inulin.

There is another, intuitive derivation of the formula. The amount of inulin that is filtered into Bowman's space each minute (called the *filtered load of inulin*) is the product of the plasma concentration of inulin and the GFR: $P_{In} \times$ GFR. The amount of inulin excreted each minute is the product of the urinary concentration of inulin and the urine flow: $U_{In} \times \dot{V}$. Since inulin, once deposited in Bowman's space, is not reabsorbed by the tubules, not secreted by them, nor metabolized, the filtered load of inulin is equal to its urinary excretion:

$$P_{In} \times GFR = U_{In} \times \dot{V}$$

$$\therefore \quad GFR = \frac{U_{In} \times \dot{V}}{P_{In}} \tag{3-1}$$

Several features of this measurement should be noted:

- *The clearance technique is not confined to the measurement of the GFR;* it can be and is applied to many substances besides inulin. The formula for all renal clearances (except the free-water clearance, see Chap. 8) is $U \times \dot{V}/P$, where U is the concentration of a given substance in the urine, $\dot{V}$ is the urine flow, and P is the concentration of the same substance in the plasma.
- Plasma, not urine, is being cleared of a given substance, in this case inulin. The units for the inulin clearance refer to the milliliters of *plasma* from which all inulin has been removed.
- The inulin clearance is independent of the plasma inulin concentration. As P_{In} increases, more inulin will be filtered so that U_{In} will rise in direct proportion to the increase in P_{In} (Fig. 3-4).
- The inulin clearance is independent of the urine flow; for a given quantity of inulin in the urine, U_{In} will fall proportionately as $\dot{V}$ rises, and vice versa.

The last two points are illustrated in Problem 3-1, at the end of this chapter.

Concept of Filtration Fraction

Not all the plasma that flows through the glomerular capillaries can be filtered into Bowman's space. This situation would be an obvious impossibility, for it would require the movement of all plasma out of the capillaries, leaving behind a solid mass of cells and colloids that could not move on into the efferent arterioles. As is shown in Figure 3-1, long before this state is reached, filtration stops because the sum of the hydrostatic pressure in Bowman's space plus the rising plasma oncotic pressure equals the hydrostatic pressure in the glomerular capillaries. Normally, only about one-fifth of the plasma entering the glomerular capillaries is filtered; this is called the *filtration fraction*, the definition and derivation of which are given in Chapter 5.

■ Clearance of Inulin: ■
A Measure of GFR

1. Infuse inulin intravenously until a constant plasma concentration of inulin is obtained
2. Determine urine volume over a known period of time so that urine flow, $\dot{V}$, can be calculated
3. Measure concentration of inulin in the urine and in a blood sample taken during the urine collection period
4. Apply Equation 3-1

Inulin: Neither Reabsorbed nor Secreted

Use of the inulin clearance as a measure of GFR is valid only if all the inulin that appears in the urine got there by filtration, i.e., only if inulin is not reabsorbed, metabolized, or secreted by the renal tubules. Proof that these conditions are met was obtained through a number of micropuncture experiments, one of which is illustrated in Figure 3-5. A proximal tubule of a rat was punctured at E from the surface of the kidney, and a column of oil, C, was injected via a micropipet in order to block the tubular lumen. This pipet was then withdrawn, leaving an opening at E through which newly formed glomerular filtrate could escape. A second pipet, A, was then inserted distal to the oil column, and a green dye was injected. This dye traversed the remainder of the proximal tubule and the loop of Henle, and reappeared on the surface of the kidney in the distal tubule belonging to this single nephron. A third pipet, B, was then inserted into the distal segment, and the remainder of the tubule was blocked with a second oil column, D.

Figure 3-5. A micropuncture experiment in a rat kidney. The symbols, as well as the rationale of the experiment, are explained in the text. The arrows indicate the direction of flow of tubular fluid. Slightly modified from Marsh, D., and Frasier, C. *Am. J. Physiol.* 209:283, 1965. Published with permission.

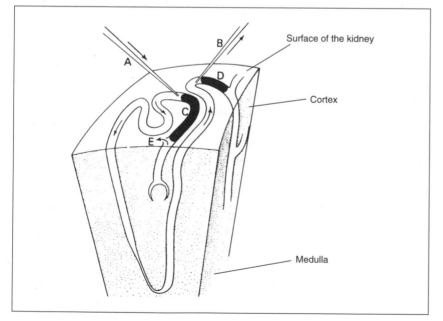

A known amount of inulin was now infused into the proximal segment through pipet A at the same time that all fluid perfusing that nephron was collected through pipet B. The fact that 99.3% of the injected inulin could be thus recovered strongly suggests that inulin was not reabsorbed. Furthermore, the rate of recovery was the same when the peritubular plasma was loaded with inulin; hence secretion of inulin was also excluded. Finally when oil block D was not present, virtually all the inulin microinjected into the proximal tubule could be recovered in the ureteral urine. Thus, inulin is not reabsorbed, metabolized, or secreted in any portion of the nephron.

Other Substances

There are substances besides inulin that are also freely filtered but not affected by passage along the renal tubules. Hence such substances, too, can be used to measure GFR. Examples include creatinine and iothalamate. Some substances meet the criteria in one species but not in others. For example, under physiological conditions, creatinine is neither reabsorbed nor secreted in the dog, and is therefore equal to the inulin clearance. In humans, however, the creatinine clearance is slightly higher than the GFR because the renal tubules secrete a small amount of creatinine. The identity of the inulin and creatinine clearances in a dog is illustrated by the calculations given in Problem 3-2 at the end of this chapter.

Clearance as a General Concept

It was emphasized above that the clearance concept is not restricted to the determination of GFR. One can measure the renal clearance of any substance, and the comparison of that clearance to that of inulin has important functional implications. For example, if, during any given time interval, less plasma is cleared of urea (a small molecule that is freely filterable) than is cleared of inulin, one can deduce that there must have been net reabsorption of urea in its course through the tubular system. (A quantitative example of this deduction is given in the Answers to Problems 4-1 and 8-1 at the end of the text.) Conversely, if, during a given time interval, more plasma is cleared of a substance than is cleared of inulin, that substance must have been added to the urine by an additional process besides glomerular filtration. That process, called *tubular secretion,* is discussed in Chapter 5.

Finally, it should be stressed that *the clearance concept is by no means restricted to renal function.* One can measure the rates at

■ **Clearances of** ■
other Substances (C_X)
Compared to Clearance
of Inulin (C_{In})

$C_X = C_{In}$
No net reabsorption or secretion of X

$C_X < C_{In}$
Net reabsorption of X

$C_X > C_{In}$
Net secretion of X

which the lungs, or the liver, or other organs remove a given substance from plasma; or one can determine the so-called total, or 'whole-body', clearance, which represents the sum of the various regional clearances. Such applications of the clearance concept are commonly used in the study of drug or hormone metabolism.

MEANING OF TF/P AND U/P FOR INULIN

Not only is inulin freely filtered, it is also a nonelectrolyte and therefore not subject to a Gibbs-Donnan effect. Hence, the concentration of inulin in Bowman's capsule fluid (B_{In}) will be identical to that in plasma (P_{In}), and P_{In} can be substituted for B_{In}. Since inulin is neither reabsorbed from nor secreted into the tubular lumen, its concentration in tubular fluid increases as water is reabsorbed from the various tubular segments; in fact, the concentration of inulin in the tubular fluid will be solely a function of the amount of water reabsorbed up to the point at which the tubule is punctured and a microsample is withdrawn.

For example, if the concentration of inulin in tubular fluid (TF_{In}) withdrawn from the proximal tubule is twice as great as that in Bowman's space (i.e., twice as great as P_{In}), it is obvious that 50% of the filtered water must have been reabsorbed. Hence a 'TF/P inulin' (i.e., the ratio of the concentration of inulin in tubular fluid to that in plasma) of 2 reflects reabsorption of one-half of the filtered water, and the formula for calculating this fraction is given in Equation 3-2:

Fraction of filtered water reabsorbed
up to point of micropuncture

$$= 1 - \frac{1}{TF/P \text{ inulin}} \qquad (3\text{-}2)$$

$$= 1 - \frac{1}{2}$$

$$= 0.5, \text{ or } 50\%$$

Micropuncture samples withdrawn from the very last segment of a proximal tubule at the surface of the kidney have inulin concentrations that are nearly 3 times greater than the concentration in plasma; that is, TF/P inulin approaches 3, and the fraction of filtered water reabsorbed would be 0.67. This, in fact, constitutes some of the experimental evidence that roughly two-thirds, or 67%, of the filtered fluid is normally reabsorbed in the proximal tubule.

By similar reasoning, the U/P inulin (the ratio of the concentration of inulin in the urine to its concentration in plasma) can be used to calculate the fraction of filtered water reabsorbed by the kidneys, as given in Equation 3-3:

$$\text{Fraction of filtered water reabsorbed by both kidneys} = 1 - \frac{1}{\text{U/P inulin}} \quad (3\text{-}3)$$

In the example given in Figure 3-4, $1 - \frac{1}{120} = 0.992$; i.e., 99.2% of the filtered water was reaborbed. This point can be verified independently by calculating that the urine flow of 1.1 mL per minute constitutes 0.8% of the amount of fluid filtered, 132 mL per minute. Expressing this point mathematically, and thereby deriving Equation 3-3:

$$\text{Fraction of filtered water excreted} \quad = \frac{\dot{V}}{\text{GFR}}$$

$$= \frac{\dot{V}}{\text{Inulin clearance}}$$

$$= \dot{V} \div \frac{U_{In} \times \dot{V}}{P_{In}}$$

$$= \frac{\dot{V}}{1} \times \frac{P_{In}}{U_{In} \times \dot{V}}$$

$$= \frac{P_{In}}{U_{In}}$$

$$\text{Fraction of filtered water reabsorbed} = 1 - \frac{P_{In}}{U_{In}}$$

$$= 1 - \frac{1}{\text{U/P inulin}} \quad (3\text{-}3)$$

Note that Equations 3-2 and 3-3 permit one to quantify important aspects about the renal handling of water without actually measuring water flow; all that is needed is the concentration of inulin in tubular fluid and plasma or in urine and plasma, respectively. This fact provides an important advantage, for it obviates the often difficult task of accurately measuring the urine flow or the even more exacting chore of measuring the flow rate of tubular fluid. This simplification can be extended to gauge the renal handling of any other substance through determination of the *clearance ratio*.

(For an explanation, see footnote b in Problem 4-1; and for a quantitative example, see Problem 6-1.)

SUMMARY

The initial step in the formation of urine is ultrafiltration of plasma in the glomerular capillaries, which act as permselective filters that discriminate on the basis of molecular size, shape, deformability, and charge. The rate of ultrafiltration is governed by: (a) the balance of Starling forces; (b) the permeability of the glomerular capillary wall to water and small solutes; (c) the total surface area of the capillaries; and (d) the rate at which plasma flows into the glomerular capillaries. The first three factors, especially point (b), are greater in glomerular than in most extrarenal capillaries; hence, the rate of glomerular filtration (GFR) far exceeds analogous movement of fluid across walls of most systemic capillaries.

The GFR can be measured by the inulin clearance, which is defined as the volume of plasma from which, in a minute's time, the kidneys remove all inulin. Normally, about one-fifth of the plasma

Problem 3-1. Sample calculations illustrating the independence of the inulin clearance from the plasma concentration of inulin (top portion) and from the rate of urine flow (lower portion) in a dog. Utilizing the data given, calculate the inulin clearances; indicate the units for clearance.

Urine flow (mL/min)	Inulin concentration		Inulin clearance ( )
	Plasma (mg/mL)	Urine (mg/mL)	
1.2	0.9	45	
1.3	1.4	68	
1.0	2.3	141	
1.4	3.8	168	
1.2	5.7	294	
1.3	0.5	23	
2.1	0.6	17	
3.1	0.4	8	
5.7	0.5	5	
6.6	0.5	4.6	

Modified from Shannon, J. A. *Am. J. Physiol.* 112:405, 1935.

Problem 3-2.   Sample calculations illustrating the identity of the inulin and creatinine clearances in a dog. Utilizing the data given, calculate the inulin and creatinine clearances; supply the units for clearance.

Urine flow (mL/min)	Inulin			Creatinine		
	Plasma (mg/dL)	Urine (mg/dL)	Clearance ( )	Plasma (mg/dL)	Urine (mg/dL)	Clearance ( )
1.0	104	5,076		13.7	673	
1.1	106	4,601		14.7	630	
0.9	108	6,017		16.0	890	
1.0	109	5,137		16.6	792	

Modified from Shannon, J. A. *Am. J. Physiol.* 112:405, 1935.

that flows through the glomerular capillaries is filtered into Bowman's space.

Since inulin, once filtered, is not removed from tubular fluid by reabsorption or catabolism, nor secreted into the tubular lumen, the degree to which it is concentrated in tubular fluid will be solely a function of the amount of filtered water that is reabsorbed. Ordinarily, nearly 70% of the filtered water is reabsorbed in the proximal tubules, and more than 99% of water entering Bowman's space is reabsorbed by the entire renal tubular system.

PROBLEM 3-3

In the steady state, an organism is in balance, which means that the output of a given substance is equal to the input of that substance. The principle of the steady state is well illustrated in the attainment of balance for inulin as this compound is infused into a subject for the measurement of the GFR. (Although the inulin clearance is seldom used to determine GFR in patients, the principle of balance when applied to urea and endogenous creatinine is so utilized.)

In the study for which data are given in Table 3-1, inulin was infused into the antecubital vein of a healthy human subject whose GFR is 120 mL per minute. The inulin was infused at a steady rate of 72 mg per minute, and periodically blood was withdrawn for determination of the plasma inulin concentration, P_{In}.

Table 3-1. Attainment of a steady state for inulin during a stable intravenous infusion of inulin in a healthy adult human.

Elapsed time (min)	Rate of inulin infusion (mg/min)	GFR (mL/min)	P_{In} (mg/mL)	Urinary excretion of inulin (mg/min)
1	72	120	0.005	
5	72	120	0.02	
10	72	120	0.05	
50	72	120	0.24	
100	72	120	0.47	
110	72	120	0.6	
120	72	120	0.6	

1. Fill in the blank column in Table 3-1. *Hint:* Knowing the properties of inulin and how it is handled by the kidneys, you can do the required calculations even though the urinary concentration of inulin and the urine flow are not given.
2. Why does the plasma concentration of inulin increase? At what point will it stop rising?
3. At what point is the steady state reached?
4. Is there a self-contradiction in saying that this person, with a GFR of 120 mL per minute, is healthy when a normal GFR was earlier stated to be 132 mL per minute (Fig. 3-4)?

SUGGESTED READINGS

Arendshorst, W. J., and Navar, L. B. Renal Circulation and Glomerular Hemodynamics. In R. W. Schrier and C. W. Gottschalk (Eds.), *Diseases of the Kidney* (5th ed.). Boston: Little, Brown, 1993. Chap. 2.

Bradley, S. E. Clearance Concept in Renal Physiology. In C. W. Gottschalk, R. W. Berliner, and G. H. Giebisch (Eds.), *Renal Physiology. People and Ideas.* Bethesda: American Physiological Society, 1987. Chap. III.

Maddox, D. A., and Brenner, B. M. Glomerular Ultrafiltration. In B. M. Brenner and F. C. Rector, Jr. (Eds.), *The Kidney* (4th ed.). Philadelphia: Saunders, 1991. Chap. 6.

Pappenheimer, J. R. Passage of molecules through capillary walls. *Physiol. Rev.* 33:387, 1953.

Smith, H. W. *The Kidney. Structure and Function in Health and Disease.* New York: Oxford University Press, 1951.

Thurau, K., Davis, J. M., and Häberle, D. A. Renal Blood Flow and Dynamics of Glomerular Filtration: Evolution of a Concept from Carl Ludwig to the Present Day. In C. W. Gottschalk, R. W. Berliner, and G. H. Giebisch (Eds.), *Renal Physiology. People and Ideas.* Bethesda: American Physiological Society, 1987. Chap. II.

Tisher, C. C., and Madsen, K. R. Anatomy of the Kidney. In B. M. Brenner and F. C. Rector, Jr. (Eds.), *The Kidney* (4th ed.). Philadelphia: Saunders, 1991. Chap. 1.

Walker, A., Bott, P., Oliver, J., and MacDowell, M. The collection and analysis of fluid from single nephrons of the mammalian kidney. *Am. J. Physiol.* 134:580, 1941.

Wearn, J. T., and Richards, A. N. Observations on the composition of glomerular urine, with particular reference to the problem of reabsorption in the renal tubules. *Am. J. Physiol.* 71:209, 1924.

Venkatachalam, M., and Kanwar, Y. Ultrastructure of the Glomerulus and Juxtaglomerular Apparatus. In E. E. Windhager (Ed.), *Handbook of Physiology, section 8: Renal Physiology,* vol. II. New York: Oxford University Press, 1991. Chap. 29.

Tubular Reabsorption

4

Water and many solutes are reabsorbed from the tubular lumen into the peritubular interstitial fluid and thence into the blood. Because the activities of water and small molecules in interstitial fluid are virtually identical to those in plasma, we often speak of reabsorption directly into the blood. The term *reabsorption* refers to the *direction* of transport, i.e., out of the tubular lumen; it is applied to all modes of transport in that direction, be they active or passive.

Generally speaking, tubular reabsorption facilitates the conservation of substances that are essential to normal function—e.g., water, glucose and other sugars, amino acids, and electrolytes. Many of these substances, such as glucose and amino acids, are reabsorbed primarily or exclusively by the proximal tubules, whereas others, such as water and sodium, are also reabsorbed at more distal sites in the nephron.

PRINCIPLES OF EPITHELIAL TRANSPORT

The process of tubular reabsorption, as well as that of tubular secretion (Chap. 5), involves transport of substances across the tubular walls, which are comprised of epithelial cells. Several characteristics of such cells—which occur also in many other organs, such as the gallbladder, intestines, lungs, and choroid plexus—are shown in Figure 4-1. Transporting epithelial cells are polarized in the sense that they are bounded by two membranes that have very different properties: the *apical* membrane, which faces the lumen, and the *basolateral* membrane, which lines the lateral intercellular spaces and faces the basement membrane and peritubular capillaries. These two membranes are separated by the *junctional complex* (or *tight junction*), a ring-like structure that surrounds each cell of the epithelium and forms its point of contact with neighboring cells. Jared Diamond aptly characterized the junctional complex by comparing it to the piece of plastic that holds a six-pack of drink cans together. In this analogy, the apical membranes are like the tops of the cans, and the basolateral membranes like the sides and bottoms of the cans.

The apical and basolateral membranes differ primarily with respect to the transporters that they contain. For example, Na-K-ATPase, the active transporter that carries Na^+ out of cells into the blood, is found only in basolateral membranes (of all nephron segments), whereas other transporters that allow Na^+ to enter the cell from the tubular lumen are found in the apical membranes (see, for example, Figs. 4-3 and 7-4). Such polarization of transporters

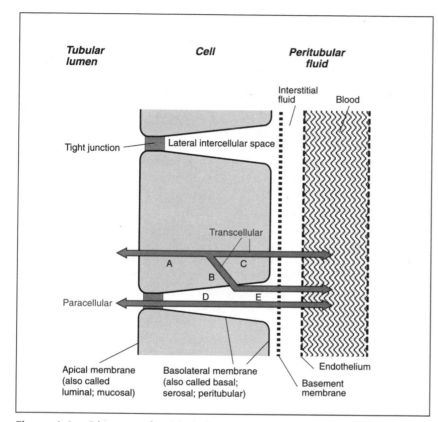

Figure 4-1. Diagram of epithelial cells that constitute the walls of renal tubules. Description is given in the text. The energy-requiring pump *Na-K-ATPase* (not shown), is found all along the basolateral membrane, which lines the intercellular spaces and is apposed to the basement membrane; Na-K-ATPase is absent from the apical membrane.

between apical and basolateral membranes in epithelia is essential to their function of transporting substances, in the net, in only one direction, e.g., from the lumen toward the blood in the case of reabsorption.

Routes of Transport

Substances can move across the epithelial cell layer by either of the two routes depicted in Figure 4-1. The *transcellular* route takes substances across the apical membrane, the cytoplasm, and the basolateral membrane (A, C or A, B, E in Fig. 4-1), whereas the *paracellular* route takes them across the tight junctions and through the lateral intercellular spaces (D, E).

Modes of Transport

As discussed in Chapter 2 (under Explanation for Differences in Composition), substances are transported either *actively* or *passively*. The process of *primary active transport* requires the direct input of energy to membrane transport proteins or *pumps,* such as Na-K-ATPase or H-ATPase, which hydrolyze adenosine triphosphate (ATP). In another form of active transport, referred to as *secondary active transport,* the driving force is the potential energy available in one of two solutes that are transported together, either in the same direction (called *cotransport* or *symport*) or in opposite directions (called *exchange* or *antiport*). That is, the energy comes from linking the 'downhill' movement of one solute (down its electrochemical gradient) to the 'uphill' movement of the other solute (against its electrochemical gradient). The most common examples of such transporters are Na^+-*cotransporters* that couple the downhill movement of Na^+ into epithelial cells to the uphill transport of other solutes into the cell across the apical membrane (described in greater detail in conjunction with Fig. 4-3). Inasmuch as the two linked solutes can go in opposite directions, secondary active transport does not necessarily imply cotransport. Thus, in many segments of the nephron, hydrogen ion secretion is driven by Na^+ moving downhill into cells in exchange for hydrogen ions moving uphill from the cells into the lumen (so-called Na-H exchange; e.g., Fig. 10-1).

A special form of active transport is *endocytosis,* by which the tiny amounts of protein that get past the glomerular filtration barrier (see previous chapter, under Ultrafiltration) are reabsorbed. In this process, protein is engulfed by the apical membrane, creating invaginations that are pinched off to form intracellular vesicles. The protein is then digested within the cell. Endocytosis is a form of active transport because it requires a direct input of metabolic energy.

In contrast to active transport, passive transport of a substance does not require any input of energy other than its own electrochemical potential gradient. For nonelectrolytes, such as urea, glucose, or water, passive transport refers to the net movement of the substance down its chemical (concentration) gradient. However, because the movement of electrolytes (ions) is subject to the forces not only of concentration but also of voltage, passive transport of an ion refers to the net movement of the ion down its *electrochemical potential difference* (see Chap. 2, under Gibbs-Donnan equilibrium). The net movement of an ion may occur down a concentration gradient and still require energy, and thus be termed active

---

■   **Modes of**   ■
Epithelial Transport

Active
— against electrochemical potential gradient
— energy from ATP, redox, other sources
— uses carriers

Secondary Active
— energy derived from flux of a coupled solute, which moves down its electrochemical potential gradient
— uses carriers

Passive (or Diffusion)
— down an electrochemical potential gradient
— simple
— facilitated: pores, channels, or carriers

Special
— Pinocytosis (endocytosis or exocytosis) requires energy; but not via carriers
— Solvent drag solute carried passively by water flow

transport, if it occurs against a relatively higher electrical potential gradient. Conversely, an ion may be transported against a concentration difference, but still be moved passively if the existing electrical potential difference favors the movement (Fig. 2-3). Passive transport may be by *simple diffusion* through the lipid matrix of cell membranes or between cells. Alternatively, passive transport may be mediated by *aqueous pores, carriers,* or *channels* within membranes, in which case it is called *facilitated diffusion.* As the term implies, facilitated diffusion of a hydrophilic substance through the lipid bilayer of cell membranes is much faster than simple diffusion.

Passive transport also may occur by a process called *solvent drag,* in which solutes are entrained by a bulk flow of water through pores that accommodate solute as well as water. For example, the movement of solutes from glomerular capillaries into Bowman's space during glomerular filtration occurs by solvent drag. Similarly, in the proximal tubule, considerable amounts of solute are transported via the paracellular pathway (D, E in Fig. 4-1) by being dragged, so to speak, in the large volume of water that is reabsorbed in this segment (Chap. 7).

QUALITATIVE EVIDENCE FOR REABSORPTION

The most obvious examples of reabsorbed substances are water and Na^+ with its main accompanying anions, Cl^- and HCO_3^-. For these substances, which are considered in subsequent chapters, more than 99% of the filtered loads are reabsorbed (see Table 1-1). In this chapter, however, we shall concentrate on the reabsorption of solutes other than sodium and its attendant anions. Glucose is a case in point. This sugar, having a molecular diameter of about 0.7 nm and not being bound to plasma proteins, is freely filtered through the glomerular capillary wall and appears in Bowman's space at the same concentration as in plasma. The fact that normally almost no glucose appears in the urine (Table 1-1) therefore shows that the sugar must be reabsorbed. Micropuncture studies have shown that more than 98% of the filtered glucose is reabsorbed in the proximal tubule, nearly all of this in the first half of the proximal tubule. Furthermore, since the concentration of glucose is much higher in plasma than in urine, glucose must be reabsorbed against a concentration gradient. This reabsorption involves a Na^+-cotransport protein that mediates secondary active transport (described in detail below).

QUANTIFYING REABSORPTION

Net reabsorption for all nephrons combined can be measured using the following formula:

Quantity excreted = Quantity filtered − Quantity reabsorbed   (4-1)

For inorganic phosphate, an electrolyte that is reabsorbed by secondary active transport on a Na^+-cotransporter:

Quantity excreted = $U_{Phos} \times \dot{V}$

Quantity filtered = $P_{Phos} \times GFR$ (called the filtered load)

where:

U_{Phos} = the concentration of inorganic phosphate in the urine
$\dot{V}$ = the rate of urine flow
P_{Phos} = the concentration of inorganic phosphate in the plasma
GFR = the glomerular filtration rate

If GFR is determined by the clearance of inulin, substituting and rearranging Equation 4-1:

$$\text{Phosphate reabsorbed} = \left(P_{Phos} \times \frac{U_{In} \times \dot{V}}{P_{In}} \right) - (U_{Phos} \times \dot{V}) \qquad (4\text{-}2)$$

A precise determination of the filtered load of a solute must correct for: (a) the effect of the Donnan equilibrium, which of course applies only to electrolytes, and (b) possible binding of the solute to plasma proteins, because the bound portion cannot be filtered. For most filtered substances, these correction factors are small or nonexistent; hence, by and large, they may be ignored, and the uncorrected plasma concentrations are used to calculate the filtered load, as above. However, for some important solutes that bind to plasma proteins (e.g., Ca^{2+}) the concentration in the filtrate may be much lower than in the plasma. Whenever important, these exceptions will be noted.

Problem 4-1 and its solution in the Answers section list raw data from an experiment that tested the characteristics of inorganic phosphate transport in dogs. A few of the derived values, converted from mg of phosphorus to mmol of phosphate (see footnote to Problem 4-1), are shown in Table 4-1, and they have been plotted in Figure 4-2.

Transport Maximum (Tm)

As shown in Figure 4-2, at low plasma concentrations all phosphate that is filtered is reabsorbed. Then the amount that is reab-

Table 4-1. Renal handling of inorganic phosphate as a function of plasma phosphate concentration.

| Plasma phosphate concentration (mmol/L) | Filtered load of phosphate (mmol/min) | Phosphate | |
		Reabsorbed (mmol/min)	Excreted (mmol/min)
0.404	0.035	0.035	0
0.329	0.027	0.027	0
1.195	0.098	0.088	0.010
3.015	0.248	0.099	0.149
4.197	0.352	0.098	0.254
10.234	0.775	0.103	0.672

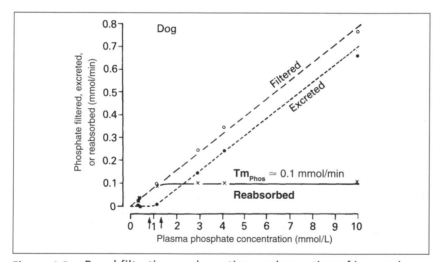

Figure 4-2. Renal filtration, reabsorption, and excretion of inorganic phosphate in dogs, plotted as a function of plasma phosphate concentration. The arrows span the range of normal plasma inorganic phosphate concentration. Plasma phosphate exists mainly in two forms: HPO_4^{2-} and $H_2PO_4^-$ (see Fig. 9-4A). Normally, small amounts of phosphate are excreted. Note that Tm_{Phos} refers to the maximal amount of phosphate that the tubules can transport per unit time. This amount varies under different physiological conditions; for example, Tm_{Phos} is decreased in the presence of elevated plasma concentrations of parathyroid hormone. Slightly modified from Pitts, R. F., and Alexander, R. S. *Am. J. Physiol.* 142:648, 1944.

sorbed reaches a maximal value that does not vary even though more and more phosphate is filtered into Bowman's space. This constant value of reabsorbed phosphate, expressed as amount per minute, is known as the *transport maximum (Tm)*. Many other substances that are reabsorbed by the kidneys have a Tm. Examples include glucose and other sugars, amino acids, uric acid, and organic solutes that are metabolic substrates (e.g., lactate and pyruvate).

Normally the plasma phosphate concentration is at a level where slightly more phosphate is filtered than the tubules can reabsorb. In other words, normally the Tm for inorganic phosphate is exceeded so that small amounts of phosphate are excreted. This fact enables the kidneys to help regulate phosphate balance: If intake of inorganic phosphate increases and its plasma concentration rises, the surcharge is excreted (Fig. 4-2); conversely, if intake decreases and the plasma concentration falls even slightly, virtually all of the filtered phosphate is conserved. Such fine adjustments are not possible for compounds such as glucose, where Tm is reached only at abnormally high plasma concentrations (Fig. 4-4). In other words, the kidney is an important regulator of phosphate balance but not of glucose balance.

CHARACTERISTICS OF CARRIER-MEDIATED TRANSPORT

The genetic messages for many channels and carriers have recently been determined by DNA sequencing, thus allowing the amino acid sequence of transport proteins to be decoded. The amino acid sequence, in turn, permits reasonable models of the structure of the carrier proteins to be developed. Such structural analyses have revealed marked similarities among many transport proteins, allowing them to be grouped into families whose members have a high degree of homology, i.e., similarity of structure and function. Furthermore, the homology extends across species, ranging from bacteria to humans. This conservation of structure during evolution is a clear indication of the importance of such transporters to survival. Most transport proteins have 6 to 12 regions (*domains*) consisting of stretches of relatively lipophilic amino acids. The lipophilic regions allow the protein to loop back and forth across the membrane, thereby forming a complex transmembrane structure that provides the route for transport. In most cases the molecular mechanisms that allow a carrier to transport a specific substance have not been established, but it is clear that these specialized proteins possess very specific binding sites for the molecules they carry.

Saturation Kinetics

The carrier that transports phosphate across the apical membrane contains specific binding sites for both Na^+ and phosphate. Because the number of carriers is limited, the total binding sites become saturated with phosphate as its concentration in the tubular fluid rises. In analogy with enzyme kinetics, the resulting approach to a maximal transport rate is referred to as *saturation kinetics,* and it provides one explanation for the nonlinear relationship shown in Figure 4-2. Saturation kinetics is a typical feature of all carriers.

Competitive Inhibition

The limited number of carriers also explains why the presence of one substance can diminish the rate of transport of another substance when both are transported by the same carrier. This phenomenon is termed *competitive inhibition* because both solutes compete for binding to the same sites. As a consequence an intravenous infusion of galactose, for example, diminishes the tubular reabsorption of glucose. Similarly, many amino acids, which are reabsorbed by several Na^+-cotransporters, compete for common carriers.

Na⁺-COTRANSPORTERS

Na^+-cotransporters are the major examples of secondary active transport, not only in the kidney but also in most other organs. We shall describe here the system for Na^+-glucose cotransport in the proximal tubule.

Figure 4-3 shows a Na^+-glucose cotransporter located in the apical membrane. The genetic message for this transporter, called *SGLT1,* has now been sequenced, and thus the amino acid sequence of this ~73,000 Dalton protein is known. In the first step of transport, two Na^+ ions combine with the cotransporter (C in Fig. 4-3) and bring about a conformational change, which enhances the affinity of C for glucose. Therefore, glucose (G) readily combines with $2Na \cdot C$, producing the ternary complex, $2Na \cdot C \cdot G$, which reorients itself within the apical membrane so as to expose the Na and G binding sites to the cytoplasm. Following this reorientation, first the Na^+ ions and then glucose dissociate from the carrier. This

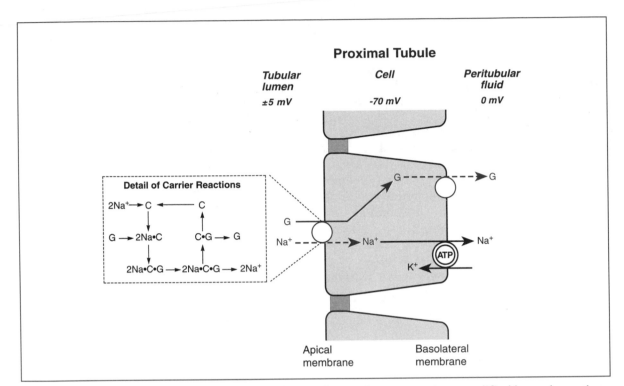

Figure 4-3. Mechanism of secondary active transport, exemplified by reabsorption of glucose in the proximal tubule via the *Na⁺-glucose cotransporter* (called *SGLT1*). Glucose crosses the apical membrane on a carrier that simultaneously transports two Na⁺ ions into the cell (shown in the insert only). Glucose moves from the cytoplasm into the peritubular fluid (interstitial space) by a carrier that mediates facilitated diffusion across the basolateral membrane; the final step, from interstitial space into the blood (see Fig. 4-1), occurs by simple diffusion. Details are given in the text. G = glucose; C = carrier or transporter; interrupted lines = passive transport; solid lines =. active or secondary active transport; double circle with 'ATP' = *NA-K-ATPase*.

process increases the concentration of glucose within the cytoplasm to the extent that there is a favorable concentration gradient for the passive movement of glucose out of the cell. Because of the size and polarity of the glucose molecule, this movement would be very slow if it occurred only by free diffusion through the basolateral membrane; however, passive glucose transport across this membrane is much faster because it is facilitated by a second carrier protein that binds only glucose and not Na⁺.

At least two passive glucose carriers are found in the basolateral membrane of the proximal tubule: *GLUT1* and *GLUT2*. Both are members of a family of passive glucose transporters (GLUT1, GLUT2, GLUT3, and so forth) that are present in many cell types.

The role of Na-K-ATPase is a key element in the overall process of glucose reabsorption. Operation of this pump keeps the intracellular concentration of Na^+ very low, thereby maintaining an electrochemical gradient for the passive movement of Na^+ from the tubular lumen into the cell (interrupted arrow). Since the transport of Na^+ and glucose are coupled, this gradient provides the energy required for uphill transport of glucose into the cell (solid arrow).

A number of compounds are reabsorbed by Na^+-cotransporters, including inorganic phosphate (Fig. 4-2), sulfate, amino acids, uric acid, and numerous organic molecules that are metabolic substrates. Furthermore, the close link of Na^+ with the process has the consequence of enabling not only the reabsorption of many compounds but also the reverse, i.e., the enhancement of Na^+ transport by the compounds (discussed in Chap. 7, under Glomerulotubular Balance). The phenomenon of cotransport is not restricted to reabsorption but applies as well to some instances of tubular secretion (Chap. 5).

GLUCOSE TITRATION CURVE

The glucose titration curve is constructed by determining the amount of glucose that is reabsorbed at increasing plasma concentrations of glucose, in the same manner as for phosphate (Fig. 4-2). If the glomerular filtration rate (GFR) stays constant, increasing the plasma concentration of glucose will lead to a progressive rise in the filtered load of glucose ($P_{Gluc} \times$ GFR), i.e., in the amount of glucose presented to the proximal tubule for reabsorption. In this way, the system is titrated to determine the plasma concentration at which the cotransporter for glucose becomes saturated and glucose is spilled in the urine. The plasma concentration of glucose at which the sugar first appears in the urine is known as the *renal threshold* for glucose.

A glucose titration curve for a healthy person is presented in Figure 4-4. It is apparent that the curve has the form that is characteristic of a Tm-limited transporter; in fact, it was the first renal Tm-limited system to be described. At low plasma glucose concentrations, all the filtered glucose is reabsorbed and 0.1% or less of the filtered load is excreted (see Table 1-1). This is the case at normal plasma glucose concentrations (denoted by the arrows on the abscissa of Figure 4-4). Then, as the maximal capacity of the

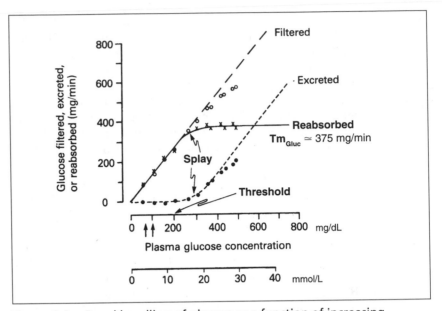

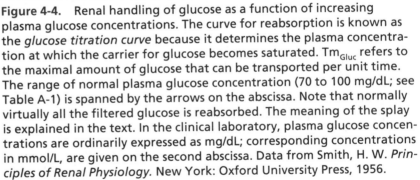

Figure 4-4. Renal handling of glucose as a function of increasing plasma glucose concentrations. The curve for reabsorption is known as the *glucose titration curve* because it determines the plasma concentration at which the carrier for glucose becomes saturated. Tm_{Gluc} refers to the maximal amount of glucose that can be transported per unit time. The range of normal plasma glucose concentration (70 to 100 mg/dL; see Table A-1) is spanned by the arrows on the abscissa. Note that normally virtually all the filtered glucose is reabsorbed. The meaning of the splay is explained in the text. In the clinical laboratory, plasma glucose concentrations are ordinarily expressed as mg/dL; corresponding concentrations in mmol/L, are given on the second abscissa. Data from Smith, H. W. *Principles of Renal Physiology.* New York: Oxford University Press, 1956.

tubules for reabsorbing glucose is reached, much more glucose is excreted in the urine. (In the experiment shown in Figure 4-4, the amount filtered, and hence that which was excreted, fell off slightly at higher plasma concentrations because the GFR decreased slightly.)

As discussed earlier in this chapter [under Transport Maximum (Tm)], the fact that normally the plasma glucose concentration is far below the value needed to saturate the reabsorptive mechanism means that the kidney is not a major regulator of glucose balance. That is, within a wide margin, virtually all of the filtered glucose will be reabsorbed whether the plasma glucose concentration rises or falls (Fig. 4-4).

Splay

Note in Figure 4-4 that Tm for glucose is approached somewhat gradually, along a curve, rather than abruptly with a sharp deflection. The curve is known as the *splay,* and it probably has two explanations. The first involves the kinetics of the chemical reaction between glucose and its carrier. Because the carrier has a finite affinity for glucose, a saturating concentration of glucose in the tubular fluid is needed to occupy all sites for glucose on the carrier. Hence, glucose is spilled in the urine before the Tm is reached, and splay results.

The second explanation involves the concept of morphological glomerulotubular imbalance. In any one person there may be an eightfold difference in the glomerular surface area available for filtration, and a twofold to threefold variation in the volume of the proximal tubule. Unless the glucose-reabsorptive capacity of each proximal tubule is tailored precisely to the glucose-filtering capacity of its own glomerulus, some nephrons will excrete glucose before Tm_{Gluc} for most nephrons is reached, and other nephrons will continue to reabsorb glucose after Tm_{Gluc} has been exceeded in most nephrons. The fact that the splay in the glucose titration curve is small means that the balance between the filtering and reabsorptive capacity of individual nephrons is remarkably precise.

The concept of *glomerulotubular balance* is not limited to glucose but may be applied to all substances that are filtered and reabsorbed. Furthermore, the term glomerulotubular balance is used in two contexts: (a) when comparing the amount of a substance filtered with the maximal capacity of the tubular system to reabsorb that substance, as in the case of glucose; and (b) when comparing the amount of a substance filtered with the *fraction* of the filtered load that the tubules reabsorb. The latter interpretation (usually referred to as *G-T balance*) has special meaning for Na^+ balance and it is discussed in detail in Chapter 7.

Glucosuria: Mutations of Na⁺-Glucose Cotransporters

In most individuals, glucosuria occurs when the plasma glucose concentration exceeds the renal threshold. The classic example is uncontrolled diabetes mellitus. Another is pregnancy, where the sugars excreted in the urine may be mainly lactose and galactose (more accurately termed *glycosuria*), or where an increase in the GFR may raise the filtered load of glucose beyond the Tm. In such instances, the renal glucose transporters are normal. There are, however, rare instances of glucosuria that can be attributed to mutations in one or more of the glucose transporters.

■   **Definitions**   ■

Filtered Load
The amount of a substance, X, that is deposited in Bowman's space by filtration:
$$GFR \times P_X$$

Transport Maximum
The maximal amount of substance X that can be reabsorbed or secreted:
$$Tm_X$$

Glomerulotubular Balance
Normal matching of proximal tubule reabsorptive capacity to the filtering capacity of its glomerulus *Alternate meaning: The phenomenon that the fraction of filtered Na^+ that is reabsorbed by the proximal tubule is constant (Chap. 7)*

One such abnormality involves SGLT1, the most common Na^+-glucose cotransporter, which is found in the intestine as well as in the kidney. It has a relatively high affinity for glucose, and an even higher affinity for galactose. This mutation, which is inherited as an autosomal recessive trait, leads to a combination of mild glucosuria (due to increased splay) and an intestinal malabsorption of galactose and glucose that produces severe and even fatal diarrhea in neonates. There also appears to be a rare mutation that leads to reduced Tm_{Gluc} and severe glucosuria. This condition results from a defect in a different Na^+-glucose cotransporter, called SGLT2, which is found in the early proximal tubule. Because virtually all of the filtered glucose is reabsorbed in the early part of the proximal tubule, it is not surprising that SGLT2 is a low-affinity, high-capacity transporter; nor is it surprising, therefore, that a defect in this particular cotransporter can lead to severe glucosuria.

PASSIVE REABSORPTION: UREA

Urea is discussed here as an example of a substance that is transported passively. The rate of reabsorption for all such substances is proportional to the concentration difference of the solute between the tubular fluid and the plasma (or interstitium), and the permeability of the tubular epithelium to the substance. The dependence of urea reabsorption on its own concentration difference is reflected in Figure 4-5A, which shows the influence of acute changes in the rate of urine flow on the excretion of urea. The rate of excretion increases markedly with increments in urine flow up to about 2 mL per minute, and thereafter it increases at a lesser rate. The increased excretion could be due to an increase in the amount filtered ($P_{Urea} \times GFR$), to a decrease in the amount of urea reabsorbed, or to a combination of the two. Since the plasma concentration of urea and the GFR stayed relatively constant in the experiment depicted in Figure 4-5, the filtered load of urea did not change; hence the increased excretion with rising urine flows must have been due to decreased tubular reabsorption, as shown in Figure 4-5B.

The increase in urine flow shown in Figure 4-5 was due to decreased reabsorption of water from the distal tubules and collecting ducts; that is, there was increased flow of tubular fluid, mainly water, in the distal convolutions and collecting ducts. Consequently, the concentration of urea in these tubular structures, and hence the difference in urea concentration between tubular and

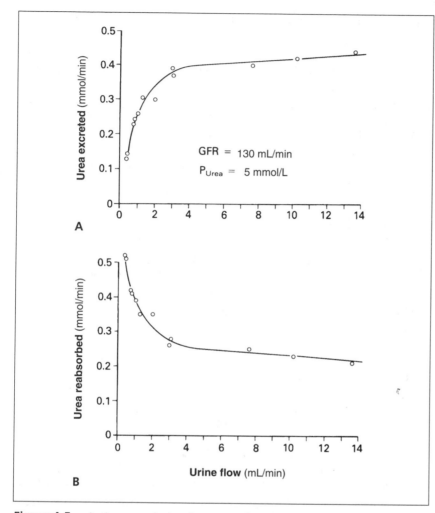

Figure 4-5. A. An experiment in a man showing the influence of the rate of urine flow on urea excretion. The points represent values in a single individual in whom urine flow was decreased by withdrawing all drinking water, and subsequently increased by having him ingest large amounts of water. Since the filtered load of urea ($P_{urea} \times$ GFR) did not change with increasing urine flow, the increased excretion must have been due to decreased reabsorption (Eq. 4-1); this fact is shown in (B). Data adapted from Austin, J. H., Stillman, E., and Van Slyke, D. D. *J. Biol. Chem.* 46:91, 1921.

interstitial fluid, declined. It is largely for this reason that the reabsorption of urea decreased.

Although this basic mechanism governs the rate of urea reabsorption throughout the nephron, the handling of urea by the kidney is actually more complicated. In the terminal portion of the inner medullary collecting duct (approximately the last 60%; Fig. 1-2A), urea is reabsorbed by facilitated diffusion, involving a saturable carrier that is enhanced by antidiuretic hormone (Fig. 8-5). It has not yet been determined whether a carrier is involved also in other nephron segments where urea is reabsorbed, such as the proximal tubule.

BIDIRECTIONAL TRANSPORT

Equation 4-1 can give a measure only of *net* reabsorption. When we describe the renal handling of a substance as involving filtration and reabsorption, we mean filtration followed by net flux from the tubular lumen to the blood. This statement does not exclude the possibility that the substance is simultaneously secreted, i.e., moved from blood into tubular fluid. In fact, for many or most substances, net tubular reabsorption or net secretion is the algebraic sum of fluxes in both directions; and the mode of transport in any one direction may be passive, active, or a combination of the two. For example, Na^+ undergoes net reabsorption, but it moves across the tubular wall in two directions, being actively reabsorbed transcellularly and passively secreted back into the lumen via the paracellular pathway.

Some substances undergo net transport in one direction in one part of the nephron, and net movement in the opposite direction in another part. Thus, K^+ (Chap. 11) is reabsorbed in proximal tubules and loops of Henle, secreted in distal tubules and cortical collecting ducts, and reabsorbed in medullary collecting ducts. For the entire kidney, there may be net reabsorption or net secretion of K^+, depending on the particular state of K^+ balance. Certain weak acids and bases, including many drugs such as antimalarials and salicylate (a metabolic product of aspirin), undergo active secretion in the proximal tubule and passive reabsorption predominantly in the distal tubule.

There are also some compounds that are both reabsorbed and secreted in a single region of the nephron. For example, uric acid undergoes net reabsorption in the first segment, S1, of the proximal tubule, then net secretion in the second segment, S2, and once again net reabsorption in the third segment, S3. In humans there is usually net reabsorption of uric acid by the entire kidney, but in other species there may be either net reabsorption or net secretion depending on the conditions.

In the preceding section, we stressed the reabsorption of urea from the collecting ducts. Actually the renal handling of urea involves other parts of the nephron as well. The scheme shown in Figure 4-6 is based on micropuncture studies, mainly in rats, at

Figure 4-6. Renal handling of urea at normal rates of urine flow. The percentages denote the proportion of the filtered amount of urea that flows at various sites along the nephron. The urea that is reabsorbed from the inner medullary collecting ducts flows into ascending vasa recta and re-enters the tubular system mainly in descending limbs of Henle belonging to short loops of Henle. By this process, called *medullary recycling of urea,* urea is returned to the inner medulla. The importance of the process, which is subserved by heterogeneity of nephrons (see Chap. 1), is discussed in Chapter 8 under Role of Urea in the Countercurrent System, Dissipation of Urea from the Inner Medulla. Data adapted from Lassiter, W. E., Gottschalk, C. W., and Mylle, M. *Am. J. Physiol.* 200:1139, 1961.

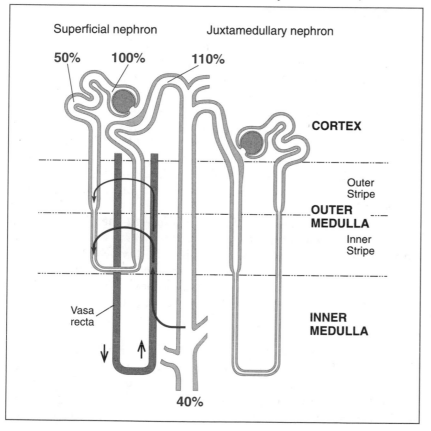

normal rates of urine flow. The percentages denote the filtered load of urea that flows along the nephron at the various sites. About 50% of the filtered urea is reabsorbed in the proximal tubules. Yet, 100% or more of the filtered amount of urea is found at the beginning of the distal tubules. Therefore, urea must diffuse into the intermediate segments, i.e., the loops of Henle. At normal rates of urine flow urea is then again reabsorbed from the inner medullary collecting ducts, so that about 40% of the filtered load of urea is excreted. Thus, urea also exhibits bidirectional transport. It undergoes net reabsorption from the proximal tubules and inner medullary collecting ducts, and net secretion into short loops of Henle, possibly including the pars recta of proximal tubules belonging to superficial nephrons. The apparent advantage of this seemingly complicated handling of urea, for the process of urinary concentration, is considered in Chapter 8 (under Role of Urea in the Countercurrent System).

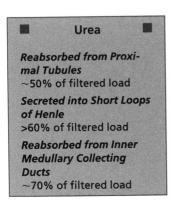

■   **Urea**   ■

Reabsorbed from Proximal Tubules
~50% of filtered load

Secreted into Short Loops of Henle
>60% of filtered load

Reabsorbed from Inner Medullary Collecting Ducts
~70% of filtered load

SUMMARY

The term *tubular reabsorption* refers to the direction of tubular transport, from tubular lumen, through peritubular interstitium, into blood. This definition applies to all modes of transport in the reabsorptive direction. Many of the compounds that undergo net tubular reabsorption are essential to homeostasis; examples include Na^+, HCO_3^-, H_2O, glucose, and amino acids.

When we speak of a compound as being handled by filtration and reabsorption, we mean filtration followed by *net* reabsorption. Such net transport can be deduced from Equation 4-1 as the difference between the amount filtered (the *filtered load*) and that which is excreted in the urine.

Epithelial cells have *apical* and *basolateral* membranes, each with very different properties. Therefore, when we describe the transport of a substance across an epithelial layer by the *transcellular* route, we have to consider two major steps: how that substance traverses the apical membrane and how it crosses the basolateral membrane. Only a single step, that across the junctional complexes, is required when a substance moves via the *paracellular* route.

Modes of transport are divided into two major categories: active and passive. The first can be *primary active,* in which there is direct input of metabolic energy into a pump, or *secondary active.* The latter type of transport (for example, *Na+-cotransport*) depends indirectly on activity of a pump even though the transported substance is not carried directly by the pump. Tubular reabsorption of Na^+ is primary active, while reabsorption of glucose, amino acids, and inorganic phosphate is secondary active. *Endocytosis* is an energy-requiring process by which the very tiny amounts of proteins that escape the glomerular filter are reabsorbed from tubular fluid.

Passive transport is the movement of a substance down its electrochemical gradient. For nonelectrolytes, only the chemical concentration gradient needs to be considered. Passive transport can occur by *simple diffusion* or by a much faster process, *facilitated diffusion*. The latter involves specialized membrane proteins called *pores, carriers,* or *channels*. Most carrier-mediated systems, whether active or passive, display the characteristics of a *transport maximum* (Tm) due to *saturation kinetics;* most also show *competitive inhibition*. A specialized form of passive transport is *solvent drag,* in which a solute is entrained in a flow of water.

The glucose titration curve displays *splay*, which reflects the finite affinity of the carrier for glucose as well as anatomical glomerulotubular imbalance. Urea is reabsorbed by facilitated diffusion, at least in the terminal portion of the inner medullary collecting duct (Fig. 1-2A). Urea also undergoes *bidirectional transport,* being reabsorbed from the proximal tubules and inner medullary collecting ducts, and secreted into the loops of Henle and partes rectae.

SUGGESTED READINGS

Benos, D. J., and Sorscher, E. J. Transport Proteins: Ion Channels. In D. W. Seldin and G. Giebisch (Eds.), *The Kidney. Physiology and Pathophysiology* (2nd ed.). New York: Raven, 1992. Chap. 20.

Berry, C. A., and Rector, F. C., Jr. Renal Transport of Glucose, Amino Acids, Sodium, Chloride, and Water. In B. M. Brenner and F. C. Rector, Jr. (Eds.), *The Kidney* (4th ed.). Philadelphia: Saunders, 1991. Chap. 7.

Burckhardt, G., and Kinne, R. K. H. Transport Proteins: Cotransporters and Countertransporters. In D. W. Seldin and G. Giebisch (Eds.), *The Kidney. Physiology and Pathophysiology* (2nd ed.). New York: Raven, 1992. Chap. 19.

Byrne, J. H., and Schultz, S. G. *An Introduction to Membrane Transport and Bioelectricity* (2nd ed.). New York: Raven Press, 1994.

Grantham, J. J., and Chonko, A. M. Renal Handling of Organic Anions and Cations; Excretion of Uric Acid. In B. M. Brenner and F. C. Rector Jr. (Eds.), *The Kidney* (4th ed.). Philadelphia: Saunders, 1991. Chap. 13.

Marsh, D. J., and Knepper, M. A. Renal Handling of Urea. In E. E. Windhager (Ed.), *Handbook of Physiology,* section 8: *Renal Physiology,* vol. II. New York: Oxford University Press, 1991. Chap. 30.

Matlin, K. S., and Caplan, M. J. Epithelial Cell Structure and Polarity. In D. W. Seldin and G. Giebisch (Eds.), *The Kidney. Physiology and Pathophysiology* (2nd ed.). New York: Raven, 1992. Chap. 16.

Murer, H., Manganel, M., and Roch-Ramel, F. Tubular Transport of Monocarboxylates, Krebs-Cycle Intermediates, and Inorganic Sulfate. In E. E. Windhager (Ed.), *Handbook of Physiology,* section 8: *Renal Physiology,* vol. II. New York: Oxford University Press, 1992. Chap. 47.

Pitts, R. F., and Alexander, R. S. The renal reabsorptive mechanism for inorganic phosphate in normal and acidotic dogs. *Am. J. Physiol.* 142:648, 1944.

Reuss, L., Russell, J. M., Jr., and Jennings, M. L. Molecular Biology and Function of Carrier Proteins. New York: Rockefeller University Press, 1993.

Schultz, S. G. Membrane Transport. In L. R. Johnson (Ed.), *Essential Medical Physiology.* New York: Raven, 1992. Chap. 2.

Silbernagl, S. Tubular Transport of Amino Acids and Small Peptides. In E. E. Windhager (Ed.), *Handbook of Physiology,* section 8: *Renal Physiology,* vol. II. New York: Oxford University Press, 1992. Chap. 41.

Silverman, M., and Turner, R. J. Glucose Transport in the Renal Proximal Tubule. In E. E. Windhager (Ed.), *Handbook of Physiology,* section 8: *Renal Physiology,* vol. II. New York: Oxford University Press, 1992. Chap. 43.

Problem 4-1. Renal handling of inorganic phosphate in dogs. Utilizing the data given, complete the blank columns.

Urine flow (mL/min)	Phosphate phosphorus[a]			Creatinine			Phosphate phosphorus[a]			Clearance ratio: phosphate clearance/creatinine clearance[b]
	Plasma (mg/dL)	Urine (mg/dL)	Clearance (mL/min)	Plasma (mg/dL)	Urine (mg/dL)	Clearance (mL/min)	Filtered (mg/min)	Excreted (mg/min)	Reabsorbed (mg/min)	
6.8	1.25	0.07		33.9	427					
9.2	2.75	0.46		31.2	283					
9.7	3.70	2.95		32.5	274					
8.7	4.64	9.10		33.3	321					
6.7	9.34	69.0		34.5	423					
8.2	13.0	95.7		34.5	352					
10.0	31.7	208		38.7	293					

[a]The values were measured as the phosphorus in phosphate; they have been converted from milligrams to millimols of inorganic phosphate in Table 4-1 and Figure 4-2.

[b]The so-called clearance ratio is the ratio of the clearance of any substance to the clearance of inulin or of creatinine, i.e., to the GFR. In the case of phosphate, the clearance ratio has the following formula: $U_{Phos} \times V/P_{Phos} \div U_{In} \times V/P_{In}$. The Vs cancel out, and the formula is reduced to $U_{Phos}/P_{Phos} \div U_{In}/P_{In}$, which has the great advantage that the clearance ratio—and the important information that it yields—can be determined without having to measure urine flow. The ratio can be applied to any substance; when the clearance ratio is <1.0, the substance in question undergoes net reabsorption; when the ratio is >1.0, the substance is secreted; and when the ratio is 1.0, the substance is, in the net, neither reabsorbed nor secreted (see Chap. 3, under Clearance as a General Concept). Numerical examples of the use of clearance ratios are given in the Answers to Problem 4-1, to Problem 4-2 (footnote), and to Problem 8-1 (*How to compute the fraction of a filtered substance that is reabsorbed*). Examples of how the clearance ratio is applied to micropuncture samples—and hence to quantifying the handling of a given substance by various tubular segments—are presented in Problem 6-1 (parts 2 and 3) and in Figure 11-3. Slightly modified from Pitts, R. F., and Alexander, R. S. *Am. J. Physiol.* 142:648, 1944. Used with permission of the American Physiological Society.

Problem 4-2. Handling of urea by the kidneys of an adult human at varying rates of urine flow. Utilizing the data given, complete the blank columns.

V̇ (mL/min)	Urine concentration		Plasma concentration		GFR (mL/min)	Urea			Urea	
	Inulin (mg/mL)	Urea (mmol/L)	Inulin (mg/mL)	Urea (mmol/L)		Filtered (mmol/min)	Excreted (mmol/min)	Reabsorbed (mmol/min)	Excreted (% of filtered load)	Reabsorbed (% of filtered load)
0.4	144	300	0.5	5						
0.8	75	263	0.5	5						
1.0	60	240	0.5	5						
3.1	20	119	0.5	5						
10.2	5.8	37	0.5	5						

Tubular Secretion

5

The term *secretion* refers to the *direction* of movement, from peritubular blood, or interstitium, or tubular cell into the tubular lumen, regardless of the mode of transport (see Chap. 4, under Principles of Epithelial Transport). The term excludes entry of substances into the tubular lumen via glomerular filtration.

Many of the substances that are secreted by renal tubules are either weak acids (organic anions) or weak bases (organic cations), both endogenous and exogenous (Table 5-1). Generally, they fall into one or more of the following categories: (1) They are foreign to the body. Drugs, such as penicillin, certain diuretics, and salicylate (a breakdown product of aspirin), are examples. (2) They are not metabolized, but are excreted unchanged in the urine, e.g., para-aminohippuric acid (PAH). (3) They are metabolized slowly, incompletely, and with difficulty, e.g., thiamine (vitamin B_1). (4) They are bound to plasma proteins and therefore cannot be filtered easily or in large amounts. Thus, tubular secretion may be viewed as a supplement to glomerular filtration and hepatic metabolism, to help in the elimination of compounds that cannot be disposed of by filtration or metabolism alone. It may also serve as a means of getting some drugs (e.g., diuretics) from the blood into the tubular fluid and thence to their sites of action in the apical membrane (Fig. 4-1) of the cell.

Table 5-1. Examples of organic anions and cations that are secreted by proximal tubules

Anions		Cations	
Endogenous	*Exogenous*	*Endogenous*	*Exogenous*
cAMP	para-aminohippurate (PAH)	Creatinine	Atropine
Salts of bile acids	Chlorothiazide and other thiazide diuretics	Epinephrine	Isoproterenol
Prostaglandins	Furosemide	Norepinephrine	Morphine
Urate	Bumetanide	Dopamine	Amiloride
Hippurate	Acetazolamide		Quinine
Oxalate	Penicillin		Cimetidine
	Probenecid		
	Salicylates (e.g., Aspirin)		

Slightly modified from Stanton, B. A., and Koeppen, B. M. In R. M. Berne and M. N. Levy, *Physiology* (3rd ed.). St. Louis: Mosby, 1992.

The fact that many secreted substances are compounds that are foreign to the body has often raised the question whether the tubular secretory mechanism normally plays any essential physiological role. It has been suggested that one such role may be the acquisition of essential metabolic substrates across the basolateral membrane (Fig. 4-1). For example, α-ketoglutarate is selectively taken up by the kidneys and the liver, and it is actively transported from the blood into renal and hepatic cells. Another role, in analogy with that cited above for diuretics, may be to transport certain endogenous compounds, such as prostaglandins, from their sites of synthesis within the kidney, via the tubular fluid, to their sites of action on tubular cells. Additionally, the presence of multiple secretory transporters that have affinities for a range of solutes may be an evolutionary adaptation that has allowed animals to excrete a wide variety of substances. The carriers involved may be analogous to the *multiple drug resistance gene product* that enables cancer cells to escape the effects of chemotherapeutic drugs by transporting them out of cells; in a like manner, renal secretory transporters may anticipate, so to speak, the threat of potentially toxic exogenous substances by being able to secrete them into the urine.

> ■ **Functional Roles** ■
> **of Secretion**
>
> ***Increased Elimination of Exogenous Solutes***
> especially drugs and toxins that bind to plasma proteins
>
> ***Increased Elimination of Metabolic Byproducts***
> especially poorly metabolized products
>
> ***Delivery of Autacoids and Drugs to Distal Nephron***
> e.g., delivery of prostaglandins and several diuretics

QUALITATIVE EVIDENCE FOR SECRETION

The possibility that some substances might be secreted was vehemently rejected for a long time. The first convincing evidence for tubular secretion appeared in 1923, when E. K. Marshall, Jr., and J. L. Vickers showed that as much as 70% of an injected dye, phenolsulfonphthalein (PSP), could appear in the urine in a single circulation through the kidneys. Since about 75% of PSP is bound to plasma proteins, only 25% was available for filtration, and only about one-fifth of that portion could be filtered (see Concept of Filtration Fraction, Chap. 3, and Filtration Fraction, below). Hence, only 5% (25% × 0.2) of the injected PSP could have reached the urine by filtration, and 65% therefore must have been secreted. Those who objected to the concept of tubular secretion, however, pointed out that PSP is a foreign substance and that Marshall's demonstration therefore might have little physiological meaning. Five years later, Marshall and A. L. Grafflin showed that endogenous compounds such as creatine and creatinine were excreted in the urine of the goosefish, *Lophius,* which has virtually no glomeruli. Nevertheless, this report was purportedly met by some obstinate skeptics with the comment that ". . . at last Marshall has found an animal that fits in with his theory."

Tubular secretion was subsequently demonstrated in numerous animals and preparations. For example, it was shown by direct visualization that PSP could be concentrated several thousand-fold within the lumina of separated tubules without glomeruli, and that this accumulation could be prevented by the metabolic poison, dinitrophenol (DNP), or by depriving the preparation of oxygen. Thus, the secretion of at least some substances must be an active transport process. The reality of tubular secretion became fully accepted with the development of the inulin clearance as a means of quantifying the rate of glomerular filtration. With this tool, as is shown in Equation 5-1, it could be clearly shown in vivo that the rate of urinary excretion of many substances far exceeded the rate at which they are filtered (see footnote b to Problem 4-1; as well as marginal box under Clearance as a General Concept, p. 54).

QUANTIFYING SECRETION

The calculation is based on the following equation:

$$\text{Quantity excreted} = \text{Quantity filtered} + \text{Quantity secreted} \qquad (5\text{-}1)$$

Using the exogenous solute para-aminohippurate (PAH) as an example:

$$\text{Quantity excreted} = U_{PAH} \times \dot{V}$$

$$\text{Quantity filtered} = P_{PAH} \times C_{In}$$

where:

U_{PAH} = the concentration of PAH in the urine (mg/mL or mg/dL)

$\dot{V}$ = the rate of urine flow (mL/min)

P_{PAH} = the concentration of PAH in the plasma (mg/mL or mg/dL) (As discussed in conjunction with Eq. 4-2, this concentration should be corrected for several factors, including the binding of PAH to plasma proteins. Since only about 10% of PAH is thus bound, however, the correction will be ignored For an example of when the correction cannot be ignored, see discussion of PSP, p. 85.)

C_{In} = the clearance of inulin, i.e., GFR (mL/min).

Substituting, and rearranging Equation 5-1:

$$\text{Quantity of PAH secreted} = (U_{PAH} \times \dot{V}) - \left(P_{PAH} \times \frac{U_{In} \times \dot{V}}{P_{In}}\right) \qquad (5\text{-}2)$$

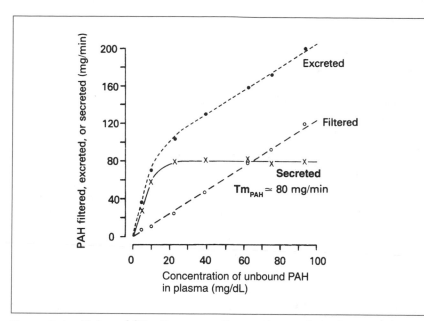

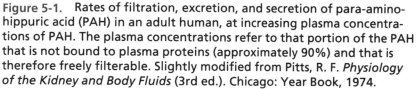

Figure 5-1. Rates of filtration, excretion, and secretion of para-amino-hippuric acid (PAH) in an adult human, at increasing plasma concentrations of PAH. The plasma concentrations refer to that portion of the PAH that is not bound to plasma proteins (approximately 90%) and that is therefore freely filterable. Slightly modified from Pitts, R. F. *Physiology of the Kidney and Body Fluids* (3rd ed.). Chicago: Year Book, 1974.

PAH is actively secreted by the proximal tubules, from the peritubular blood into the tubular lumen. Thus, an energy-consuming carrier must be involved, and one would anticipate that it would have a limited capacity to secrete PAH and related solutes. In other words, there should be a transport maximum, Tm, for PAH. The existence of this maximum is shown in Figure 5-1, which depicts the handling of PAH by the kidneys of a normal adult human as the plasma concentration of PAH is raised progressively by intravenous infusion. Note that, at plasma concentrations above 20 mg/dL, PAH secretion becomes constant because Tm_{PAH} has been reached. In a normal adult person, the maximal amount of PAH that can be transported by all proximal tubular cells combined is approximately 80 mg/min.

MEASUREMENT OF RENAL PLASMA FLOW

In Chapter 3 we stressed that about one-fifth of the plasma that enters the glomerular capillaries is filtered into Bowman's space.

Inulin can get into the tubular system only by filtration. Therefore, only about one-fifth of the inulin can be removed from the plasma as blood courses through the kidneys at any one time. In contrast, a substance like PAH, which besides being filtered also undergoes active tubular secretion, can be almost 'completely' removed. This has been proved by simultaneously sampling arterial and renal venous blood; as the blood enters the kidney, it has a finite concentration of PAH, and as the blood leaves the kidney, the concentration is virtually zero.

Obviously, 'complete' removal in a single circuit of the blood through the kidneys is possible only if the secretory Tm for PAH has not been reached. Consequently, the procedure for *estimating* renal plasma flow with PAH is as follows:

1. Infuse PAH intravenously at a rate that will result in a steady, low plasma concentration, which will not saturate the secretory transport mechanism, i.e., which will maintain the rate of secretion well below Tm.
2. Measure the concentration of PAH in the urine; U_{PAH} = 25.5 mg/mL (2,550 mg/dL).
3. Measure the rate of urine flow; $\dot{V}$ = 1.1 mL/min.
4. Calculate the rate of urinary excretion of PAH; $U_{PAH} \times \dot{V}$ = 28 mg/min.
5. Measure the concentration of PAH in arterial plasma; P_{PAH} = 0.05 mg/mL (5 mg/dL)
6. Now you can ask the following question: If each milliliter of plasma flowing through the glomeruli and peritubular vessels contributed 0.05 mg of PAH to the urine (which must be so if the renal venous concentration of PAH is zero), how many milliliters of plasma must have passed through the kidneys in order to have excreted 28 mg of PAH?

$$28 \text{ mg} \div \frac{0.05 \text{ mg}}{\text{mL}} = \frac{28 \text{ mg}}{1} \times \frac{\text{mL}}{0.05 \text{ mg}} = 560 \text{ mL}$$

Since 28 mg was excreted in 1 minute, 560 mL of plasma must have passed through the kidneys during this 1 minute. Note that, when we express the value in milliliters per minute, we have calculated the *clearance of PAH*, $U_{PAH} \times \dot{V}/P_{PAH}$.

Effective Renal Plasma Flow (ERPF)

In the above description, the word *complete* has been qualified because actually the concentration of PAH in renal venous blood is not zero but rather about one-tenth of its concentration in renal arterial blood. This is so not only because some blood flows through areas of the kidney that do not remove PAH (e.g., the renal capsule, the renal pelvis, the perirenal fat) but also because the circulation in certain areas, such as the outer medulla, does not come into contact with the tubular epithelium and because some tubular epithelium does not remove PAH completely. Since the procedure described above measures the flow that traverses tissue that *effectively* removes PAH from the plasma, the rate of flow thus determined is called the *effective renal plasma flow* (ERPF). Hence, at low plasma concentration of PAH, the clearance of PAH is a measure of ERPF.

$$C_{PAH} = \frac{U_{PAH} \times \dot{V}}{P_{PAH}} = ERPF \ (mL/min) \qquad (5\text{-}3)$$

Exact Renal Plasma Flow (RPF). Extraction of PAH

By simultaneously measuring the concentration of PAH in renal arterial and renal venous plasma, one can determine exactly how much PAH was extracted from each milliliter of plasma flowing through the kidneys. In this way one can precisely measure the renal plasma flow (RPF), as opposed to the ERPF. In fact, whenever an exact determination of RPF is needed—now limited almost exclusively to animal research—the extraction of PAH is measured. [In most studies on humans, the state of the renal circulation is assessed by some form of radiographic analysis such as Doppler ultrasound, not by extraction, or it is approximated as the ERPF (Eq. 5-3).] Measurement of extraction is necessary because only 85 to 90% of PAH is removed from the renal circulation under control conditions, and also because the rate of extraction can vary by 20% or more during various physiological and experimental conditions. This fact and sample calculations of RPF using the extraction of PAH are given in Problem 5-1 and in the corresponding Answer.

Moreover, one can measure RPF precisely by determining the extraction of any one of a number of substances. This point can be illustrated for inulin. If the urinary concentration of inulin is 150 mg/mL, and the urine flow is 1.1 mL/min, the urinary excretion of inulin is 165 mg/min. If, while this excretion rate was measured, the concentration of inulin in renal arterial plasma was 1.25 mg/mL, and that in renal venous plasma was 1.00 mg/mL, each milliliter of plasma traversing the kidneys must have contributed 0.25 mg to the 165 mg that was excreted. Hence the RPF must have been

$$\frac{165 \ mg}{min} \div \frac{0.25 \ mg}{mL} = \frac{165 \ mg}{min} \times \frac{mL}{0.25 \ mg} = 660 \ mL/min = RPF \quad \nearrow \quad \text{bigger than GFR 125 GFR}$$

It will be apparent that this method of measuring RPF is an application of the Fick principle (see Eq. 6-2). The urinary excretion of inulin is in a sense the renal consumption of inulin and thus analogous to the $\dot{V}_{O_2}$ of Equation 6-2; and the concentration of 0.25 mg/mL is the difference between the renal arterial and renal venous concentrations of inulin and is thus analogous to the a-v oxygen difference of Equation 6-2. Thus, the formula for measuring RPF by substance X (be it PAH, or inulin, or some other substance) is:

$$RPF = \frac{U_X \times \dot{V}}{Pa_X - Pv_X} \qquad (5\text{-}4)$$

where:

Pa_X = the concentration of substance X in renal arterial plasma
Pv_X = the concentration of X in renal venous plasma.

The reason PAH, rather than inulin, is ordinarily used for this purpose is that the a-v difference is greater for PAH, so that errors

Figure 5-2. Application of the principle of balance to the derivation of Equation 5-4. Symbols are explained in the text.

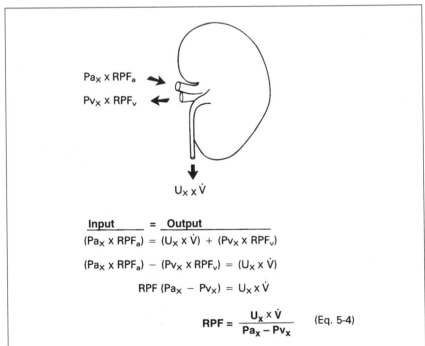

due to measurement influence the results less with PAH than with inulin.

Another way of deriving Equation 5-4 is through the principle of balance. The input of substance X to the kidney is equal to the product of the concentration of X in renal arterial plasma, Pa_X, and the plasma flow rate in the renal artery, RPF_a (Fig. 5-2). The output of X by the kidney is equal to the urinary output of X ($U_X \times \dot{V}$) plus the flow of X in the renal vein ($Pv_X \times RPF_v$). (The small difference between RPF in the renal artery and that in the renal vein, which is due to urine flow, may be ignored in this example.) In the steady state, input equals output, and solving the balance equation in Figure 5-2 leads to Equation 5-4.

CALCULATION OF RENAL BLOOD FLOW (RBF)

If the hematocrit (Hct)—i.e., the fraction of whole blood that is cells—is 0.45 or 45%, the fraction of whole blood that is plasma is 0.55. Hence, by considerations of proportionality:

$$\frac{RPF}{0.55} = \frac{RBF}{1.00}, \text{ and}$$

$$RBF = \frac{RPF}{0.55} = \frac{RPF}{1.00 - Hct}$$

(5-5)

Substituting 660 mL/min for RPF,

$$RBF = \frac{660}{1.00 - 0.45} = \frac{660}{0.55} = 1{,}200 \text{ mL/min}$$

FILTRATION FRACTION (FF)

The filtration fraction, alluded to in Chapter 3, is that fraction of the plasma flowing through the kidneys that is filtered into Bowman's space. It is calculated by the following formula:

$$FF = \frac{GFR}{RPF}$$

(5-6)

Substituting 132 mL/min for GFR (see Fig. 3-4) and 660 mL/min for RPF (above)

$$FF = \frac{132}{660} = 0.20$$

This is simply restating that normally about one-fifth, or 20%, of the plasma entering the glomerular capillaries is filtered. Changes in this value can alter the oncotic pressure in peritubular capillaries and thereby the reabsorption of tubular fluid (see Fig. 7-10).

SUMMARY

Tubular secretion refers to the transport of substances into the tubular lumen by means other than glomerular filtration. Secretion defines the direction of transport, not the mode. When we speak of a substance as being filtered and secreted, we usually mean *net* secretion; this net transport can be quantified by means of Equation 5-1.

The process of secretion may be viewed as helping the body to get rid of potentially harmful compounds, especially when they are bound to plasma proteins and therefore cannot be filtered in large amounts. Secretion may also serve as a means to get metabolic substrates into tubular cells, and to bring certain drugs and certain endogenous compounds (see Table 5-1) that act at the apical membrane of tubular cells to these sites.

At low plasma concentrations—i.e., below Tm_{PAH}, when the secretory transport for PAH is operating below its maximal capacity—85 to 90% of the PAH is removed from the plasma in a single circuit through the kidneys. Hence, at low plasma concentrations of PAH, the clearance of PAH, C_{PAH}, yields a fairly close approximation of the renal plasma flow; this approximation is known as the effective renal plasma flow (ERPF). The exact renal plasma flow (RPF) can be determined by measuring the renal extraction of PAH and applying the Fick principle.

The rate of renal blood flow (RBF) can be calculated by means of a simple proportionality if the fraction of whole blood that is made up of cells (the hematocrit) is known.

The filtration fraction (FF) is normally about 0.20; that is, normally about 20% of the plasma that traverses the kidneys is filtered into Bowman's space.

Problem 5-1. Determination of renal plasma flow (RPF), renal blood flow (RBF), and filtration fraction (FF), using PAH and inulin in dogs. The extraction of PAH changes during the postnatal period, when these data were obtained. Utilizing the data given, fill in the blank columns.

Age (days)	Urine flow (μL per min per g of kidney)[c]	U_{PAH} (mg/dL)	Pa_{PAH}[a] (mg/dL)	Pv_{PAH}[a] (mg/dL)	RPF (μL per min per g of kidney)[c]	RBF[b] (μL per min per g of kidney)[c]	C_{In} (μL per min per g of kidney)[c]	FF
2	3.8	104	2.60	2.16			130	
21	2.7	283	1.70	1.08			270	
40	5.2	664	3.00	1.23			630	
60	3.2	672	1.20	0.34			790	
74	2.3	3,516	3.10	0.52			1,200	

[a]Pa_{PAH} and Pv_{PAH} = concentration of PAH in arterial and renal venous plasma, respectively.
[b]Assume that the hematocrit = 0.45.
[c]Values have been expressed per gram of kidney in order to correct for any changes that might be due to growth of the kidney during the postnatal period. Abstracted from Horster, M., and Valtin, H. *J. Clin. Invest.* 50:779, 1971.

SUGGESTED READINGS

Grantham, J. J., and Chonko, A. M. Renal Handling of Organic Anions and Cations; Excretion of Uric Acid. In B. M. Brenner and F. C. Rector, Jr. (Eds.), *The Kidney* (4th ed.). Philadelphia: Saunders, 1991. Chap. 13.

Marshall, E. K., Jr., and Vickers, J. L. The mechanism of the elimination of phenolsulphonphthalein by the kidney: A proof of secretion by the convoluted tubules. *Bull. Johns Hopkins Hosp.* 34:1, 1923.

Roch-Ramel, F., Besseghir, K., and Murer, H. Renal Excretion and Tubular Transport of Organic Anions and Cations. In E. E. Windhager (Ed.), *Handbook of Physiology.* Section 8: *Renal Physiology.* New York: Oxford University Press, 1992. Vol. I, Chap. 48.

Shannon, J. A. The renal excretion of phenol red by the aglomerular fishes, *Opsanus tau* and *Lophius piscatorius. J. Cell. Comp. Physiol.* 11:315, 1938.

Renal Hemodynamics and Oxygen Consumption

6

The two kidneys of an adult human together weigh about 300 g, and thus constitute less than 0.5% of the body weight. Yet, they are perfused by an amount of blood that is equal to 20 to 25% of the cardiac output, i.e., in excess of 1,000 mL per minute. The reason for this very high rate of perfusion is probably related to the evolutionary development of an organ with a high filtering capacity, as discussed in Chapter 1 (under Evolution).

In addition to the high rate of flow, the renal circulation has a number of other characteristic features, some of which are unique. These include: (a) differences in glomerular filtration rate (GFR) and in renal blood flow (RBF) that depend on the type of nephron, (b) selective changes in GFR and RBF, (c) autoregulation of GFR and RBF, and (d) renal oxygen consumption. We begin this chapter by describing the resistances in the renal vasculature; we then describe the features listed above, and end by considering the control of the renal circulation.

HYDROSTATIC PRESSURES AND RESISTANCES IN THE RENAL VASCULAR TREE

Hydrostatic pressures in the major renal vessels are shown in Figure 6-1. The data are from dogs; although absolute values in humans and other species might be slightly different, the profile is almost certainly similar. Of particular importance is the large decrease in pressure that occurs in the afferent and efferent arterioles, which identifies these two vessels as the major sites of vascular resistance. Changes in the resistance within either of these vessels will alter the renal blood flow (RBF); but both resistances interact to determine the hydrostatic pressure within the glomerular capillaries, and hence the rate of glomerular ultrafiltration (see Fig. 3-1 and Fig. 6-3).

REGIONAL DIFFERENCES IN GLOMERULAR FILTRATION AND IN BLOOD FLOW

Two types of nephron, the superficial and the juxtamedullary, were described in Chapter 1. Besides having anatomical distinctions, these nephrons also differ functionally (see Chap. 1, under Heterogeneity of Nephrons). As shown in Figure 6-2, under control conditions (Normal) the so-called *single nephron glomerular filtration rate* (snGFR, as distinct from GFR, which refers to the

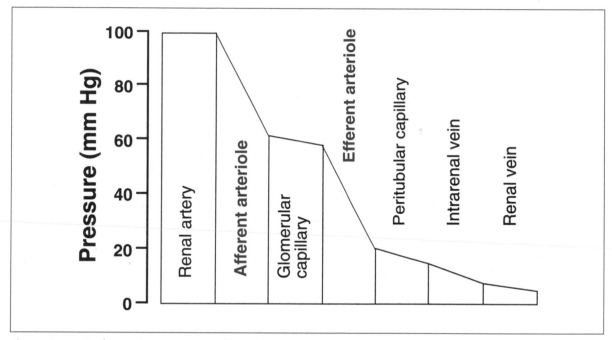

Figure 6-1. Hydrostatic pressure profile in the renal vascular tree of dogs. Data from Navar, L. G., et al. Renal Circulation. In S. G. Massry and R. J. Glassock (Eds.), *Textbook of Nephrology* (2nd ed.). Baltimore: Williams & Wilkins, 1989. Chap. 2.

glomerular filtration rate of the entire kidney) of a juxtamedullary nephron is greater than that of a nephron lying in more superficial parts of the cortex. Furthermore, differential changes in these filtration rates occur during various conditions. For example, during water diuresis (defined at the beginning of Chap. 7; also called diabetes insipidus), when the antidiuretic hormone (ADH, or vasopressin) is absent, there is a reduction in the snGFR of juxtamedullary nephrons but no change in that of superficial nephrons. That ADH is responsible for this change, indirectly or directly, is shown by the restoration of the snGFR, mostly in juxtamedullary nephrons, when animals with diabetes insipidus are treated with the hormone (diabetes insipidus plus exogenous ADH in Fig. 6-2).

Regional differences exist also for renal blood flow (see box in the margin). Nearly all of the blood that enters the kidneys through the renal arteries flows through the glomeruli and thereafter traverses the peritubular capillaries to perfuse the tubular structures in the cortex. Considering that about one-quarter of the cardiac output goes to the kidneys, this amounts to a perfusion rate per unit of cortical tissue that is more than 100 times higher than that

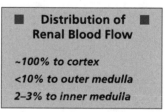

■ **Distribution of** ■
Renal Blood Flow

~100% to cortex

<10% to outer medulla

2–3% to inner medulla

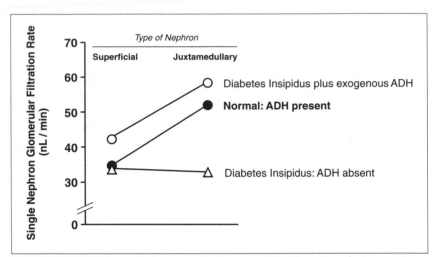

Figure 6-2. Nephron heterogeneity in regard to the rate of glomerular filtration in single glomeruli (snGFR) of the two major types of nephron. The experiments were conducted in two strains of rat: those that have the antidiuretic hormone (ADH, or vasopressin) and those that lack this hormone (so-called Brattleboro rats with diabetes insipidus). Detailed description is given in the text. Note the small units for snGFR (*nano*liters per minute). Slightly modified from Trinh-Trang-Tan, M.-M., et al. *Am. J. Physiol.* 240 (*Renal Fluid Electrolyte Physiol.* 9):F372, 1981; and *Am. J. Physiol.* 246 (*Renal Fluid Electrolyte Physiol.* 15):F879, 1984.

of resting muscle. Less than 10% of the total renal blood flow enters the medulla, and only 2 to 3% reaches the inner medulla. Again, however, since total renal blood flow is so great, the absolute flow even for inner medulla (when expressed per unit of tissue) is still approximately the same as that of resting muscle. The functional importance of regional differences, not only in blood flow but also in snGFR, will become clear later; they play a critical role in the renal conservation of water (discussed in Chap. 8, under Countercurrent Exchange in Vasa Recta).

SELECTIVE AND INDEPENDENT CHANGES IN GFR AND RBF

The renal circulation is unique in that it consists of two capillary beds in series, the glomerular capillaries followed by the peritubular capillaries (see Fig. 1-2B). This fact, combined with two resistances that can be influenced independently of one another (the afferent and efferent arterioles), makes it possible to have either parallel or divergent shifts in glomerular filtration and renal blood flow. This point is illustrated in Figure 6-3. We assume that the hydrostatic pressure in the renal artery (called the *renal perfusion pressure*) does not change in the following examples.

If resistance decreases in the afferent arterioles, then there will be an increase in RBF; this conclusion follows from the relationship

$$RBF = \frac{\Delta P}{R} \tag{6-1}$$

where:

RBF = the rate of renal blood flow
ΔP = the difference in hydrostatic pressure between the renal artery and the renal vein (Fig. 6-1)
R = the vascular resistance [mainly afferent plus efferent arteriolar resistances (Fig. 6-1)]

In the example just cited, when the resistance of the afferent arterioles decreases, the hydrostatic pressure within the glomerular

Figure 6-3. Changes in renal blood flow (RBF) and glomerular filtration rate (GFR) that occur when resistance is altered in either the afferent or efferent arterioles, provided that the renal perfusion pressure does not change. The changes in RBF and GFR are not usually in exact proportion to one another, as might be implied by arrows of equal length. For details and for exceptions to this schema, see text.

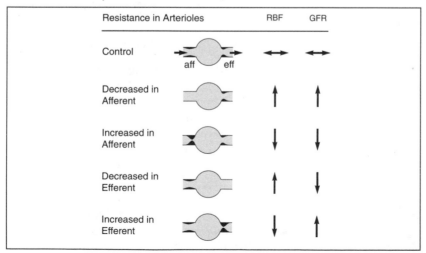

capillaries (P_c, Eq. 2-8) rises, because a larger fraction of the renal arterial pressure is transmitted to the glomerular capillaries. According to Equation 2-8, this increase in P_c contributes to an increase in GFR (note that Equation 2-8, not Equation 6-1, must be used to assess changes in GFR). Thus, decreased resistance in afferent arterioles will lead to an increase in both the RBF and the GFR. The opposite reasoning applies when resistance in the afferent arterioles is increased: According to Equation 6-1, RBF will diminish, and because P_c in Equation 2-8 falls, there also will be a decrease in GFR (Fig. 6-3).

When resistance is altered predominantly or solely in efferent arterioles, divergent changes in RBF and GFR occur. As shown in Figure 6-3, a decrease in efferent arteriolar resistance leads to an increase in RBF because R of Equation 6-1 has fallen; but now, because of a simultaneous decrease in P_c, the GFR will be reduced. Conversely, when resistance in efferent arterioles is increased, RBF falls (Eq. 6-1) while GFR rises (due largely to an increase in P_c; Eq. 2-8).

While Figure 6-3 presents a useful exercise in understanding the consequences of two resistances in series (afferent and efferent), the situation is not usually as simple as in the examples cited above. For one thing, simultaneous changes in both afferent and efferent resistances are more common than is a change in only one of them. Even then, however, the same reasoning applies, although the analysis gets more complicated. And then, recall that GFR is determined not only by P_c, but also by the renal plasma flow (a derivative of RBF; Eq. 5-5), which exerts its influence on GFR through another important Starling force, the plasma oncotic pressure, π_c (see Chap. 3, under Forces Involved in Glomerular Ultrafiltration, last paragraph). Therefore, the changes in RBF and GFR are not usually proportional, as implied by arrows of equal length in Figure 6-3, although the direction of the changes hold for most situations. One example of a more complicated situation will suffice: Suppose that resistance is increased simultaneously in both the afferent and efferent arterioles. By Equation 6-1, increased resistance in either locale will lead to a fall in RBF, and since resistance is increased at two sites, the fall in RBF may be marked. The GFR, however, cannot be predicted so readily: If the increase in resistance is greater in the afferent than in the efferent arteriole, GFR is likely to decline, whereas if the reverse is the case, GFR may increase.

By and large, and in most physiological circumstances, the basic concept is that when the *net* change of resistance occurs in afferent arterioles, RBF and GFR change in the same direction, whereas when the *net* change occurs in efferent arterioles, RBF and GFR will move in opposite directions.

AUTOREGULATION OF GFR AND RBF

The phenomenon of autoregulation is illustrated in Figure 6-4, which portrays the GFR and the RBF measured simultaneously in dogs as their renal arterial pressure is varied. Note that over a range of pressure from about 80 to 180 mm Hg, a 100% increase in perfusion pressure causes an increase in RBF of less than 10%. This, by the formula RBF = $\Delta P/R$, must mean that somehow an increase in perfusion pressure is accompanied by a nearly equivalent increase in vascular resistance, so that RBF is nearly unaltered. By the deductions referred to in relation to Figure 6-3, the simultaneous 'constancy' of GFR and RBF (shown in Fig. 6-4) indicates that the predominant change in resistance occurs in the afferent arterioles.

Autoregulation persists even after complete renal denervation, after adrenal demedullation (which prevents production of catecholamines), and in a completely isolated kidney perfused with plasma in vitro. Hence, as the term is meant to indicate, autoregulation is an intrinsic phenomenon that must be due to a change exclusively within the kidney, and that is brought about when the arterial perfusion pressure is altered.

The mechanism of autoregulation has not been identified fully. Many investigators believe that it involves two processes in varying combination: (a) myogenic and (b) tubuloglomerular feedback.

> ■ **Autoregulation** ■
>
> *Renal Blood Flow (RBF) and Glomerular Filtration Rate (GFR) are both kept fairly constant*
> Therefore, resistance probably changes primarily in afferent arterioles
> *Proposed Mechanisms*
> Myogenic (Bayliss)
> Tubuloglomerular feedback (TGF)

Myogenic (Bayliss) Mechanism

The myogenic mechanism, described by W. M. Bayliss in 1902, involves an intrinsic property of arterial smooth muscle whereby that muscle contracts or relaxes in response to increases or decreases in vascular wall tension, respectively. There is an immediate and fleeting response (a matter of a few seconds only) during which, say, a rise in perfusion pressure is followed by an increase in vessel radius, so that blood flow does go up. But almost immediately thereafter, the resulting stretch of the vessel wall quickly elicits contraction, so that within 30 seconds of the pressure increase, flow is returned nearly to the control value. The opposite chain of events occurs when perfusion pressure is decreased. It is possible that the link between a change in vessel radius and subsequent contraction or relaxation is variable entry of calcium into cells through channels, which ultimately influences the state of myosin light chains.

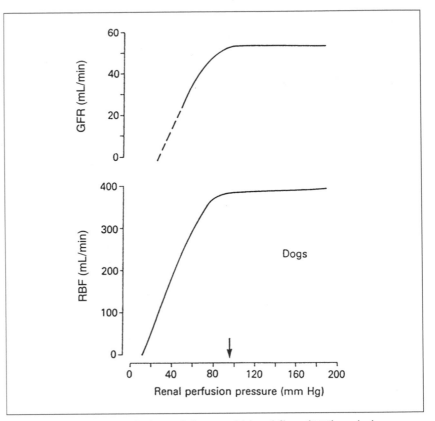

Figure 6-4. Autoregulation of the renal blood flow (RBF) and glomerular filtration rate (GFR) in dogs as the renal perfusion pressure is varied. The arrow indicates the approximate normal mean pressure in the renal arteries. The fact that RBF and GFR are simultaneously kept constant must mean that the net change in resistance occurs in the afferent arterioles. Note that within the so-called autoregulatory range of approximately 80 to 180 mm Hg (and assuming a hematocrit of 45%—Eq. 5-5), the filtration fraction in this example is 0.25, or 25%. Adapted from Navar, L. G. *Am. J. Physiol.* 234 (*Renal Fluid Electrolyte Physiol.* 3):F357, 1978.

Tubuloglomerular Feedback (TGF)

This mechanism, as the name implies, involves a feedback loop, illustrated in Figure 6-5, in which the flow rate of tubular fluid, or some derivative thereof, is sensed at the macula densa of the juxtaglomerular apparatus (JGA; see Fig. 1-3) and in turn governs the filtration rate of the single glomerulus (snGFR) to which that JGA is apposed. For example (Fig. 6-5), it has been shown that

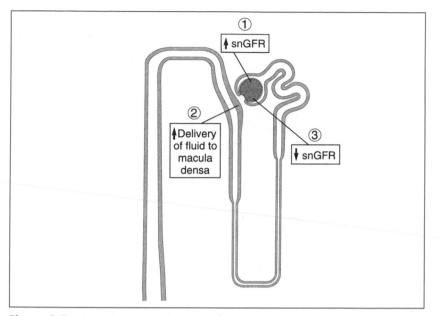

Figure 6-5. Regulation of the single nephron glomerular filtration rate (snGFR) by the tubuloglomerular feedback mechanism. The sequential steps are described in the text.

when an increase in the snGFR (step 1) is mimicked by microperfusion of a single loop of Henle at an increased rate (step 2), the snGFR in that particular nephron is reduced (step 3), mainly because of a decreased hydrostatic pressure in glomerular capillaries (see Fig. 3-1; P_c of Eq. 2-8). The opposite also holds, although to a lesser degree: When tubular flow rate through the loop of Henle is decreased, P_c and snGFR are increased.

The major unknowns about tubuloglomerular feedback concern the variable(s) that is sensed at the JGA as well as the effector substance(s) that alters the tone of the arteriolar smooth muscle—probably of the afferent arteriole. It is possible that the specialized macula densa cells of the distal tubule (see Fig. 1-3) monitor the delivery of solute or NaCl within the tubular fluid at this point; but it is not known whether the variable that is sensed is the concentration of Na^+ or of Cl^-, or the amount of NaCl that is reabsorbed, or some other correlate of the tubular flow rate—or whether indeed it is Na^+ or Cl^- at all rather than some other solute(s) or osmolality. Nor is it settled whether the effector mechanism involves adenosine and ATP, or a noncyclooxygenase prostanoid, or some other substances that have been suggested.

Tubuloglomerular feedback and autoregulation may have evolved to subserve the critical function of salt balance (see Chap. 7, under Renal Regulation of Na^+ Balance). That is, as snGFR increases and therefore an abnormally large amount of NaCl is filtered, this fact might be quickly sensed at the JGA and corrected through a negative feedback loop that decreases the snGFR. The concomitant autoregulation of RBF (Fig. 6-4) could be a mere by-product of one mechanism by which the kidneys maintain salt balance; or, since the rate of plasma flow through glomerular capillaries can in part determine the rate of glomerular filtration (see Chap. 3, under Forces Involved in Glomerular Ultrafiltration), autoregulation of RBF might be an integral part of autoregulation of GFR.

RENAL OXYGEN CONSUMPTION

According to the Fick principle, the oxygen consumption of an organ, $\dot{V}_{O_2}$, is related directly to the rate of blood flow to that organ, $\dot{Q}$, and to the difference in oxygen content between the artery, Ca_{O_2}, and vein, Cv_{O_2}, of that organ.

$$\dot{V}_{O_2} = \dot{Q}(Ca_{O_2} - Cv_{O_2}) \quad (6\text{-}2)$$

In most organs, such as skeletal muscle, the resting oxygen consumption remains constant as the blood flow to that organ is reduced. Consequently, the arteriovenous (a-v) oxygen content difference rises in proportion to the decrease in flow (Eq. 6-2). The heart is an exception, since even at rest the coronary a-v oxygen difference is very high, approximately 11 vol%. Therefore, when coronary blood flow decreases, the oxygen supply to the myocardium is deficient. For this reason, the heart is known as a flow-limited organ.

There are two seeming paradoxes about renal oxygen consumption: (1) Even though this consumption per weight of renal tissue is greater than that of any other organ save the heart, the renal a-v oxygen difference is only about 1.7 vol%, probably the lowest of any organ. (2) Despite the very low a-v oxygen difference, the kidneys do not initially extract more oxygen from each unit of blood as renal blood flow is reduced. The solution to these paradoxes is illustrated in Figure 6-6; it involves the fact that the main renal requirement for oxidative energy is the tubular reabsorption of sodium.

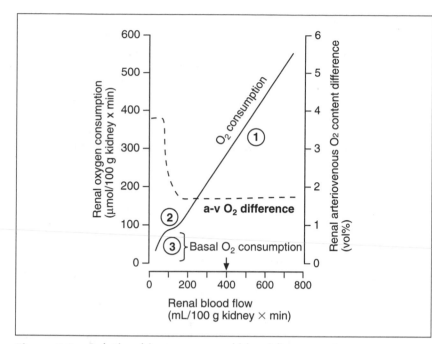

Figure 6-6. Relationship among renal blood flow, renal oxygen consumption, and renal arteriovenous oxygen content difference (a-v O_2 difference) in dogs. The circled steps are explained in the text. The arrow indicates the approximate normal value for renal blood flow in dogs. Based on data from Kramer, K., and Deetjen, P. *Pflügers Arch. Ges. Physiol.* 271:782, 1960; Lassen, N. A., Munck, O., and Thaysen, J. H. *Acta Physiol. Scand.* 51:371, 1961; Deetjen, P., and Kramer, K. *Pflügers Arch. Ges. Physiol.* 273:636, 1961.

As is shown in Figure 6-6, the relationship among renal blood flow, renal oxygen consumption, and renal a-v oxygen difference goes through three phases as the blood flow is decreased. At first (step 1), down to a blood flow of approximately 150 mL per 100 g of kidney per minute, the oxygen consumption decreases proportionally, so that the a-v oxygen difference does not change. As blood flow decreases further (step 2), the kidneys extract more oxygen from each unit of blood flowing through them. At extremely low levels of renal blood flow (below approximately 75 mL per 100 g of kidney per minute; step 3), no more oxygen can be extracted even as the flow decreases; consequently, at this point the renal cells will undergo ischemic damage and they may die.

The three phases have functional and pathophysiological correlates. During the first phase, decreasing amounts of Na^+ are filtered and hence presented to the tubules for reabsorption; i.e., as renal blood flow decreases, so does the GFR and hence, at a constant plasma Na^+ concentration, so does the filtered load of Na^+ (GFR $\times$ P_{Na}). The need to reabsorb virtually all of the filtered Na^+ (Table 1-1) accounts for the vast majority of oxygen consumption by the kidneys. During the second phase, GFR has ceased, and at this point, as RBF decreases further, the kidneys extract more oxygen from each volume of blood flowing through them, thereby supplying the basal need to keep renal cells alive and functioning. This need, of approximately 100 μmol oxygen per 100 g kidney per minute, normally comprises about one-third of total renal oxygen consumption, and is similar to that of other epithelial tissues. If RBF decreases beyond this point, during the third phase, renal cells suffer ischemic damage. The three phases explain why RBF can be reduced severely, as in shock, without causing renal cellular damage—because basal oxygen consumption is not compromised until phase 3 is reached. Figure 6-6 also shows why a condition known as acute renal failure due to hypoperfusion with blood can be prevented if the hypotension or shock is reversed quickly, before irreversible damage to renal cells has occurred.

Sodium reabsorption is an active process (see Chap. 7), which depends largely on energy derived from oxidative metabolism. This deduction fits well with the fact that most of the filtered sodium is reabsorbed in the proximal and distal tubules (see Fig. 7-7), i.e., in the renal cortex, which has a very high rate of aerobic metabolism; in contrast, renal medullary structures derive much energy from anaerobic as well as from aerobic metabolism. The cost of reabsorbing filtered sodium is about 1 μmol of oxygen for every 28 μmols of sodium reabsorbed.

CONTROL OF RENAL CIRCULATION

Normally, from moment to moment, renal blood flow (RBF) and GFR are kept quite constant through autoregulation (Fig. 6-4). But during physiological and pathological perturbations—e.g., heavy exercise, emotional stress, liver and heart failure, changes in the intake of salt, hemorrhage—autoregulation is overridden and profound changes in the renal circulation occur. The sympathetic nervous system, numerous hormones including autacoids (some of which are listed in Table 6-1), and endothelial factors all affect the resistances of the afferent and efferent arterioles, and thus alter RBF and GFR.

Sympathetic Nervous System

One of the most important regulators of RBF and GFR is the sympathetic nervous system. Sympathetic efferent nerves innervate both the afferent and efferent arterioles, and increases in the rate of firing of these nerves cause constriction of both arterioles. In general, a moderate increase in sympathetic input causes a decrease in RBF and relatively minor changes in GFR, so that filtration fraction (FF) (Chap. 5, under Filtration Fraction) rises. Stronger sympathetic output, as occurs in trauma and shock, can increase the sum of the two arteriolar resistances sufficiently to diminish RBF greatly and to cause cessation of glomerular filtration.

Renin and Angiotensin

The *renin-angiotensin-aldosterone* system is described in detail in Chapter 7. It plays a central role not only in Na$^+$ and water balance, but also, through angiotensin II (AII), as a regulator of RBF and GFR. Renin, which is secreted by the juxtaglomerular apparatus (JGA; Fig. 1-2A), is involved, ultimately, in the formation of AII (see Fig. 7-8). It is possible that both systemically circulating AII and AII produced locally within the kidney influence the renal

Table 6-1. Influence of various vasoactive compounds on afferent and efferent arterioles.

Substance	Afferent arteriole	Efferent arteriole
Acetylcholine	relax	relax
Nitric oxide (often referred to as *the* EDRF)	relax	relax
Dopamine	relax	relax
Bradykinin	relax?	relax
Prostacyclin	relax	relax
Prostaglandin E$_2$	relax*	no effect
Prostaglandin I$_2$	relax*	relax*
Calcitonin gene-related peptide	relax*	no effect
Norepinephrine	constrict	constrict
Angiotensin II	constrict	constrict
Endothelin	constrict	constrict
Thromboxane	constrict	constrict
Vasopressin	no effect	constrict
Atrial natriuretic peptide	no effect	no effect

*Relaxation of norepinephrine-induced tone.

circulation. Angiotensin II increases the resistance of both afferent and efferent arterioles (Table 6-1); it therefore decreases RBF and, at high concentrations, also the GFR.

Endothelial Factors

The endothelium has been undeservedly ignored in the past, being perceived as just the passive wall of a tube carrying blood. It is now known that endothelial cells possess a variety of receptors and that, in response to activation of those receptors, they release various agents, some of which have potent vasoactive effects. These agents are characterized as *autacrine* or *paracrine* because they are hormones or very similar to hormones, but act on the same or adjacent cells, respectively, rather than on target cells that are far removed from where the substance (hormone) is produced. The endothelial factors are classed into two groups: *endothelium-derived relaxing factors* (EDRF) and *endothelium-derived contracting factors* (EDCF). Among EDRF are *nitric oxide* (NO) and *prostacyclin,* which can both produce profound relaxation of vascular smooth muscle, including the afferent and efferent arterioles. Among EDCF are *endothelin, thromboxane,* and *angiotensin* (discussed above); they constrict vascular smooth muscle, including that of renal arterioles.

It has been proposed that mesangial cells also may play a role in governing RBF and GFR, although there is no agreement on this point. Mesangial cells are specialized cells located in the glomerulus and in the juxtaglomerular apparatus; they contain contractile elements that can be stimulated by most of the autacoids (i.e., self-produced agents) that affect afferent and efferent arteriolar resistances. Although these cells are not part of the glomerular capillaries and arterioles, and hence not endothelial cells, they are closely apposed or even attached to these structures. It is possible, therefore, that the contractile state of mesangial cells may affect the number of open glomerular capillaries and thus the total surface area available for filtration. Since this area is a component of the ultrafiltration coefficient (K_f of Eq. 2-8), GFR could be regulated, in part, by mesangial cells. An alternative view, however, is that the contractility of mesangial cells merely lends structural support to glomerular capillaries but does not alter their surface area.

Hemorrhage

The afferent and efferent arterioles, and mesangial cells, are constantly receiving numerous neural and humoral inputs, and their state of constriction can be viewed as deriving from the algebraic sum of these varied inputs. The interplay of the various factors can be very important in many clinical situations. For example, non-steroidal anti-inflammatory drugs that inhibit cyclooxygenase decrease the production of prostacyclin and other prostaglandins. By themselves these drugs do little to alter RBF or GFR; during stress or trauma, however, the resulting decrease in prostaglandin production can exacerbate the vasoconstrictor effects of increased sympathetic tone and circulating catecholamines, and thus lead to a potentially damaging decrease in RBF. One paradigm of trauma and stress is hemorrhage, which particularly exemplifies the complex interplay of the many factors that regulate RBF and GFR.

The renal circulation is exquisitely sensitive to blood loss. Even relatively small hemorrhages, which do not decrease the systemic blood pressure measurably, can result in striking decreases in the renal blood flow. The mechanisms that bring about this effect are shown in Figure 6-7. We will consider first the events that lead to adjustment of the renal circulation (solid arrows), and then other events that, through their actions on the kidneys, tend to restore the extracellular fluid (ECF) volume and the blood pressure (broken arrows). Blood is lost from the plasma compartment, and hemorrhage therefore leads to a reduction of the ECF volume (Fig. 2-1) and—by the relationship that *systemic arterial pressure = cardiac output × peripheral resistance*—to a decline of systemic blood pressure. These two changes are sensed by volume receptors and pressure (or baro-) receptors. Stimulation of the aortic arch and carotid sinus evokes an increase in sympathetic outflow and catecholamines, and these changes, plus stimulation of renal baroreceptors (see Fig. 7-9), increase secretion of renin at the juxtaglomerular apparatus and consequent production of angiotensin II. It is mainly these vasoconstrictor substances that then constrict the afferent or efferent arteriole, or both (Table 6-1), which leads to a decrease in RBF. These effects contribute to an increase in total peripheral resistance (TPR), which tends to restore the systemic blood pressure. The concomitant decline in GFR probably has several causes: the decrease in RBF, the decrease in the hydrostatic pressure within glomerular capillaries (P_c of Eq. 2-8; Fig. 3-1), and the differential effects of vasoconstrictors and vasodilators (of endothelial and other origin) on the afferent and efferent arterioles (Fig. 6-3 and Table 6-1). The decline in GFR promotes the renal retention of Na^+ and water.

Simultaneously with the above changes, and partly as a result of them, there are influences that bring about the renal retention of Na^+ and water through direct actions on the renal tubules: (a) increased secretion of renin, brought about not only by renal baroreceptors but also by increased sympathetic outflow (Fig. 6-7), leads,

■　**Sensors of Changes in Blood Volume and Extracellular Fluid Volume**

High-pressure baro-receptors
aortic arch
carotid sinus
kidneys

Low-pressure, volume receptors
cardiac atria
pulmonary vessels
hepatic vessels (?)

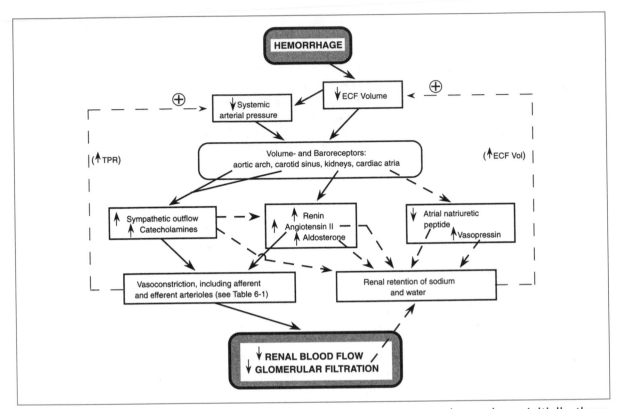

Figure 6-7.　Regulation of renal function in response to hemorrhage. Initially, there is a decrease in renal blood flow and glomerular filtration rate caused by the mechanisms designated by solid arrows. These mechanisms, plus some others (broken heavy arrows), lead to compensatory mechanisms (broken light arrows) that restore systemic arterial pressure and extracellular fluid (ECF) volume to or toward normal. The compensatory mechanisms include an increase in total peripheral resistance (TPR) and an increase in ECF volume following renal retention of sodium and water.

ultimately, to increased plasma levels of angiotensin II and aldosterone; (b) increased sympathetic outflow and catecholamines, as well as (c) increased angiotensin II exert a direct effect on renal tubules; (d) the plasma concentration of atrial natriuretic peptide (ANP) is lowered, perhaps to zero, by low-pressure receptors and volume receptors in the cardiac atria; and (e) the plasma concentration of vasopressin is raised by these receptors. As a result of the renal retention of Na$^+$ and water, the ECF volume, previously lowered by hemorrhage, tends to be restored (Fig. 6-7, broken arrow on right).

SUMMARY

The mammalian renal circulation has a number of unique features. 1. The renal circulation consists of two capillary beds in series (the glomerular capillaries followed by the peritubular capillaries). The fact that these capillary networks are preceded and separated by the two sites of major vascular resistance in the kidney (the afferent and efferent arterioles, respectively) makes it possible to change GFR and RBF independently of one another and sometimes in opposite directions. 2. There are striking regional differences, with nearly 100% of the total RBF perfusing the cortex and less than 10% of RBF entering the medulla. The single nephron glomerular filtration rate (snGFR) is greater in juxtamedullary nephrons than in superficial nephrons, and the rates of filtration in these nephrons may change independently of one another. 3. Ordinarily GFR and RBF are held relatively constant through autoregulation, a process that is thought to be effected by two factors: (a) an intrinsic property of arteriolar smooth muscle called the myogenic mechanism and (b) tubuloglomerular feedback. 4. Per unit of tissue weight, the kidneys are perfused by more blood and they consume more oxygen than does almost any other organ. Yet, the renal arteriovenous (a-v) oxygen content difference is lower than that of other organs. The explanation for this fact is that under normal conditions, renal oxygen consumption is governed by the need to reabsorb virtually all of the filtered Na^+, not by the basal energy requirements of renal cells.

These unique features are best understood in the context of salt and water balance. Probably through evolutionary forces, the kidney became an organ of high-filtering capacity. As a necessary concomitant, the RBF far exceeds the basal oxygen requirements. In most terrestrial mammals, the potential liability of high filtration is counteracted by virtually complete reabsorption of the filtered water and Na^+. The latter requires energy (see Chap. 7) and is, in fact, the process that accounts for the high rate of renal oxygen consumption. The *raison d'être* for autoregulation of the GFR may well be the regulation of Na^+ balance; if even just a small increase in GFR were left unchecked, so much more Na^+ would be filtered that the organism would be in immediate danger of Na^+ depletion and of a fatal reduction in extracellular fluid volume. Simultaneous autoregulation of the blood flow might be a mere coincidental event or it might be an integral part of the mechanism by which the GFR is finely tuned. Finally, the intrarenal distribution of the blood flow and glomerular filtration rate also may be governed primarily by the need for the conservation of Na^+ (Chap. 7) and of water (Chap. 8).

The renal circulation is regulated by a large number of vasodilator and vasoconstrictor substances that act on the afferent or efferent arterioles, or on both. In any given circumstance, several of these substances can act simultaneously, and they often dampen one another, ultimately to produce an integrated response.

PROBLEM 6-1

This problem has been adapted from two reports: Horster, M., and Thurau, K. *Pflügers Arch. Ges. Physiol.* 301:162, 1968; Jamison, R. L. *Am. J. Physiol.* 218:46, 1969.

An anesthetized rat, which weighed 140 g, was prepared for renal micropuncture. The animal was given inulin by intravenous infusion to attain a steady plasma concentration for this compound. A late segment of a proximal tubule was punctured at the surface of the kidney, and a droplet of oil was instilled into the tubular lumen through the micropipet. (To visualize this procedure, see Fig. 3-5.) All of the tubular fluid flowing just proximal to the oil droplet was then collected for a period of 3 minutes, during which time a sample of blood was obtained from a femoral artery. This procedure was repeated three times in other proximal tubules.

Next, the papilla was exposed by incision of the renal pelvis (see Fig. 1-1A; rats have only a single papilla), the bend of a loop of Henle was punctured, and tubular fluid was collected quantitatively, as described above for a proximal tubule. Again, samples of arterial blood were obtained during each collection of tubular fluid. This procedure was applied to two other bends of loops of Henle.

Each sample of tubular fluid was analyzed for its total volume and its concentration of inulin and of Na^+. Each sample of arterial blood was centrifuged, and the plasma was analyzed for its concentration of inulin and Na^+. Average values for the two types of collection are given in Table 6-2.

1. What was the glomerular filtration rate of single nephrons (snGFR) at the surface of the kidney? What was the snGFR of nephrons arising deep in the cortex? Explain the difference.
2. What fraction of the glomerular filtrate was reabsorbed by the end of the proximal tubule at the surface of the kidney? What fraction had been reabsorbed up to the bend of the loop of Henle?

Table 6-2. Results obtained on micropuncture samples.

Flow rate of tubular fluid ($\dot{v}$) (nL/min)	Concentrations in tubular fluid (TF)		Concentrations in arterial plasma (P)	
	Na⁺ (mmol/L)	Inulin (mg/dL)	Na⁺ (mmol/L)	Inulin (mg/dL)
Micropunctures of proximal tubules:				
11.21	140	209	137	98
Micropunctures of bends of loops of Henle:				
9.14	283	583	138	93

3. What fraction of the filtered Na^+ was reabsorbed up to the end of the proximal tubule at the surface of the kidney? What fraction of the filtered Na^+ had been reabsorbed up to the bend of the loop of Henle?

SUGGESTED READINGS

Ahrendshorst, W. J., and Navar, L. G. Renal Circulation and Glomerular Hemodynamics. In R. W. Schrier and C. W. Gottschalk (Eds.), *Diseases of the Kidney* (5th ed.). Boston: Little, Brown, 1993. Chap. 2.

Cohen, J. J., and Kamm, D. E. Renal Metabolism: Relation to Renal Function. In B. M. Brenner and F. C. Rector, Jr. (Eds.), *The Kidney* (2nd ed.). Philadelphia: Saunders, 1981.

Dworkin, L. D., and Brenner, B. M. The Renal Circulations. In B. M. Brenner and F. C. Rector, Jr. (Eds.), *The Kidney* (4th ed.). Philadelphia: Saunders, 1991. Chap. 5.

Edwards, R. M. Angiotensin II receptor subtypes in the kidney. *J. Am. Soc. Nephrol.* 3:1643, 1993.

Gullans, S. R., and Hebert, S. C. Metabolic Basis of Ion Transport. In B. M. Brenner and F. C. Rector, Jr. (Eds.), *The Kidney* (4th ed.). Philadelphia: Saunders, 1991. Chap. 2.

Moss, N. G., Colindres, R. E., and Gottschalk, C. W. Neural Control of Renal Function. In E. E. Windhager (Ed.), *Handbook of Physiology,* section 8: *Renal Physiology,* vol. I. New York: Oxford University Press, 1992. Chap. 24.

Navar, L. G., Carmines, P. K., and Paul, R. V. Renal Circulation. In S. G. Massry and R. J. Glassock (Eds.), *Textbook of Nephrology* (2nd ed.). Baltimore: Williams & Wilkins, 1989. Chap. 2.

Schnermann, J., Häberle, D. A., Davis, J. M., and Thurau, K. Tubuloglomerular Feedback Control of Renal Vascular Resistance. In E. E. Windhager (Ed.), *Handbook of Physiology,* section 8: *Renal Physiology,* vol. II. New York: Oxford University Press, 1992. Chap. 34.

Na⁺ and H₂O Transport. Na⁺ Balance

7

Continued

Challenges to Na⁺ Balance:
  2. Changes in Na⁺ Intake
    Changes in GFR
    Changes in Na⁺ Reabsorption
  Tuners of Na⁺ Balance

SUMMARY

■   **Terminology**   ■

Osmolality   the concentration of discrete solute particles in solution

Isosmotic   having the same osmolality as plasma (but can also refer to comparison with fluids other than plasma). The prefixes hypo- and hyper- refer to osmolalities below or above that of normal plasma

Na+ Balance   the normal equality between Na⁺ intake and Na⁺ output by the body. This balance ensures constancy of extracellular fluid volume

Diuresis   urine flow above usual levels

Water Diuresis   increased urine flow due to decreased reabsorption of 'free' water (i.e., water without solute)

Osmotic Diuresis   high rate of water excretion caused by the filtration of poorly reabsorbed solutes such as mannitol

Antidiuresis   low rate of water excretion (usually <0.5 mL/min) as hyperosmotic urine

Natriuresis   rate of urinary Na⁺ excretion above usual levels

Among the most important functions of the kidney are the maintenance of normal osmolality and normal volume of the body fluids. The osmolality of these fluids is determined by the total number of discrete—and hence osmotically active—solutes within those compartments (see Chap. 2, under Osmolality in the Major Compartments, p. 26). When solutes are in relative excess of water, all the body fluid compartments become *hyperosmotic* compared to normal plasma, which has an osmolality of about 287 mOsm/kg (milliosmols per kg H₂O; for explanation of this notation, see Table A-1 in the Appendix). Conversely, when there is a relative excess of water or a deficit of solutes, the body fluid compartments become *hyposmotic,* i.e., less than approximately 287 mOsm/kg.

Because the extracellular fluid (ECF) compartment includes the plasma (Fig. 2-1), the volume of ECF is very important in the dynamics of the cardiovascular system. In the condition known as *volume contraction* a low extracellular fluid volume is accompanied by reduced venous return and reduced cardiac output. In generalized edema, there is an excess of extracellular fluid volume, which, because of an enlarged plasma volume, can lead to heart failure and pulmonary edema.

As discussed in Chapter 2 (under Maintenance of Compartment Size. Importance of Total Solute Content, p. 30) and in this chapter, the total body content of Na⁺ usually determines the volume of extracellular fluid because Na⁺ and the accompanying anions, Cl⁻ and HCO₃⁻, are the primary solutes in this compartment. The normal and constant volume of the extracellular fluid compartment depends on the ability of the kidneys to adjust the total daily excretion of Na⁺ so that it matches exactly the daily intake of this ion. This equilibrium of Na⁺ intake and output is referred to as *Na⁺ balance,* or simply salt balance because Na⁺ and Cl⁻ are usually transported together. When the body loses more salt than is taken in, the individual is said to be in *negative Na⁺ balance,* and extracellular fluid volume decreases. Conversely, *positive Na⁺ balance* occurs when Na⁺ intake exceeds output, and then extracellular fluid volume increases, which ultimately leads to edema (see Chap. 2, under Edema).

Of course, the volume of the body fluid compartments is also determined by the balance between the amount of water taken in and the amount lost in the urine and by other routes (Table A-4). A urine flow above the usual average of approximately 1 mL/min is called *diuresis*. Urine osmolality can range from hyposmotic to hyperosmotic to plasma (see Chap. 8). When the urine flow is high and its Na$^+$ concentration is high, the rate of urinary Na$^+$ excretion ($U_{Na} \times \dot{V}$) is higher than the normal average, a condition called *natriuresis*. But when the urine flow is high and it contains only small amounts of solute, the condition is referred to as a *water diuresis,* because there is a loss of free water (i.e., water without solutes) from the body (discussed in Chap. 8 under Free Water, p. 176). Water diuresis is the normal response to drinking large volumes of water (Problem 8-1), but it can also occur abnormally because of some aberration in the antidiuretic hormone (ADH or vasopressin) system.

As the name implies, antidiuretic hormone reduces urine flow, a condition referred to as *antidiuresis*. In this state, water is conserved through avid reabsorption so that the solutes requisite for balance are excreted in a small volume. Consequently, the urine is hyperosmotic to plasma; in humans, urine osmolality can be as high as 1,200 mOsm/kg (discussed in Chap. 8).

In summary, the balance of both salt and water in the body depends critically on the rate at which the kidney reabsorbs these substances and returns them to the plasma. This chapter presents the major transport mechanisms responsible for these reabsorptive processes in the different regions of the nephron; it concludes with a discussion of how the processes for Na$^+$ are regulated under normal conditions and in some pathological circumstances. Regulatory processes for water are detailed in Chapter 8.

CORRELATION OF Na$^+$ AND H$_2$O REABSORPTION

Even though the kidneys can regulate the reabsorption of salt and water independently of one another (illustrated in Problem 8-1), the reabsorption of water is linked directly to the reabsorption of salt. A key element to understanding this (seemingly paradoxical) linkage was the theoretical demonstration that, if hyperosmotic urine were to be formed through active transport of water, the expenditure of energy required would be more than 1,000 times the amount of energy that could be produced by renal metabolism. In fact, to date, active water transport has not been demonstrated in any biological system. It was clear, therefore, that water reabsorption by renal tubules (and, in fact, by all epithelia) is a passive process that depends on osmotic gradients between the tubular fluid and the peritubular interstitial fluid and plasma. Hence, water diffuses passively in response to an osmotic gradient set up mainly by NaCl and NaHCO$_3$ and, to a lesser extent, by organic solutes that are transported with Na$^+$ (see Chap. 4, under Na$^+$ Co-transporters, p. 69).

Na$^+$ AND H$_2$O REABSORPTION IN PROXIMAL TUBULES

It was pointed out in Chapter 4 (under Principles of Epithelial Transport) that epithelial cells (unlike blood cells, for example) have two membranes with different properties (Figs. 4-1 and 4-3). Therefore, transport of substances across epithelia is a two-step process, first across the apical membrane and then across the basolateral membrane (in the case of reabsorption), and vice versa (in the case of secretion). Furthermore, in analyzing the transport of a charged particle, such as Na$^+$, we must take into account not only the chemical concentration difference across each membrane, but also the electrical potential difference ($\Delta\Psi$; see Eq. 2-7). These points are illustrated for the proximal tubule in Figure 7-1.

Early Proximal Tubule

Because transport is different in the first half of the proximal tubule than it is in the second half, we divide this tubule into 'early' and 'late' portions. Electrical potential differences for the early proximal tubule are shown at the top in Figure 7-1A; they were measured by inserting microelectrodes into the tubular lumen and into the cell, taking peritubular fluid as a zero reference. The $\Delta\Psi$ across the apical membrane is approximately 66 millivolts (mV), with the interior of the cell being negative with respect to the lumen. Therefore, a positively charged ion such as Na$^+$ can enter the cell passively (as reflected by interrupted arrows), i.e., down its *electrochemical gradient:* Both the chemical concentration difference [being approximately 140 mmol/L in the tubular fluid and much lower within the cell (Fig. 2-2)] and the electrical potential difference favor entry into the cell. In the early proximal tubule, this entry occurs by two means: (a) by Na$^+$-cotransport (see Fig. 4-3), not only with glucose, as shown in Figure 7-1A, but also with inorganic phosphate, sulfate, amino acids, and other organic acids; and (b) by a Na⁺/H⁺ exchanger. Once inside the cell, however, the Na⁺ must be transported actively in order to get out of the cell across the basolateral membrane: Not only does it have to be transported against a chemical concentration difference (from the low concentration within cells to one of approximately 140 mmol/L in peritubular fluid, i.e., interstitial fluid and blood) but also against a $\Delta\Psi$ of approximately 70 mV, since the interior of the cell is negative with respect to the peritubular fluid. This active transport is accomplished by Na-K-ATPase, where the 'ATP' within the concentric circles (carrier) indicates a direct input of energy; these pumps are distributed not only in the membrane facing the peritubular fluid (as shown), but also along the membrane that faces the intercellular space, i.e., along the entire basolateral membrane.

The glucose and other compounds that are cotransported across the apical membrane enter the peritubular space passively, primarily by facilitated diffusion because the diffusional permeability of the basolateral membrane for these substances is low (Fig. 4-3). The HCO_3^-, which was formed within the cell from the processing of CO_2 (described in detail in Chap. 10), also moves out of the cell by facilitated diffusion. The last process is important because it means that in the early proximal tubule Na⁺ is reabsorbed mostly with HCO_3^-. The fact that HCO_3^- is preferentially reabsorbed in this manner (and that the reabsorption of water follows the reabsorption of Na⁺ and HCO_3^-; see below, under Coupling of Solute and Water Transport) produces an increasing concentration of Cl⁻ within the tubular fluid as it approaches the late proximal tubule.

Late Proximal Tubule

The reabsorption of glucose, inorganic phosphate, amino acids, and other organic acids is virtually completed by the end of the early proximal tubule; therefore, cotransport is no longer a major mode of entry for Na⁺ into the cell in the late proximal tubule. It still enters the cell passively, but now primarily by a Na⁺/H⁺ exchanger (Fig. 7-1B). Then, as in the early proximal tubule, Na⁺ must leave the cell actively, via Na-K-ATPase. Na⁺/H⁺ exchangers are common transporters in many cell types, where they raise intracellular pH by driving H⁺ ions out of cells in exchange for Na⁺ entry into cells. At least three different forms of this ubiquitous transporter have been cloned and sequenced, and one form is found in the basolateral membrane of many renal tubular cells as well as of other epithelia. However, the form present in the apical membrane of the proximal tubule (Fig. 7-1B) is different, probably

Figure 7-1. Modes of reabsorption of Na⁺ in the proximal tubule, which is divided
into an early portion (A, approximately the first half)
and a late portion (B, approximately the second half,
including the pars recta).
Broken arrows indicate passive transport; circles represent carriers; and the
slanted parallel bars crossing
the basolateral membrane
represent specialized proteins, which are ion channels. The circle with 'ATP' in
the center is the sodium
pump or Na-K-ATPase,
which, unlike the other carriers shown here, requires a
direct input of energy in the
form of ATP hydrolysis. Although Na-K-ATPase is
shown here only in the basal
membrane, it must be realized that this active carrier is
also present in the lateral
membranes bordering the
intercellular spaces. Note
that the interior of the cell
has a negative voltage with
respect to both tubular lumen and peritubular fluid.
C.A. = carbonic anhydrase.

A. Events in the early
proximal tubule. Details are
described in the text. Note
that in this segment, Na⁺ is
reabsorbed in conjunction
with HCO_3^- as well as with
glucose and other solutes,
including inorganic phos-
phate and organic acids, but
not with Cl⁻. The production
of H⁺ and HCO_3^- within cells
from the splitting of water
and the processing of CO_2 is
detailed in Chapter 10.

B. Events in the late proximal tubule. Details are described in the text. Note
that in this segment, Na⁺ is
reabsorbed almost exclu-
sively with Cl⁻.

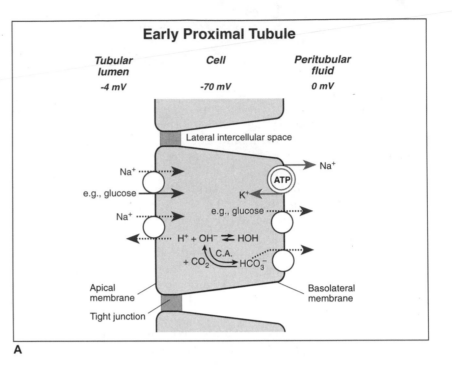

A

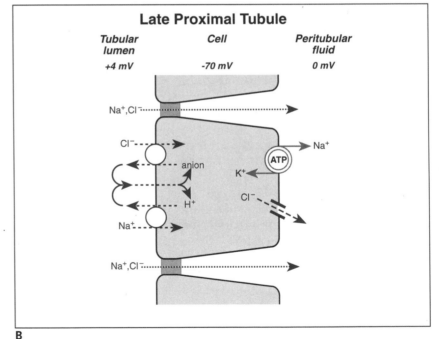

B

because it is regulated in response to the requirements for H^+ secretion in the proximal tubule (discussed in Chap. 10).

Whereas in the early proximal tubule, Na^+ is reabsorbed preferentially with HCO_3^- (Fig. 7-1A), in the late proximal tubule it is accompanied mostly by Cl^- (Fig. 7-1B). As indicated by the broken arrows, Cl^- can be transported passively across the epithelium of late proximal tubules; two routes are involved, transcellular and paracellular (Fig. 4-1). Reabsorption across the cell can occur passively because the reabsorptive processes of Na^+, HCO_3^-, and water in the early proximal tubule raise the concentration of Cl^- in the tubular fluid. This fact, coupled with the low concentration of Cl^- within cells (Fig. 2-2), makes it possible for the chemical concentration gradient to overcome the 'unfavorable' electrical potential gradient and for Cl^- to enter the cell passively; this conclusion is based on the Nernst equation (Eq. 2-7). Similarly, Cl^- can cross the basolateral membrane passively even though it has to go from the low concentration within cells into a peritubular concentration of approximately 100 mmol/L, because there is a large $\Delta\Psi$ oriented with the peritubular fluid positive with respect to the interior of the cell. Note, in Figure 7-1B, that Cl^- enters the cell in exchange for a small organic anion such as formate, which simultaneously exits the cell on a common anion exchanger protein. This process occurs in parallel with Na^+/H^+ exchange so that the net result is the reabsorption of NaCl.

Reabsorption of Cl^- by the paracellular route occurs down a favorable chemical concentration gradient, which 'overcomes' the slightly unfavorable $\Delta\Psi$ (Fig. 7-1B). The Cl^- concentration is approximately 120 mmol/L within late proximal tubular fluid as opposed to about 100 mmol/L in peritubular fluid. As the negatively charged Cl^- ions diffuse through the tight junctions and along the intercellular spaces, the late tubular lumen becomes slightly positive with respect to peritubular fluid (Fig. 7-1B), and Na^+ therefore can flow passively along these spaces, down the favorable $\Delta\Psi$. There is as yet no agreement on what proportion of Na^+ is reabsorbed passively in the entire proximal tubule and what proportion is reabsorbed actively; it is possible that approximately one-third is passive and two-thirds active.

Coupling of Solute and Water Transport

Inasmuch as the transport of water is passive in all biological systems, water must flow in response to pressure differences, be they hydrostatic or osmotic, or both. For the proximal tubule, the force is predominantly or exclusively osmotic, and therefore the required differences in osmolality must be generated by the reabsorptive processes that we have just reviewed—i.e., by the reabsorption of Na^+ with HCO_3^- and with Cl^-, and in cotransport with other solutes (Fig. 7-1). We might expect, therefore, that the osmolality of blood (which probably is in osmotic equilibrium with interstitial fluid) would be higher than the osmolality of proximal tubular fluid. Yet, initially when such measurements were taken, these osmolalities appeared to be equal. In retrospect, this apparent equality arose from the limits of sensitivity of the osmolality measurements in tiny amounts of tubular fluid (in the range of nanoliters); i.e., such osmometers are accurate to at best ±3 mOsm/kg, and a smaller difference between tubular fluid and blood, if it existed, could not be detected.

As reviewed for urea (Chap. 4), the rate of transport of a substance that is carried passively across a membrane, be it a solvent (e.g., H_2O) or a solute, depends on the chemical concentration difference for that substance on the two sides of the membrane, as well as on the permeability of the membrane for the substance. If that permeability is very high, then only a small concentration difference will be required to move large amounts of the substance. That is the situation for the proximal tubule in regard to H_2O (and to certain solutes), which is partly why the proximal tubule is called a 'leaky epithelium.' Both the apical and basolateral membranes of proximal tubular cells, as well as the tight junctions and lateral intercellular spaces, are exceedingly permeable to H_2O, so that only a very small osmotic gradient (perhaps 2 to 5 mOsm/kg) will suffice to move very large amounts of H_2O from the tubular lumen into the peritubular space. Initially, a gradient of that size could not be detected by standard means; but recently, through several careful experimental approaches, it has been shown that solute reabsorption causes the proximal tubular fluid to become slightly dilute, while simultaneously the osmolality of peritubular fluid becomes slightly higher than in the blood (Figs. 7-2A and B). Although the difference in osmolality is small, it is sufficient to cause a large osmotic water flow because of the high osmotic water permeability. Recall that approximately two-thirds of the water that is filtered into Bowman's space is reabsorbed in the proximal tubule (see Chap. 3, under Meaning of TF/P and U/P for Inulin).

Our current understanding of the process that couples solute and water transport in the proximal tubule is shown in Figure 7-2, which incorporates the solute transport processes illustrated in Figure 7-1. The description is limited to Na^+ and water; elsewhere (e.g., Chaps. 5 and 11) we consider other transport processes in the proximal tubule, such as secretion of organic acids or reabsorption of K^+. In the early proximal tubule, Na^+ is reabsorbed predominantly as the HCO_3^- salt, as well as by cotransport with various solutes such as glucose. Almost certainly the reabsorbate—i.e., the fluid that is reabsorbed—is initially slightly hypertonic to the fluid in the tubular lumen. Therefore, the fluid in the lumen becomes slightly hypotonic and the interstitial fluid surrounding the tubule slightly hypertonic. It is this small difference in the osmolality that is thought to supply the driving force for the passive reabsorption of water, at least in the early proximal tubule. The route for water transport in this segment is both paracellular (D–E in Fig. 4-1) and transcellular (A–C or A–B–E in Fig. 4-1).

In the late proximal tubule, the composition of the luminal fluid has been altered by the preferential reabsorption of HCO_3^- and of solutes such as glucose in the early proximal tubule. Thus, the Cl^- concentration is now greater in the luminal fluid than in the blood or the interstitial fluid, while the HCO_3^- concentration is lower. This difference in anion composition produces an additional osmotic force for water reabsorption as a consequence of the fact that HCO_3^- has a higher reflection coefficient than does Cl^-. The reflection coefficient, σ, is an index of the osmotic effectiveness of a solute. Theoretically, the definition of an osmotic pressure difference involves a semipermeable membrane, i.e., a membrane that is permeable only to water but not to solutes. However, biological membranes actually have varying permeabilities to different solutes, and hence a correction factor must be applied when calculating the osmotic pressure developed by a permeable solute. If that solute is truly impermeable, we can think of it as being 'reflected' by the membrane ('bounced off' the membrane), thereby producing the full theoretical osmotic pressure. Such a solute would have a reflection coefficient of 1.0. Conversely, a solute that permeates the membrane as easily as water would have a reflection coefficient of zero. Thus, the usual range of reflection coefficients is zero to 1.0.

In the late proximal tubule the reflection coefficient for Cl^- is less than that for HCO_3^-. Consequently, HCO_3^- produces a larger osmotic force in the reabsorptive direction than does Cl^- in the opposite direction, even though the Cl^- concentration is higher in tubular fluid than in the interstitium and blood. Other solutes, such as glucose and amino acids, are almost completely absent from the late proximal tubular fluid. Because these solutes have reflection coefficients of approximately 1.0, they also add to the osmotic driving force for water reabsorption in this segment. Finally, the osmotic flow of water across the epithelium, which here too, occurs through both the transcellular and paracellular routes (Fig. 7-2B), results in passive reabsorption of Na⁺ and Cl⁻ by

■   **Coupling of**   ■
Solute and Water
Transport

Direct, obligatory coupling only in proximal tubules

Reabsorption of two-thirds of filtered sodium followed by reabsorption of two-thirds of filtered water

Peritubular fluid hyperosmotic

Tubular fluid hyposmotic

Reflection coefficient greater for bicarbonate than for chloride

Figure 7-2.
  A, B. Coupling of solute and water transport in the early (A) and late (B) proximal tubule. These two diagrams show the net movements of solute and water that result from the transport processes shown in Figure 7-1A and 7-1B. Details are described in the text. Lumen negative and lumen positive refer to the transepithelial electrical potential difference ($\Delta\Psi$; see Fig. 7-1A and 7-1B, respectively). σ = reflection coefficient. The true structure of proximal tubular epithelium is shown in C and D.
  C. Electron micrograph of early proximal tubular epithelium from a rat. The lateral intercellular spaces follow a serpentine course, so it is seldom possible to observe a single channel extending from the apex to the base of the cell. Note the abundant mitochondria, which supply the energy mainly for active Na+ transport, via Na-K-ATPase, all along the basolateral membrane. Micrograph kindly supplied by C. C. Tisher.
  D. Three-dimensional model of an early proximal tubular cell, constructed by morphometric and modeling techniques. Scanning electron micrographs have proved this model to be remarkably correct (see Welling, D. J., and Welling, L. W. *Fed. Proc.* 38:121, 1979). The lateral cellular processes of one cell interdigitate with corresponding processes of adjacent cells

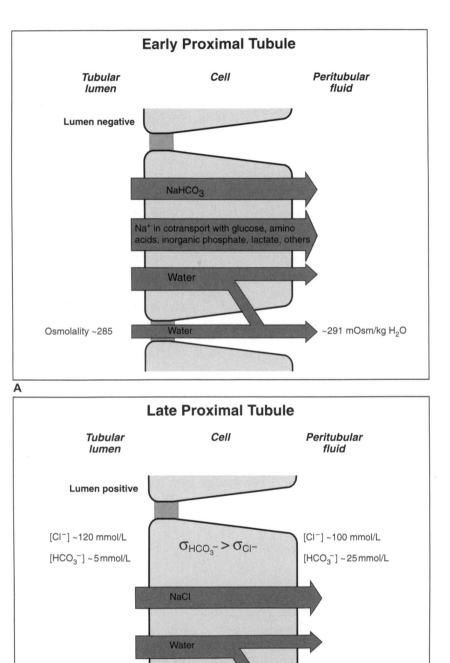

Early Proximal Tubule

Tubular lumen　　　Cell　　　Peritubular fluid

Lumen negative

NaHCO$_3$

Na+ in cotransport with glucose, amino acids, inorganic phosphate, lactate, others

Water

Osmolality ~285　　Water　　~291 mOsm/kg H$_2$O

A

Late Proximal Tubule

Tubular lumen　　　Cell　　　Peritubular fluid

Lumen positive

[Cl$^-$] ~120 mmol/L　　$\sigma_{HCO_3^-} > \sigma_{Cl^-}$　　[Cl$^-$] ~100 mmol/L

[HCO$_3^-$] ~5 mmol/L　　　　[HCO$_3^-$] ~25 mmol/L

NaCl

Water

Osmolality ~285　　Water　　~291 mOsm/kg H$_2$O

B

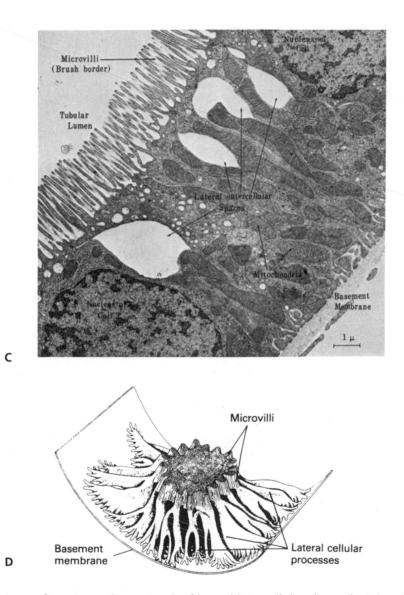

C

D

to produce a complex network of lateral intercellular channels. It is primarily the high salt and water permeabilities of the junctional complexes at the ends of these spaces (the tight junctions, Fig. 4-1), that cause proximal tubules to be 'leaky.' The configuration of late proximal tubular cells is similar but less complex. From Welling, L. W., and Welling, D. J. *Kidney Int.* 9:385, 1976. Published with permission.

solvent drag (see box on p. 64). Solvent drag probably accounts for the large proportion of Na⁺ that is reabsorbed passively in the proximal tubule.

Na⁺ AND H₂O REABSORPTION IN OTHER PARTS OF NEPHRON

In this section, we shall simplify the description by largely ignoring heterogeneity of nephrons (see Chap. 1, under Heterogeneity of Nephrons, p. 7), differences among species, as well as certain other differences between segments of nephrons.

Several parts of the nephron are not accessible to micropuncture, which, by and large, can be applied only to structures that appear at the surface of the kidney or at the very tip of the papilla (see Fig. 1-2A). In such instances, data are obtained through an in vitro technique called the *isolated perfused tubule,* which is described in the legend to Figure 7-3.

Figure 7-3.   Preparation of an isolated perfused renal tubule. A segment of tubule (in this instance, a proximal convoluted tubule from a rabbit) is held between two micropipets and suspended in a medium of varying composition. The segment is approximately 2 mm long. Fluid is perfused through the pipet on the left and is collected through the pipet on the right; the electrical potential difference ($\Delta\Psi$) can also be measured. By this technique, valuable information has been gained on parts of the nephron that are not ordinarily accessible to micropuncture (e.g., pars recta, loop of Henle, collecting duct, convolutions of juxtamedullary nephrons). From Burg, M. B., et al. *Am. J. Physiol.* 215:788, 1968.

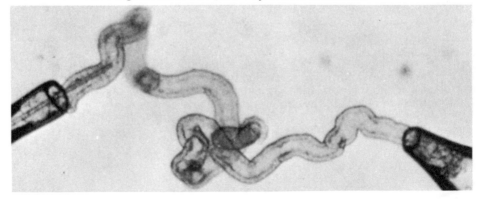

Loop of Henle

Thin Descending Limb

Descending limbs of Henle are highly permeable to water, and they ordinarily reabsorb up to approximately 20% of the water that is filtered. This water moves, however, in response to hyperosmolality of the interstitium arising from a countercurrent system (described in Chap. 8), not, as in proximal tubules, from coupling of solute and water flow. The thin descending limb may be moderately permeable to Na^+ and Cl^- and to urea, but these solutes are secreted (down their concentration gradients) into this segment, not reabsorbed from it. Almost certainly, all solutes are transported passively in thin descending limbs, some possibly via ion channels. This segment may or may not have a slight—perhaps 2 to 4 mV—lumen-negative transepithelial voltage ($\Delta\Psi$).

Thin Ascending Limb

This segment is especially permeable to Cl^- but also to Na^+, and the reabsorption of both is largely (possibly exclusively) passive. Water, however, cannot follow because these segments are virtually impermeable to water (discussed further in Chap. 8). There is no detectable $\Delta\Psi$.

Thick Ascending Limb

This segment constitutes an important site of Na^+ transport; ascending thick limbs of Henle ordinarily reabsorb approximately 25% of the filtered Na^+ (Fig. 7-7). They also appear to have considerable reserve for reabsorbing more Na^+ so that, as a general rule, if the proximal tubules fail to recapture the usual two-thirds of the filtered Na^+, the thick ascending limbs compensate partially by reabsorbing more. That fact probably explains why diuretics that act on the proximal tubules are much less effective in increasing the urinary excretion of Na^+ and water than are the so-called loop-diuretics, which inhibit the specialized cotransporter in the thick ascending limbs of Henle (described next).

The major solute transporters in the thick ascending limb are shown in Figure 7-4. We are already familiar with several of the elements: the Na-K-ATPase in the basolateral membrane (remember that this pump lies also all along the lateral membrane, which lines the lateral intercellular spaces), the Na^+/H^+ exchanger in the apical membrane, and the processing of CO_2 (which is described further in Chapter 10). Na^+ enters the cell mainly by what is known as the *Na:K:2Cl cotransporter* (or *symporter*). The driving force for this cotransporter comes from the large electrochemical

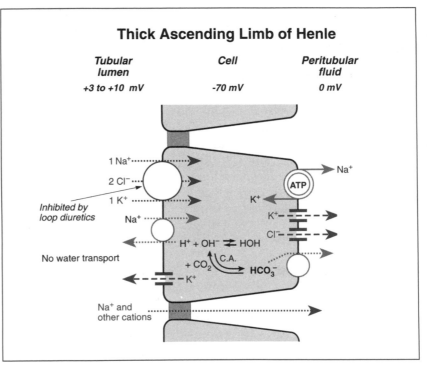

Figure 7-4. Modes of Na⁺ reabsorption in the thick ascending limb of the loop of Henle. The various symbols have the same meaning as those given in the legend for Figure 7-1. C.A. = carbonic anhydrase. The large circle in the apical membrane is the *Na:K:2Cl cotransporter,* so named because it is a single carrier that transports all three ions in those proportions. It is this carrier that is inhibited by the powerful 'loop' diuretics, such as furosemide and bumetanide. Note that tubular fluid is positive with respect to peritubular fluid, and that the interior of the cell is negative to both. Details are described in the text.

potential difference favoring entry of Na⁺ into the cell. This force makes it possible for K⁺ and Cl⁻ to be transported across the apical membrane against their electrochemical gradients. To exit the cell, Na⁺ must be transported actively, by Na-K-ATPase, while K⁺ and Cl⁻ cross into the peritubular fluid passively. Some K⁺ also returns to the lumen via a specific channel in the apical membrane. The fact that the apical membrane has a channel only for K⁺ while the basolateral membrane has channels for both K⁺ and Cl⁻ accounts for the lumen-positive transepithelial $\Delta\Psi$; that $\Delta\Psi$, in turn, permits Na⁺ and other cations (K⁺, Ca²⁺, Mg²⁺) to be moved passively, along the lateral intercellular spaces, from tubular lumen into peritubular fluid. In the thick ascending limb of Henle, approximately one-half of the Na$^+$ traverses the epithelium by the transcellular route and one-half by the paracellular route.

The Na:K:2Cl symporter has been cloned and sequenced. It is similar to transporters that are activated in many cells in response to changes in cellular volume, i.e., in situations where movement of ions in or out of cells alters intracellular osmolality and thus helps to regulate cellular volume. This cotransporter, which in the kidney is normally active only in thick ascending limbs of Henle, is important particularly because it is the target of some of the most potent diuretics. These diuretics, called *loop diuretics* and exemplified by furosemide and bumetanide, inhibit the cotransporter by binding to the Cl$^-$ site, thereby preventing the cotransporter from cycling. The resultant inhibition of net NaCl reabsorption leads to increased excretion of these ions and with them, of water.

As is true for thin ascending limbs, so also in the case of thick ascending limbs, there is no coupling of solute and water transport. The thick limbs are highly impermeable to water, so that water cannot follow the reabsorption of solute. This property of thin and thick limbs is critical for both diluting and concentrating the urine, a process that is described in detail in Chapter 8.

Distal Tubule

The distal tubule has two segments with very different properties, the *early distal tubule,* which extends from about the juxtaglomerular apparatus to the middle of the distal convolution (Fig. 1-2A), and the *late distal tubule,* which is the remaining distal convolution (also known as the connecting tubule) until it joins the cortical collecting duct. Because the late distal tubule is very similar to the collecting duct, its features are described along with the latter.

Early Distal Tubule

Here (Fig. 7-5) Na$^+$ enters the cell passively via a symporter with Cl$^-$. This cotransporter also has been cloned and sequenced; it is the target of another class of diuretic agents, the thiazide diuretics (e.g., hydrochlorothiazide). Na$^+$ enters the lateral intercellular spaces and the peritubular fluid actively via Na-K-ATPase, and Cl$^-$ does so passively via a channel. As with the thin and thick ascending limbs of Henle, water transport is not coupled to solute transport because the early distal epithelium is virtually impermeable to water.

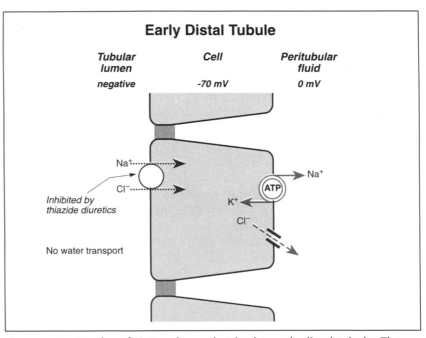

Figure 7-5.   Modes of Na⁺ reabsorption in the early distal tubule. The various symbols have the same meaning as those given in the legend for Figure 7-1. 'Lumen negative' refers to the transepithelial electrical potential difference ($\Delta\Psi$), with tubular fluid being slightly negative in respect to peritubular fluid; the interior of the cell is negative to both. Details are described in the text.

Late Distal Tubule and Collecting Duct

As stated above, the late distal tubule and the collecting duct are very similar, both anatomically and functionally. There are two major cell types in these tubular segments: (a) the principal cell and (b) the intercalated cell. Only the former reabsorbs Na⁺, and we will therefore describe only principal cells here. Intercalated cells are responsible for secreting H⁺—not, however, in conjunction with Na⁺ reabsorption, as in the proximal tubule and thick ascending limb of Henle (Figs. 7-1A, B and 7-4)—and their function is discussed fully in Chapter 10.

Reabsorption of Na⁺ by principal cells is shown in Figure 7-6. Sodium can move across the apical membrane passively, by facilitated diffusion through a channel and down both a favorable chemical and electrical potential gradient. The channel protein is a com-

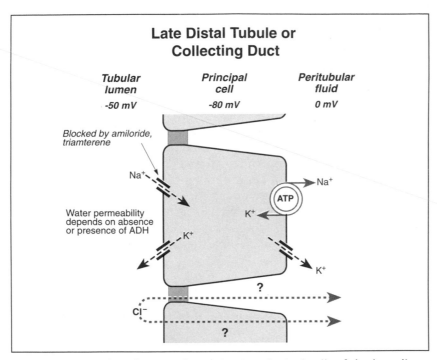

Figure 7-6. Modes of Na⁺ reabsorption in principal cells of the late distal tubule and collecting duct. The various symbols have the same meaning as those given in the legend for Figure 7-1. The question marks above and below the dashed arrows with Cl⁻ indicate that we do not yet know the mode of transport for this ion.

plex of multiple subunits, one of which is the channel itself while the remainder are regulatory in nature. Thus far, the conducting portion of a similar Na⁺-specific channel in the colon, as well as two regulatory subunits, have been cloned and sequenced. The channel can be blocked by yet another class of diuretics that includes amiloride and triamterene. These diuretics, however, are not remarkably effective as natriuretic agents (i.e., increasing the urinary excretion of Na⁺) because only a small fraction of the filtered Na⁺ is reabsorbed in late distal tubules and collecting ducts, as compared with the more proximal regions of the nephron (Fig. 7-7). Na⁺ moves out of the cell actively via Na-K-ATPase. The reabsorbed Na⁺ is accompanied mainly by Cl⁻, but neither the mechanism(s) nor routes of transport for Cl⁻ have been worked out fully.

It is likely that Cl^- moves passively, certainly via the paracellular route where it can move down the lumen-negative $\Delta\Psi$. It may also be transported by the transcellular route, possibly as a neutral NaCl salt or possibly via a channel in the basolateral membrane. Water transport in the late distal tubule and collecting duct varies with the plasma concentration of the antidiuretic hormone (ADH, or vasopressin), which alters the water permeability of these segments (Table 7-1). This property, which is essential in determining the osmolality of the urine, is discussed in detail in Chapter 8.

The K^+ that is built up within the cell by Na-K-ATPase leaves the cell via channels in both the apical and basolateral membranes. The relative rates of K^+ movement through these two routes determine the rate of net K^+ secretion into the lumen, and that varies, in turn, with the dietary intake of K^+ and hence with the need for K^+ balance; details are discussed in Chapter 11.

Table 7-1.   Some properties of various parts of the nephron.[a] In most instances, the electrical potential difference ($\Delta\Psi$) has a range of values along a given part; for the sake of clarity, only a single representative value is indicated.

Part of nephron	Transepithelial $\Delta\Psi$[b] lumen relative to peritubular fluid mV	Ion that is actively reabsorbed	Permeability to water ADH[b] present	Permeability to water ADH absent
Proximal tubule				
Early	−4	Na⁺	+++	+++
Late	+2	Na⁺	+++	+++
Loop of Henle				
Thin descending	0 (?)	none	++++	++++
Thin ascending	0 (?)	none (?); Na⁺ (?)	0[c]	0
Thick ascending	+10	Na⁺ and Cl⁻	0	0
Distal tubule				
Early	−10	Na⁺ and Cl⁻	0	0
Late	−40	Na⁺	+++	0
Collecting duct				
Cortical	−25	Na⁺	+++	0
Outer medullary	−7	Na⁺	+++	0
Inner medullary	−2	Na⁺	+++	0

[a]A more complete listing of the permeability characteristics of various parts of the nephron is given in tabular form in Jamison, R. L. Urine Concentration and Dilution. The Roles of Antidiuretic Hormone and Urea. In Brenner, B. M., and Rector, F. C., Jr. (Eds.), *The Kidney* (2nd ed.). Philadelphia: Saunders, 1981. Chap. 11.
[b]ADH = antidiuretic hormone (Chap. 8); $\Delta\Psi$ = electrical potential difference.
[c]Virtually zero, although most biological membranes are not totally impermeable to water.

Final modulation of Na$^+$ reabsorption takes place in collecting ducts, probably mainly in inner medullary collecting ducts, where the epithelium can pump Na$^+$ against very large concentration gradients. Whereas earlier parts of the nephron, especially the proximal tubules, reabsorb large amounts of Na$^+$ against a relatively small or no chemical concentration difference, the collecting ducts transport lesser amounts but can do so to a point where the concentration of Na$^+$ in the tubular fluid may become vanishingly small (<1.0 mmol/L).

RENAL REGULATION OF Na$^+$ BALANCE

We often speak of 'Na$^+$ balance' or 'dietary intake of Na$^+$' when we really mean NaCl, or salt. It should be borne in mind that in all the body fluids, including blood and urine, as well as in food and drink, cationic Na$^+$ occurs in combination with anions so that electroneutrality exists. Although the predominant anion is usually Cl$^-$, that is not always the case; for example, patients being treated with NaHCO$_3$ may ingest a great deal of Na$^+$ that is not in the form of ordinary table salt, or NaCl. Because of these exceptions, because even normally intake of Na$^+$ is not exclusively in the form of the chloride salt, and because Na$^+$ and Cl$^-$ do not always move together in the nephron, we will continue to use the terms *Na$^+$ balance, Na$^+$ handling,* and *dietary Na$^+$* in the ensuing discussion.

Amounts of Na$^+$ Reabsorbed in Various Parts of Nephron

The handling of Na$^+$ by the kidneys of a normal adult human is depicted in Figure 7-7, in which the single nephron represents both kidneys. With a glomerular filtration rate of 180 liters per day (Table 1-1) and a plasma Na$^+$ concentration of 140 mmol/L, the filtered load of Na$^+$ is 180 × 140, or 25,200 mmol per day. [Strictly speaking, this value should be lowered by the Donnan factor of about 0.95, but, as stated in Chapter 4 (under Quantifying Reabsorption), such corrections are customarily ignored.] Of the 25,200 mmol filtered, roughly 67%, or 16,800 mmol per day, is reabsorbed in the proximal tubules. Normal urine flow is about 1 mL per minute; since there are 1,440 minutes in 24 hours, normal urine flow is approximately 1,500 mL per day. At a typical urinary Na$^+$ concentration of about 100 mmol/L (see Answer to Problem 11-1), the daily urinary excretion of Na$^+$ is about 150 mmol or just 0.6% of the filtered load. Hence, nearly 33% of the filtered load of Na$^+$ is reabsorbed beyond the proximal tubules. This reabsorption is ap-

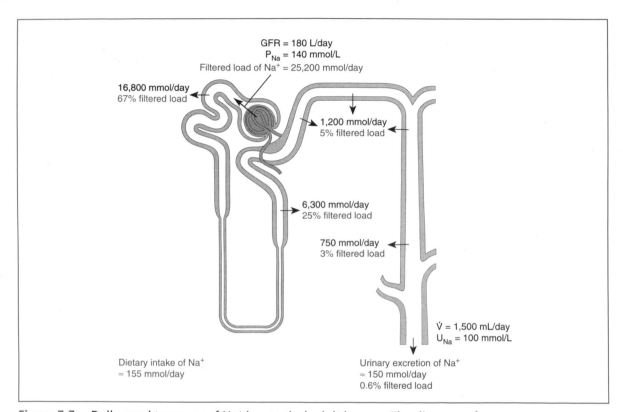

Figure 7-7. Daily renal turnover of Na⁺ in a typical adult human. The diagram of the nephron represents the composite of the roughly two million nephrons of both kidneys. In the steady state, the organism is by definition in 'balance.' For Na⁺ this means that the daily output of Na⁺ equals the daily intake. Na⁺ is excreted mainly by the kidneys; the difference between the rate of urinary excretion of Na⁺ and the daily intake is made up by extrarenal routes, such as sweat, saliva, and other gastrointestinal secretions. Ordinarily, the extrarenal losses of Na⁺ are negligible, although such losses can be great during sweating or in certain clinical states, such as surgical drainage of gastrointestinal fluids. GFR = glomerular filtration rate; P_{Na} and U_{Na} = plasma and urinary concentration of sodium, respectively.

portioned as follows: approximately 25% or 6,300 mmol per day in the loops of Henle; about 5% or 1,200 mmol per day in the distal tubules; and about 3% or 750 mmol per day in the collecting ducts.

Normally, then, about 99.4% of the filtered Na⁺ is reabsorbed (Table 1-1). It is obvious that, given a normal dietary intake of Na⁺ of around 150 mmol per day (the range is very wide, from approximately 30 to 250 mmol per day), any change in the glomerular filtration rate (GFR) or in the rate of tubular Na⁺ reabsorption could seriously threaten Na⁺ balance and hence the maintenance of the extracellular volume (Chap. 2, under Maintenance of Compartment Size. Importance of Total Solute Content). Or, a change in the dietary intake of Na⁺ would pose a similar threat unless the GFR or tubular reabsorptive rate were quickly adjusted. The fact that the extracellular fluid volume is normally kept at quite a constant value shows that physiologic adjustments must quickly come into play when Na⁺ balance is challenged. These adjustments are discussed next. Because the renin-angiotensin-aldosterone system plays a major role in some of the adjustments, we will digress briefly to describe that system.

Percentage of Filtered Sodium Reabsorbed along Nephron	
~67%	proximal
~25%	ascending limb of Henle
~5%	distal
~3%	collecting duct

The Renin-Angiotensin-Aldosterone System

Through both direct and indirect effects, the components of this system, especially angiotensin II, influence not only Na⁺ balance, but also renal and systemic hemodynamics (as reviewed in Fig. 6-7) as well as water balance. The multiple actions of angiotensin II will be reviewed later.

Production of Angiotensin II and Aldosterone

The dynamics of the system and its regulation of Na⁺ balance, extracellular fluid (ECF) volume, and vascular resistance, and hence of systemic blood pressure, are shown in Figure 7-8. *Renin* is secreted by the juxtaglomerular apparatus (JGA) in the kidney, from granular cells that are located mainly or exclusively in the afferent arterioles (Fig. 1-3). Renin is a proteolytic enzyme that splits a decapeptide from *angiotensinogen,* an α₂-globulin substrate that is produced by the liver. The decapeptide *angiotensin I,* may have little physiological action of its own; it is converted to an active octapeptide, *Angiotensin II,* through the loss of two terminal amino acids under the influence of *Angiotensin Converting Enzyme* (ACE). The conversion occurs mainly in the lungs, but also in the kidneys and perhaps in other organs.

Control of Renin Release

The production of renin is the rate-limiting step for the renin-angiotensin-aldosterone system (Fig. 7-8). It is therefore important to understand the factors that regulate the secretion of renin. These factors are shown in Figure 7-9; note that, in addition to a direct effect of angiotensin II, they constitute a negative feedback system that involves the many actions of angiotensin II that are shown in Figs. 6-7 and 7-8. There are three major components of this feedback: (a) baroreception in the afferent arterioles, (b) alteration of

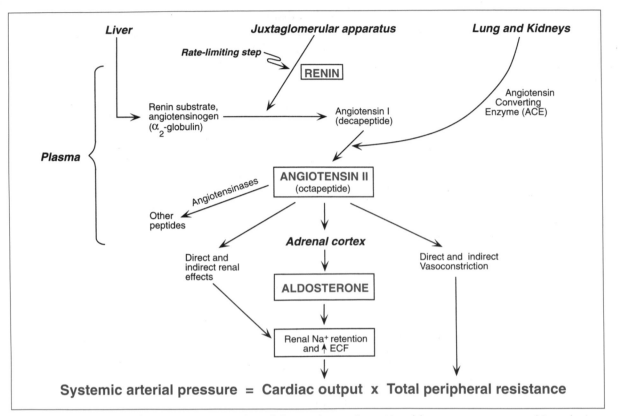

Figure 7-8. Dynamics of the renin-angiotensin-aldosterone system and its relation to systemic arterial blood pressure. Details are described in the text. Note how the many effects of angiotensin II (discussed further below, in conjunction with Table 7-2) are logically coordinated to support normal blood pressure. This task is accomplished by raising total peripheral resistance and by stimulating Na⁺ reabsorption and expanding the extracellular fluid (ECF) volume.

the amount of NaCl flowing at the macula densa, and (c) the influence of sympathetic nerves on the arterioles of the JGA. Depending on the circumstances, these three may act together in a coordinated manner, or one or more may predominate.

Baroreceptor Mechanism

An increase in renal perfusion pressure decreases the release of renin. The opposite is also true: A moderate to marked decrease in renal perfusion pressure, whether induced by hemorrhage or by

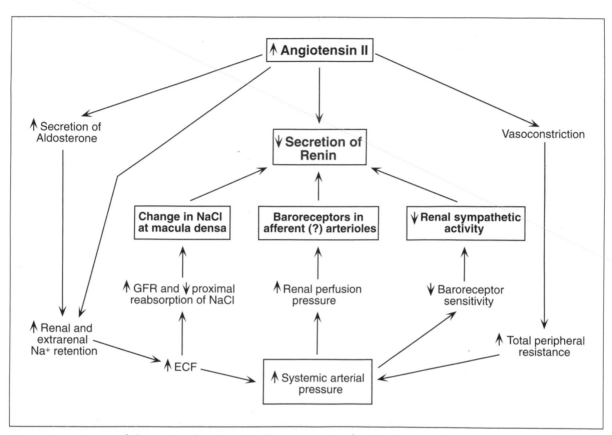

Figure 7-9. Some of the major direct and indirect negative feedback loops that regulate the secretion of renin and hence the level of angiotensin II. Details are given in the text. Note that, as described in the legend to Figure 7-8, angiotensin II acts in two ways: to reduce Na+ excretion and to increase total peripheral resistance (TPR). By these two means, angiotensin II maintains or raises systemic blood pressure. The diagram depicts a typical negative feedback control system: As blood pressure and extracellular fluid (ECF) volume rise, production of renin, and thus of angiotensin II (Fig. 7-8), is reduced until homeostasis is again achieved.

constriction of the aorta above the renal arteries, stimulates the release of renin.

Macula Densa Mechanism

Changes in the delivery of tubular fluid to the macula densa (see Chap. 1, under Juxtaglomerular Apparatus, and Fig. 1-3) alter the release of renin. But the direction of the change is still not clear—i.e., whether an increased delivery of fluid and of NaCl to the macula densa leads to an increase or to a decrease of renin secretion. It is for this reason that Figure 7-9 speaks of a 'change in NaCl at macula densa' and does not specify the direction or the nature of the change (i.e., whether the sensed variable is the concentration or the amount of NaCl, or indeed whether it is Na^+ or Cl^- at all).

Recall that the JGA is also the site for the mediation of tubuloglomerular feedback (TGF; Fig. 6-5). Given the constrictor action of angiotensin II on the afferent and efferent arterioles (Table 6-1), it is tempting to conclude that angiotensin II modulates the glomerular filtration rate during TGF (Fig. 6-5); this, however, is almost certainly not the case. Just how TGF is mediated is still not known (see p. 103). To avoid confusion, therefore, it is important to separate the two actions of the JGA: one, as the site for TGF; and the other, as the site for the production of renin.

Sympathetic Nervous System and Catecholamines

The arterioles of the JGA are innervated by sympathetic nerve fibers. Electrical stimulation of the renal nerves, as well as stimulation of β-adrenergic receptors by isoproterenol, increases the release of renin, whereas renal denervation and β-adrenergic blockade by propranolol have the opposite effect. It can be shown experimentally that these effects are distinct from those that act via baroreceptors or the macula densa.

Other Influences

Several other factors, in addition to those shown in Fig. 7-9, may play a role in the control of renin release. (1) There is an inverse correlation between the plasma concentration of K^+ and Ca^{2+} and the release of renin. (2) Vasopressin and atrial natriuretic peptide (ANP), even at physiological doses, inhibit the release of renin. (3) Prostaglandins E_2 and I_2 stimulate the production or release of renin.

Actions of Angiotensin II

Angiotensin II, which arises from the action of renin (Fig. 7-8), has multiple actions, both within the kidney and outside of it (Table 7-2). The net effect of these actions is mainly threefold: (1) Through retention of Na^+—in proximal tubules, both as a direct effect and through an increase in filtration fraction (Fig. 7-10), and more distally as well as in extrarenal organs via aldosterone—it increases extracellular fluid volume and hence cardiac output; (2) by its potent direct vasoconstrictor action, and through its influence on sympathetic and vagal tone, and baroreceptor sensitivity, it increases total peripheral resistance; and (3) by stimulating thirst

Table 7-2.   Multiple actions of angiotensin II.

Renal	Extrarenal
Increase Na⁺ reabsorption in proximal tubules through direct effect through increased filtration fraction (FF) (Fig. 7-10)	Arteriolar vasoconstriction
	Increase sympathetic outflow and catecholamines
	Decrease vagal tone
	Increase baroreceptor sensitivity
Increase sensitivity of tubulo-glomerular feedback (TGF)	Decrease capillary permeability
	Increase aldosterone secretion
Decrease renin secretion	Increase ADH secretion
Decrease medullary blood flow	Increase thirst

and release of ADH, as well as by decreasing medullary blood flow, it promotes the acquisition as well as the renal retention of water (discussed in Chap. 8), and thereby augments volume.

Challenges to Na⁺ Balance:
1. Spontaneous Changes in GFR

Given a stable plasma concentration for Na⁺, changes in GFR markedly alter the filtered load of Na⁺. Hence, unless such changes are quickly accompanied by physiologic adjustments, a decrease in GFR would lead to a surfeit of body Na⁺, and an increase in GFR might lead to fatal Na⁺ depletion. The following quantitative example will illustrate this point. Working with the values depicted in Figure 7-7: If GFR were to increase by just 2%, the filtered load of Na⁺ would increase to 183.6 × 140 = 25,704 mmol per day. [Although such small changes in GFR have not been documented (because inulin clearance can be measured to an accuracy of only ±10%), it is very likely that alterations of a few percent in GFR occur frequently, e.g., as we undergo changes in posture, our degree of activity, and possibly our emotional state.] Note that the extra amount filtered because of this very small increase in GFR—504 mmol per day—is three times greater than the daily intake of Na⁺! Therefore, if the absolute amount of Na⁺ reabsorbed *were* to remain 25,050 mmol per day (Fig. 7-7), the daily excretion of Na⁺ would rise to 654 mmol, an intolerably high value. In fact, this does not happen because two physiological compensations set in: glomerulo-tubular balance (G-T balance) and autoregulation of the GFR.

Glomerulotubular Balance

It was pointed out in Chapter 4 (under Splay, p. 73) that, when used in the context of Na⁺ balance, G-T balance has a different connotation from the one that is derived from the glucose titration curve. In the present context, G-T balance refers to the fact that under steady-state conditions a constant fraction of the filtered Na$^+$ is reabsorbed in the proximal tubules despite variations in GFR. Normally, this fraction is about 0.67, or 67% (Fig. 7-7). In the hypothetical example described above, in which GFR had increased by 2%, G-T balance would have adjusted Na$^+$ reabsorption in the proximal tubules to 25,704 $\times$ 0.67, or 17,222 mmol per day. This adjustment therefore would 'recapture' all but 82 mmol of the extra amount of Na$^+$ filtered (504 $-$ 422 mmol), and this remainder would be reabsorbed in the loops of Henle, distal tubules, and collecting ducts.

At least two processes are thought to be responsible for G-T balance: (1) changes in filtration fraction (FF = GFR/RPF; see Chap. 5, under Filtration Fraction, p. 91) and consequent changes in the oncotic pressure within peritubular capillaries; and (2) Na$^+$-cotransport (Chap. 4, Fig. 4-3).

(1) The first effect is shown in Figure 7-10. For example, if GFR increases without a rise in renal plasma flow (RPF) (step 1)—as might occur if resistance in afferent arterioles is decreased at the same time that resistance in efferent arterioles is increased (see also Fig. 6-3)—a greater amount of plasma water will be removed (i.e., filtered into Bowman's space) from each unit of plasma flowing through the glomerular capillaries. Consequently, the plasma proteins, which are not filtered, will be dissolved in less plasma and the plasma oncotic pressure (π_c) will rise (step 2). Simultaneously, if the increased resistance in efferent arterioles exceeds the decreased resistance in afferent vessels, the hydrostatic pressure within peritubular capillaries (P$_c$) will fall. Since the plasma oncotic pressure and the hydrostatic pressure within peritubular capillaries are two of the important Starling forces (Fig. 2-5) that govern the reabsorption of Na$^+$ and water from the proximal tubule, this reabsorption will increase as filtration fraction rises (step 3).

(2) Another possible mechanism for G-T balance may relate to the phenomenon of cotransport (described in Chap. 4), in which the reabsorption of Na$^+$ is linked to that of various organic solutes. The proposal is that, because these solutes are reabsorbed virtually completely in the early proximal tubule, an increased filtered load of organic solutes will be followed automatically by an equal increment in reabsorption, not only of the organic solutes but also, through cotransport, of Na$^+$.

Autoregulation of GFR

This phenomenon, which is illustrated in Figure 6-4, involves the relative constancy of the total filtration rate (GFR) and of the

■ **Adjustments to** ■
Spontaneous (Primary)
Changes in GFR

Glomerulotubular balance
(G-T balance)

Autoregulation of GFR

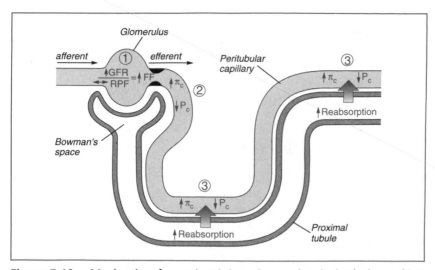

Figure 7-10. Mechanism for maintaining glomerulotubular balance (G-T balance) through changes in filtration fraction (FF) and consequent changes in Starling forces. G-T balance refers to the phenomenon that when GFR increases or decreases *as an initial event* (as, for example, with changes in posture), reabsorption of Na⁺ and water in the proximal tubules increases or decreases, respectively, so that roughly two-thirds of the glomerular filtrate continues to be reabsorbed. Shown here are the changes that ensue when FF increases. Details are described in the text. GFR = glomerular filtration rate; RPF = renal plasma flow; π_c = plasma oncotic pressure; P_c = hydrostatic pressure within capillary.

glomerular filtration rate of single nephrons (snGFR). Whenever there is a tendency for the GFR to increase, whether it be through increased renal arterial perfusion pressure (Fig. 6-4) or through some other means (Fig. 6-5), a negative feedback mechanism is activated, which tends to return the GFR to the normal level. As discussed in Chapter 6 (under Autoregulation of RBF and GFR), at least part of this feedback appears to involve the juxtaglomerular apparatus (JGA). Whatever the mechanism, it seems likely that autoregulation, by tending to keep the filtered load of Na⁺ constant, is a major means whereby serious Na⁺ wastage is prevented.

Thus the threat to Na⁺ balance that would be occasioned by spontaneous changes in GFR is ordinarily combated by relative constancy of the so-called proximal fractional reabsorption (G-T balance), by adjustments of the reabsorptive rate in more distal parts, and by a feedback mechanism that tends quickly to return the GFR toward the normal level (autoregulation).

Challenges to Na⁺ Balance:
2. Changes in Na⁺ Intake

Alterations in the acquisition of Na^+ pose a second major threat to Na^+ balance. For example, unless a decrease in Na^+ intake is accompanied by decreased excretion, depletion of Na^+ and hence of extracellular fluid volume would quickly ensue. Conversely, a large increase in Na^+ intake might quickly lead to an augmentation of total body Na^+ followed by expansion of the extracellular fluid compartment—unless there were a rapid increase in the urinary excretion of Na^+. Such expansion is manifested as generalized edema (see Chap. 2, under Edema), and, when marked, can cause heart failure and pulmonary edema. Physiological adjustments in the rate of Na^+ excretion do in fact set in quickly; those that occur in response to an increase in Na^+ intake are shown in Figure 7-11.

Note in this diagram that an increased intake of Na^+ leads to the appropriate response of increased renal excretion of Na^+, and that it does so through an expansion of the extracellular fluid (ECF) volume, which in turn leads to increased systemic arterial pressure. When the intake of Na^+ rises, there is a momentary increase in plasma osmolality, which stimulates thirst (Fig. 8-7C). Drinking is then augmented until the plasma osmolality returns to normal—but now at an expanded ECF volume, which, through an increase in cardiac output, raises the systemic arterial pressure. It is because of this chain of events that an increased Na^+ intake is equated with *'volume expansion,'* a term that always refers to enlargement of the *ECF* volume; and it is for this reason that increased Na^+ intake and volume expansion elicit the same physiological responses, even when the expansion is brought about by means other than Na^+ intake (e.g., by increasing plasma oncotic pressure through an intravenous infusion of salt-poor albumin). The mechanisms that are then set into motion result from the stimulation of low-pressure volume receptors (the cardiac atria and pulmonary vessels) and high-pressure baroreceptors (aortic arch, carotid sinus, kidneys, and possibly other organs).

Changes in GFR

An increase in Na^+ intake often is accompanied by a rise in GFR, which raises the filtered load of Na^+ and, other things being equal, the urinary excretion of Na^+. The argument may seem self-contradictory, since we have just reviewed physiological compensations

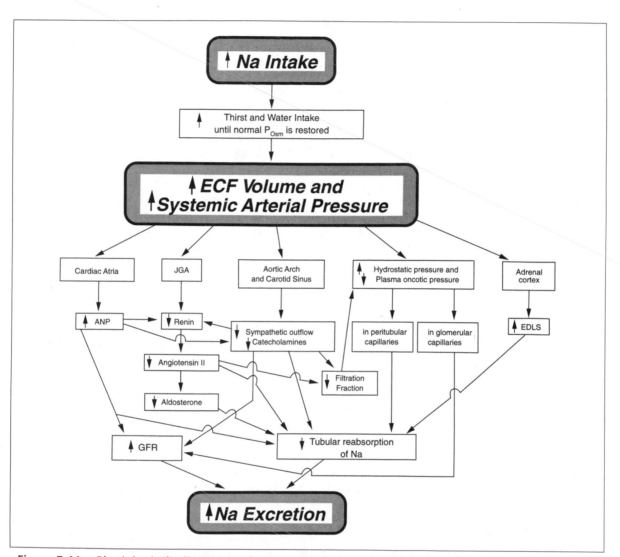

Figure 7-11. Physiological adjustments that maintain balance for Na$^+$ when the intake of Na$^+$ is increased. Details are described in the text. Under these circumstances of volume expansion, the increase in glomerular filtration rate (GFR) is a secondary event, and mechanisms such as autoregulation of GFR, glomerulotubular balance (G-T balance), and tubuloglomerular feedback (TGF) are attenuated or abolished. P$_{Osm}$ = plasma osmolality; ECF = extracellular fluid; JGA = juxtaglomerular apparatus; ANP = atrial natriuretic peptide; EDLS = endogenous digitalis-like substance; GFR = glomerular filtration rate.

that minimize Na^+ excretion when GFR is increased. The solution to this apparent paradox lies in the distinction between a spontaneous (*primary*) and a compensatory (*secondary*) increase in GFR. When the latter occurs, as in response to augmented Na^+ intake, it is usually not accompanied by G-T balance or by autoregulation. That is, whatever the mechanisms are that bring about G-T balance and autoregulation, these mechanisms appear to be attenuated or abolished by a high intake of Na^+.

The increase in GFR is brought about by several mechanisms. Volume expansion, by diluting the plasma proteins, leads to *decreased plasma oncotic pressure* as well as to *increased systemic arterial pressure*. Both of these changes occur also within glomerular capillaries, where they lead to increased filtration (Fig. 3-1). In addition, dilation of the cardiac atria stimulates the secretion of *atrial natriuretic peptide* (ANP), which probably increases GFR; and baroreceptor reflexes lead to *decreased sympathetic tone*, which increases GFR through a reduction in afferent arteriolar resistance and an increase in RBF.

Changes in Na⁺ Reabsorption

As the many arrows in Figure 7-11 indicate, there are many changes that lead to decreased tubular reabsorption of Na^+: (1) *decreased aldosterone;* (2) *decreased angiotensin II;* (3) *decreased sympathetic tone and catecholamines;* (4) *decreased filtration fraction giving rise to changes in Starling forces;* and (5) possibly *increased ANP* or *ouabain-like natriuretic hormones* (also called *endogenous digitalis-like substances (EDLS),* or both.

The role of aldosterone in the regulation of Na^+ excretion is well established. Aldosterone stimulates Na^+ reabsorption in late distal tubules and cortical collecting ducts, and a decreased concentration of this hormone in blood has the opposite effect. Aldosterone exerts its cellular action by interacting with specific chromosomal receptors in the cell nucleus, and this event is followed by increased production of messenger RNAs (mRNAs) and hence by increased synthesis of certain proteins. These proteins augment Na^+ transport by three means: (a) increasing the permeability of the apical membrane to Na^+; (b) increasing the amount of Na-K-ATPase (the 'Na⁺ pump') in basolateral membranes; and (c) increasing the activity of enzyme(s) in the Krebs citric acid cycle that catalyze the formation of adenosine triphosphate (ATP) and thus enhance the supply of energy to the Na^+ pump.

Activation of baroreceptors in the kidney (possibly in the afferent arterioles), increased flow of fluid past the macula densa, and

■ **Adjustments to** ■
Changes in Sodium
Intake

Secondary Changes in GFR

Altered Sodium
Reabsorption
— renin-angiotensin-aldosterone
— sympathetic tone and catecholamines
— filtration fraction and Starling forces (Figs. 7-10 and 7-11)
— atrial natriuretic peptide (ANP)?
— other natriuretic hormones? e.g., endogenous digitalis-like substance (EDLS)?

decreased sympathetic activity all inhibit the release of renin at the juxtaglomerular apparatus (see Fig. 7-9), and that inhibition, in turn, causes reduced formation of angiotensin II (Fig. 7-8). The last change inhibits the reabsorption of Na$^+$ in proximal tubules by slowing the Na$^+$/H$^+$ exchanger (Figs. 7-1A and B). The decrease in angiotensin II also results in decreased stimulation of aldosterone secretion from the adrenal cortex and hence in decreased reabsorption of Na$^+$ from late distal tubules and cortical collecting ducts. Finally, the changes in angiotensin II and sympathetic tone act on the afferent and efferent arterioles in such a way (Table 6-1) as to decrease filtration fraction which, through raising hydrostatic pressure and lowering plasma oncotic pressure in peritubular capillaries, decreases proximal reabsorption of Na$^+$ (Fig. 7-11). [Note that this chain of events is consistent with Figure 7-10, where an increased filtration fraction leads to increased reabsorption of Na$^+$. What is confusing is that in both Figures 7-10 and 7-11 we have indicated increases in GFR; yet, Na$^+$ reabsorption is increased in the former while it is decreased in the latter. As noted above, the distinction is between a *primary* or *initial* (Fig. 7-10) versus a *secondary* or *compensatory* (Fig. 7-11) increase in GFR.]

Thus far, the release of atrial natriuretic peptide (ANP) from cardiac atria has been demonstrated conclusively only during severe volume expansion, not in response to the relatively small changes in Na$^+$ intake that occur from moment to moment. Hence, the role of this hormone in the daily regulation of Na$^+$ excretion remains uncertain. Nevertheless, the peptide can reduce Na$^+$ reabsorption from proximal tubules by inhibiting sympathetic tone and catecholamines, and from late distal tubules and collecting ducts by inhibiting the secretion of aldosterone. In addition, ANP may act directly on collecting ducts to decrease Na$^+$ reabsorption.

Similarly, the role of ouabain or a closely related ouabain-like compound (e.g., EDLS), in the regulation of Na$^+$ excretion remains to be defined. It is possible that this compound(s), which is synthesized in the adrenal cortex and has the same basic structure as do adrenal steroids, is the elusive *natriuretic hormone,* which was first proposed by H. E. deWardener and has been sought for many years by numerous investigators. It belongs to a class of substances called cardiac glycosides, because they increase the contractile strength of the heart. The prototype is digitalis (*Foxglove*), which is why the ouabain-like compound is referred to as *endogenous digitalis-like substance* (EDLS). This substance(s) exerts its action by inhibiting the ubiquitous Na$^+$ pump (Na-K-ATPase) and increasing intracellular Ca^{2+}. Its action as a natriuretic hormone may derive from EDLS acting on specific isoforms of Na-K-ATPase in the nephron.

At first glance, it may seem that Figure 7-11 portrays a series of confusing interacting events. That, however, is in the nature of physiological responses to perturbations that could threaten survival. Any function as vital as the preservation of Na⁺ balance, and hence of the extracellular fluid volume, is bound to be regulated by many variables acting harmoniously as a backup, fail-safe system. In that respect, note that, by and large, the interactions among the variables in Figure 7-11 abet one another in the common goal of maintaining Na⁺ balance.

Tuners of Na⁺ Balance

Various portions of the nephron appear to play different roles in the maintenance of Na⁺ balance. It is useful to think of the proximal tubules as 'coarse tuners', which recapture the bulk of filtered Na⁺ and water; of the loops of Henle as 'medium tuners', which tend to compensate for failure of the proximal tubules to reabsorb the requisite amounts; and of the late distal tubules and collecting ducts as 'fine tuners', where precise adjustments of Na⁺ and H₂O reabsorption, and hence of their excretion, are made.

SUMMARY

The amounts of H₂O, and of Na⁺ with its attendant anions, that are filtered every day exceed their daily intakes by more than a hundredfold (see Table 1-1). For this reason, Na⁺ and H₂O balance—i.e., the equality between intake and output—depends critically on the tubular reabsorption of these substances. Some features of Na⁺ and H₂O transport along the nephron are summarized in Table 7-1. In most parts of the nephron, Na⁺ reabsorption is active, and it is the primary process that is followed by passive reabsorption of H₂O. Exceptions include the thin descending limb of Henle, in which all solutes appear to be transported passively, and the thin ascending limb of Henle, in which Na⁺ reabsorption may be mostly or wholly passive. Reabsorption of H₂O is passive throughout.

Approximately 67% of the Na⁺ that is filtered is reabsorbed in the proximal tubules. The reabsorptive process differs in the early as opposed to the late proximal tubule. In the early proximal tubule, Na⁺ is reabsorbed mainly as NaHCO₃ and in cotransport with glucose, inorganic phosphate, amino acids, and other organic acids; in contrast, in the late proximal tubule, Na+ is reabsorbed mainly as NaCl. In the entire proximal tubule, approximately two-thirds of Na+ reabsorption is active (by the transcellular route) while roughly one-third is passive (by the paracellular route).

Water transport in proximal tubules is coupled very tightly to Na+ transport under all conditions. Consequently, approximately 67% of the filtered water, as well as of the filtered Na+, is reabsorbed. Initially, the fluid that is reabsorbed is very slightly hyperosmotic to plasma. Therefore, the fluid within the tubular lumen becomes slightly hyposmotic to plasma (perhaps 285 mOsm/kg) while the peritubular fluid becomes slightly hyperosmotic (perhaps 291 mOsm/kg). Because the water permeability of proximal tubules is so very high, this small osmotic difference suffices to reabsorb such a large fraction of the filtered H_2O.

In thin descending limbs of Henle, the movement of both solute and water is passive (Table 7-1). These segments are highly permeable to H_2O, and as much as 10 to 20% of filtered H_2O is reabsorbed from them. Some Na+, Cl−, and urea may diffuse passively into thin descending limbs (i.e., they may be secreted into this segment but not reabsorbed from it).

Ascending thin limbs are virtually impermeable to H_2O (Table 7-1). They reabsorb Na+ and Cl−, possibly entirely by the passive mode. They are quite permeable to urea, and this solute is secreted into thin ascending limbs.

Thick ascending limbs of Henle constitute an important site for Na+ and Cl− transport. Approximately 25% of the filtered load of Na+ is reabsorbed from these segments, and this value can increase considerably if more fluid is delivered into the loops of Henle out of proximal tubules. In thick ascending limbs, Na+ and Cl− are reabsorbed by a symporter, which transports 1 Na+, 1 K+, and 2 Cl−s across the apical membrane. It is this symporter that is inhibited by the so-called loop diuretics. Like thin ascending limbs, thick ascending limbs of Henle are virtually impermeable to H_2O, a fact that gives rise to the 'single effect' of the countercurrent multiplier that is essential for rendering urine hyperosmotic to plasma (discussed in Chap. 8).

The distal tubule is divided into two parts, early and late. In early distal tubules, Na+ and Cl− enter the cell by a symporter that is located in the apical membrane. Na+ leaves the cell via Na-K-ATPase, and Cl− leaves through a channel. This segment, like the ascending limbs of Henle, is virtually impermeable to H_2O.

The late distal tubule is so similar to the collecting duct that the two are described together. These segments contain two types of cell, the intercalated cell and the principal cell. Only the latter transports Na^+, where the ion enters the cell through a channel and exits via Na-K-ATPase. Although the details of Cl^- reabsorption in late distal tubules and collecting ducts have not yet been worked out, the mode of transport is likely to be wholly or mostly passive. It is in this, the final part of the nephron, that fine tuning of Na^+ reabsorption, and hence of Na^+ balance, takes place. The fine tuning occurs especially in inner medullary collecting ducts, where Na^+ can be reabsorbed against a very large concentration gradient. Late distal tubules and collecting ducts have a very low water permeability in the absence of the antidiuretic hormone (ADH or vasopressin) and a very high water permeability in its presence. Hence, water transport in these segments varies directly with the concentration of ADH in plasma.

Normally, approximately 67% of the filtered Na^+ is reabsorbed in proximal tubules, about 25% in loops of Henle, about 5% in distal tubules, and nearly 3% in collecting ducts. For H_2O the figures are: approximately 67% in proximal tubules, 10 to 20% in loops of Henle, 10 to 15% in late distal tubules (with ADH present), and about 1% in collecting ducts.

In a healthy person, there are two major threats to Na^+ balance: (a) spontaneous (primary) changes in glomerular filtration rate (GFR) and hence in the filtered load of Na^+, and (b) changes in Na^+ intake. The first threat is countered by the physiological compensations of glomerulotubular (G-T) balance and by autoregulation of the GFR. The second is counteracted by compensatory (secondary) changes in GFR and by altering the tubular reabsorption of Na^+. Maintenance of Na^+ balance is a vital function, which is controlled by many, interacting variables. Among those that come into play in response to an increase in Na^+ intake (volume expansion) are: decreased sympathetic tone and catecholamines, decreased renin-angiotensin-aldosterone, change in Starling forces arising from a decreased filtration fraction, and possibly increased atrial natriuretic peptide (ANP) and increased endogenous digitalis-like substance (EDLS).

PROBLEM 7-1

What is a normal dietary intake of sodium for a typical adult human? How much sodium is contained in the salt-poor or low-salt diet that is prescribed for many patients? Express your answer as grams, millimols, and milliequivalents per day.

PROBLEM 7-2

A hospitalized patient has a plasma Na^+ concentration of 112 mmol/L (normal 136 to 146 mmol/L; Table A-1). It is decided that this abnormality should be quickly corrected, at least partially. If it is desired to raise the plasma Na^+ concentration to 132 mmol/L, how much 5% NaCl solution (5 g NaCl per dL H_2O) should be infused intravenously? The patient weighs 53 kg; atomic weights are given in Table A-5 in the Appendix.

[*Note:* Because a low plasma Na^+ concentration (called *hyponatremia*) represents a relative excess of H_2O over Na^+, many patients with hyponatremia are treated through restriction of fluid intake. Sometimes, however, a very low plasma Na^+ concentration (as in this instance) is treated by giving NaCl.]

SUGGESTED READINGS

Blaustein, M. P. Physiological effects of endogenous ouabain: control of intracellular Ca²⁺ stores and cell responsiveness. *Am. J. Physiol.* 264 (*Cell Physiol.* 33):C1367, 1993.

Brenner, B. M., Ballermann, B. J., Gunning, M. E., and Zeidel, M. L. Diverse biological actions of atrial natriuretic peptide. *Physiol. Rev.* 70:665, 1990.

DeWardener, H. E. Control of Sodium Excretion. In C. W. Gottschalk, R. W. Berliner, and G. H. Giebisch (Eds.), *Renal Physiology. People and Ideas.* Bethesda: American Physiological Society, 1987. Chap. VII.

Hackenthal, E., Paul, M., Ganten, D., and Taugner, R. Morphology, physiology, and molecular biology of renin secretion. *Physiol. Rev.* 70:1067, 1990.

Hollenberg, N. K., and Ingelfinger, J. R. The Renin-Angiotensin System. In R. G. Narins (Ed.), *Maxwell & Kleeman's Clinical Disorders of Fluid and Electrolyte Metabolism* (5th ed.). New York: McGraw-Hill, 1994. Chap. 16.

Koeppen, B. M. Mechanisms of Segmental Sodium and Chloride Reabsorption. In D. W. Seldin and G. Giebisch (Eds.), *The Regulation of Sodium and Chloride Balance.* New York: Raven Press, 1990, Chap. 3.

Kopp, U. C., and DiBona, G. F. The Neural Control of Renal Function. In D. W. Seldin and G. Giebisch (Eds.), *The Kidney. Physiology and Pathophysiology* (2nd ed.). New York: Raven, 1992. Chap. 33.

Méndez, R. E., and Brenner, B. M. Glomerulotubular Balance and the Regulation of Sodium Excretion by Intrarenal Hemodynamics. In D. W. Seldin and G. Giebisch (Eds.), *The Regulation of Sodium and Chloride Balance*. New York: Raven Press, 1990. Chap. 4.

Rossier, B. C., and Palmer, L. G. Mechanisms of Aldosterone Action on Sodium and Potassium Transport. In D. W. Seldin and G. Giebisch (Eds.), *The Kidney. Physiology and Pathophysiology* (2nd ed.). New York: Raven, 1992. Chap. 38.

Schafer, J. A. Transepithelial osmolality differences, hydraulic conductivities, and volume absorption in the proximal tubule. *Annu. Rev. Physiol.* 52:709, 1990.

Seldin, D. W., and Giebisch, G. (Eds.). *The Regulation of Sodium and Chloride Balance*. New York: Raven Press, 1990.
This excellent monograph begins with an extensive section on sodium and chloride balance in health, and then continues with a consideration of abnormal states.

Concentration and Dilution of Urine: H₂O Balance

8

Even though water reabsorption is a passive event that follows the reabsorption of solutes, especially Na^+, water balance can be regulated independently of Na^+ balance. This task is accomplished through changes in the blood concentration of antidiuretic hormone (ADH or vasopressin), which adjusts the amount of water that is reabsorbed from the late distal tubules and collecting ducts. When the concentration of ADH is high, so is the water permeability of these parts of the nephron (Table 7-1). Consequently, much water is reabsorbed and hyperosmotic urine is formed—up to about 1,200 mOsm/kg in humans (the state of antidiuresis, defined in the marginal box on p. 116). Conversely, at low concentrations of ADH the water permeability of late distal tubules and collecting ducts is reduced (Table 7-1). This state results in little water reabsorption from these parts and the formation of hyposmotic urine— down to about 50 mOsm/kg in humans (water diuresis). (The terms *isosmotic, hyperosmotic,* and *hyposmotic* are defined in the box on p. 116. Except when specified, the comparison in the present chapter is with the osmolality of normal plasma.)

In this chapter we shall discuss first how ADH regulates the water permeability of late distal tubules and collecting ducts; second, how the kidneys can form either hyperosmotic or hyposmotic urine, depending on the requirements of water balance; and third, how the body maintains water balance by regulating the acquisition of water through thirst and the retention or excretion of water through modulated secretion of ADH.

MODULATION OF WATER PERMEABILITY BY ADH

The means by which ADH changes the water permeability of late distal tubules and collecting ducts is shown in Figure 8-1A. The action is exerted on principal cells (some properties of which were described in conjunction with Fig. 7-6). When ADH binds to a specific receptor (called the V_2 *receptor*) located on the basolateral membrane of these cells, a stimulatory guanine nucleotide (GTP)-binding protein (*G-protein;* not shown in Fig. 8-1A) is activated, and that activation in turn stimulates an enzyme, *adenylate cyclase,* which is located within the membrane. The enzyme converts adenosine triphosphate (ATP) to the intracellular meditor, *cyclic 3',5'-adenosine monophosphate* (cAMP), and the formation of cAMP sets off a cascade of events that culminates in the incorporation of *water channels* into the apical membrane. The cascade includes: activation of a specific protein kinase, called *protein kinase*

A (PKA), which phosphorylates as yet unidentified proteins; involvement of cytoskeletal elements, including microfilaments and microtubules, which may in part be the targets of the phosphorylation; and a shuttling mechanism by which specific cytoplasmic vesicles insert water channels into the apical membrane and remove the channels from that membrane.

The shuttling mechanism is an evolutionary variation of an important biological phenomenon called *receptor-mediated endocytosis*. It is the main mechanism by which ADH regulates the water permeability of late distal tubules and collecting ducts. When ADH is present in the plasma (Table 7-1), channels are inserted into the apical membrane (called *exocytosis*), and when the plasma concentration of ADH falls or is low, the channels are removed from the membrane (*endocytosis*). Water channels in the apical membrane can be visualized by the technique of freeze-fracture electron microscopy, where the channels appear as clusters of *intramembranous particles* (IMPs; Fig. 8-1B, C). By and large, the number of channels correlates with the plasma concentration of ADH and hence with the water permeability of late distal tubules and collecting ducts. That correlation, however, can be modulated by the activity of a specific *cAMP-phosphodiesterase,* which breaks down cAMP to the inactive *5'-adenosine monophosphate* (5'-AMP), by autacoids such as prostaglandins, and by other substances such as calcium and protein kinase C.

Largely through the techniques of molecular and cellular biology it has been shown that there are many water channels throughout the animal and plant kingdoms. Most are relatively small proteins (25,000 to 30,000 Daltons) that belong to a family of water channels called *MIP26* (Membrane Integral Protein, molecular weight 26,000 Daltons). They are found in a large variety of fluid-transporting tissues, including not only the kidneys but also the eye (lens), lungs (alveoli), choroid plexus, yeast and other plants, and most notably red blood cells (the last called *CHIP28,* standing for CHannel-forming Integral Protein with a molecular weight of 28,000 Daltons). [Recall that red blood cells are highly permeable to water regardless of the presence or absence of ADH, and that they swell and often burst when surrounded by hyposmotic plasma (called *hemolysis*), and shrink when the plasma is hyperosmotic.]

One member of the MIP26 family is the channel that responds to ADH as portrayed in Figure 8-1A. This channel, called *WCH-CD* (Water CHannel-Collecting Duct), has been cloned and sequenced. As expected, WCH-CD is localized exclusively to the apical membranes of principal cells in late distal tubules and collecting ducts.

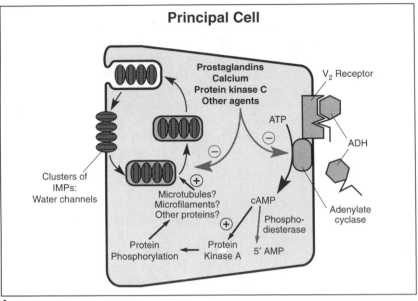

A

Figure 8-1. A. Chain of events whereby antidiuretic hormone (ADH) increases the permeability to water of the apical membrane of late distal tubules and collecting ducts. Some of the schema is based on experiments that were conducted on other membranes that are also sensitive to ADH, most notably the skin and urinary bladder of frogs and toads. Note that the receptors for ADH lie in the basolateral membrane, whereas the increased permeability is induced in the apical membrane through insertion of water channels. The question marks indicate steps that have not yet been defined fully. Details are described in the text. ATP = adenosine triphosphate; cAMP = cyclic 3′,5′-adenosine monophosphate; 5′AMP = 5′-adenosine monophosphate; IMPs = intramembranous particles.

B, C. Freeze-fracture electron micrographs, showing surfaces within the fracture of the apical membrane from collecting ducts of a Brattleboro rat that lacks ADH (B) and a Brattleboro rat that was treated with ADH (C). The arrows point to some clusters of intramembranous particles (IMPs) that were incorporated into the membrane through fusion with cytoplasmic vesicles. IMPs are thought to be water channels, and the clusters are probably the sites of increased water flow. Note that there are no clusters in (B), when ADH was absent. The encircled arrowheads indicate the shadowing direction. From Harmanci, M. D., et al. *Am. J. Physiol.* 235 (*Renal Fluid Electrolyte Physiol.* 4): F440, 1978. Analogous changes in response to ADH were demonstrated earlier in anuran membranes (e.g., Chevalier, J., et al. *Cell Tissue Res.* 152:129, 1974; Kachadorian, W. A., et al. *Science* 190:67, 1975).

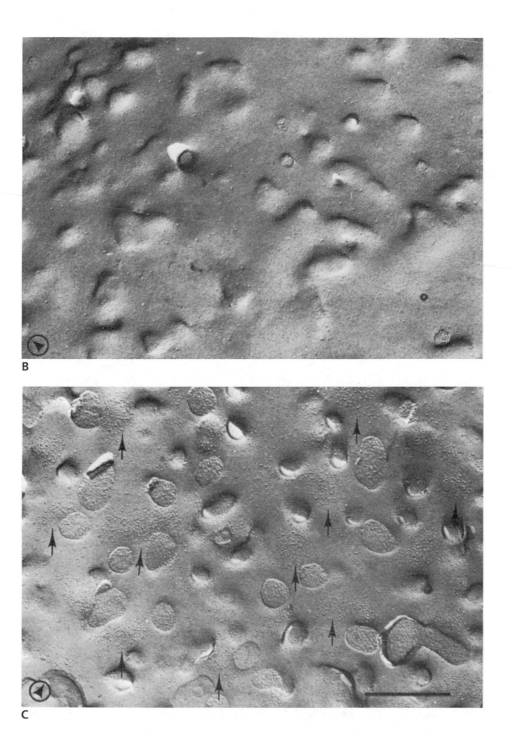

B

C

WCH-CD
— modulated by ADH
— in apical membranes
  of late distal tubules
  and collecting ducts
WCH-3
— modulated by hormones???
— in basolateral membranes of late distal
  tubules and collecting
  ducts
CHIP28
— not modulated
— in proximal tubules
  and descending limbs
  of Henle; apical and
  basolateral
  membranes

It appears that the WCH-CD protein passes through the membrane four times, and that four of these proteins form a tetramer that imparts very specific and high permeability for water.

In addition, there are other water channels along the nephron, as would be expected because diffusion of water through a lipid bilayer would be relatively slow. Rapid flow of water across biological membranes requires facilitated transport. Thus, a protein very similar to CHIP28, called *CHIP28k* (k for kidney), is found in the entire proximal tubule and in the descending limb of Henle's loop—i.e., in the most water-permeable parts of the nephron (Table 7-1); CHIP28k is found in both the apical and basolateral membranes of these nephron segments. Like CHIP28, CHIP28k is not affected by ADH. There is preliminary evidence for yet a third water channel in the kidney, *WCH-3*; it is different from CHIP28, is found in basolateral membranes of late distal tubules and collecting ducts, and may or may not be subject to hormonal regulation. No water channels have been found in those parts of the nephron that are always impermeable to water, namely, the thin and thick ascending limbs of Henle (Table 7-1).

It has been proposed that water channels be renamed *aquaporins,* with modifying suffixes that designate precisely which channel one is talking about—CHIP28, CHIP28k, WCH-CD, WCH-3, MIP26, or any of numerous others. Although that term—aquaporin—implies pores, the water transporters that have been studied thus far behave more like channels than like simple pores; i.e., the channels exhibit a great degree of specificity for water and they exclude solutes that are of the same size as or smaller than water (e.g., H^+). Such selectivity indicates specific interaction of the water molecule with elements of the water channel, just as is seen with channels that transport ions.

THE COUNTERCURRENT MECHANISM

As we have seen (Table 7-1), in all parts of the nephron except the thin limbs of the loops of Henle, the transport of Na^+ is active, while water reabsorption is passive. Given these prerequisites, it is conceptually easy to form hyposmotic urine: The kidneys actively reabsorb Na^+ (and its anions) from an isosmotic glomerular filtrate while much of the water is retained within the tubules. It proved more difficult, however, to conceive a system that will produce hyperosmotic urine through the passive reabsorption of water, as this process requires the buildup of hyperosmotic fluid in the tissues that surround the tubules. The problem of hyperosmotic urine formation through passive water reabsorption puzzled renal physiologists for many years until W. Kuhn and K. Ryffel proposed the countercurrent mechanism. The principle of this mechanism in a normal human being concentrating urine to 1,200 mOsm/kg is illustrated in Figure 8-2A.

Formation of Hyperosmotic (Concentrated) Urine

The process is thought to occur through the following sequence of events:

1. The fluid in Bowman's capsule, being an ultrafiltrate of plasma, has an osmolality of approximately 287 mOsm/kg, the mean value for normal plasma (Table A-1 in the Appendix).

2. Approximately two-thirds of the glomerular filtrate is reabsorbed in the proximal tubules (Fig. 7-7), in just slightly hyperosmotic proportions (see Chap. 7, under Coupling of Solute and Water Transport). Consequently, tubular fluid at the end of the proximal tubule is just slightly hyposmotic (Fig. 7-2B).

3. The ascending limbs of Henle, both thin and thick, are quite impermeable to water (Table 7-1). Therefore, in this segment NaCl is reabsorbed to the virtual exclusion of water, a process that renders the outer and inner medullary interstitium hyperosmotic to plasma. This process is abetted by the loops of Henle acting as countercurrent multipliers (described below). Since fluid having an osmolality of 285 mOsm/kg entered the loops of Henle and in the net, NaCl was withdrawn, tubular fluid at the beginning of the distal tubule is hyposmotic.

4. With a high concentration of ADH in the blood, the membranes lining the late distal tubules and collecting ducts are highly permeable to water (Table 7-1). Hence, all along these tubular segments, water diffuses passively down the osmotic gradient between tubular fluid and cortical, outer medullary, and inner medullary interstitium. The tubular fluid is thereby concentrated until osmotic equilibrium with the interstitium is reached, and this progressive concentration of tubular fluid takes place even though some NaCl continues to be reabsorbed from the distal tubules and collecting ducts.

This is called the countercurrent system, for at least three reasons: (a) the loops of Henle act as countercurrent multipliers; (b) the vasa recta act as countercurrent exchangers (described below); and (c) it is the countercurrent arrangement of the entire nephron that gives the tubular fluid in collecting ducts a chance to flow through an area of interstitial hyperosmolality, thereby per-

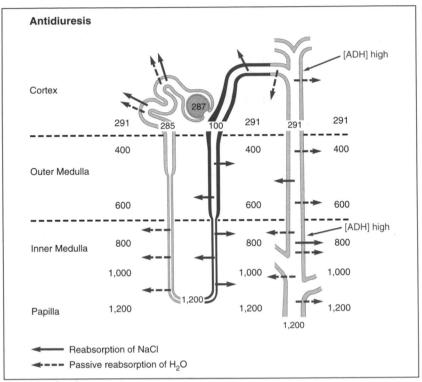

A

Figure 8-2. Operation of the renal countercurrent system in a normal human being. Red boundaries indicate very low permeability to water. The numbers refer to the osmolality (mOsm/kg) of either tubular or interstitial fluid. Solid arrows denote reabsorption of NaCl, which is active except in the thin ascending limbs of Henle, where it may be largely passive (see Table 7-1; Countercurrent Multiplication in the Inner Medulla, p. 171); arrows with dashed line denote passive reabsorption of water. The number of arrows in each part of the nephron signifies semiquantitatively the amounts of solute transported relative to water. For example, in ascending limbs of Henle, solute is reabsorbed to the virtual exclusion of water (but not complete exclusion, since renal membranes are not wholly impervious to water).

A. During antidiuresis.

B. During water diuresis. It is possible (but not known for certain) that the osmolality of tubular fluid at the early distal tubule is slightly higher in water diuresis than in antidiuresis. The important changes from antidiuresis are: (1) the lower interstitial osmolality in the medulla and papilla; (2) the virtual absence of ADH; and hence (3) the lack of osmotic equilibration between fluid in the collecting duct and the surrounding interstitium.

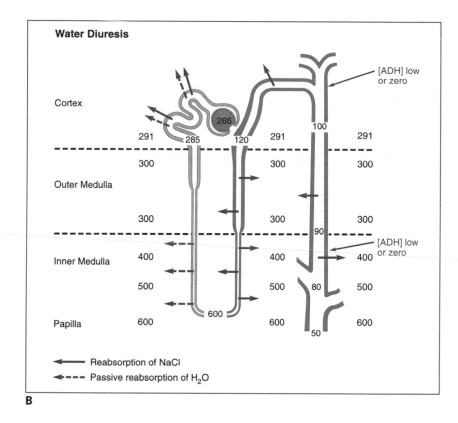

Water Diuresis

- [ADH] low or zero

Cortex

Outer Medulla

Inner Medulla

Papilla

285

291   285   120   291   100   291
300   300   300
300   300   300
              90
400   400   →   400   [ADH] low or zero
500   500   80   500
600   600   600
       600   50

⟵   Reabsorption of NaCl
⟵--- Passive reabsorption of H$_2$O

B

mitting concentration of urine through the passive reabsorption of water.

Formation of Hyposmotic (Dilute) Urine

During the formation of dilute urine (Fig. 8-2B), the sequence is qualitatively identical up to the beginning of the distal tubule. (For reasons cited in part 4 of Table 8-1, there is a quantitative difference in that the osmolality of the papillary interstitium is only about one-half the value that it is during antidiuresis.) Now, in water diuresis, the blood concentration of ADH is low or zero, so that the membranes lining the late distal tubules and collecting ducts are relatively impermeable to water (Table 7-1). Hence, very little water is reabsorbed even though an osmotic gradient between tubular lumen and interstitium persists. Some NaCl continues to be reabsorbed, which accounts for the further dilution of

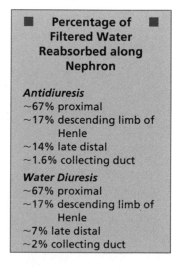

■   **Percentage of**   ■
**Filtered Water
Reabsorbed along
Nephron**

Antidiuresis
~67% proximal
~17% descending limb of Henle
~14% late distal
~1.6% collecting duct

Water Diuresis
~67% proximal
~17% descending limb of Henle
~7% late distal
~2% collecting duct

tubular fluid from approximately 120 mOsm/kg at the beginning of the distal tubule to perhaps 50 mOsm/kg in the urine.

Historical Hints

It is of interest that although the countercurrent hypothesis became accepted as the mechanism only around 1960, strong hints on where to search for the mechanism were extant in the literature for at least 50 years. In 1909, K. Peter pointed to the correlation between the length of thin loops of Henle in different species of mammals and the degree to which they could concentrate the urine. For example, in the Australian hopping mouse, which lives in the desert near Alice Springs and can concentrate its urine to perhaps 9,000 mOsm/kg, some long loops of Henle reach all the way into the ureter, whereas in rodents that do not live in arid habitats and concentrate their urine to about 2,500 mOsm/kg, the long loops are not nearly so extended, reaching only to the tip of the papilla. In 1925, E. H. Starling and E. B. Verney pointed out (albeit in a footnote) that there is a correspondence between the ability to make urine hyperosmotic to plasma, and the presence of medullary loops of Henle. This point was again made by E. K. Marshall, Jr., in 1934, when he emphasized in a review that only birds and mammals could render urine hyperosmotic to plasma, and only in these animals did one find medullary thin loops of Henle (see Fig. 1-4).

All this evidence suggested to investigators that urine must be concentrated within the loops of Henle. Then micropuncture studies showed that tubular fluid even in late portions of the distal tubules is either hyposmotic or isosmotic (Fig. 8-2A, B), but not hyperosmotic. It therefore was clear that the fluid must become hyperosmotic in the collecting ducts.

The correct role of the loops of Henle was first suggested in 1942 by two Swiss workers, W. Kuhn and K. Ryffel, who published a paper entitled "Production of concentrated solutions from diluted ones solely by membrane effects: A model for renal function." However, their countercurrent theory was largely ignored because it seemed unnecessarily complicated compared to active reabsorption of water. Nevertheless, the Swiss group persisted, and in 1951 H. Wirz, B. Hargitay, and W. Kuhn reproposed the countercurrent theory and presented preliminary experimental evidence (discussed below) supporting their hypothesis. By 1960 the experimental evidence in its favor became so overwhelming that the hypothesis was accepted.

COUNTERCURRENT MULTIPLICATION
IN LOOPS OF HENLE

One form of countercurrent multiplication is depicted in Figure 8-3. (It is to be stressed that the process of multiplication takes place in the loops of Henle, whereas that of countercurrent exchange, discussed later, occurs in the vasa recta.) We will illustrate the buildup of the so-called *corticomedullary interstitial osmotic gradient* by showing schematic, stepwise events as they are thought to occur in the thick ascending limb of Henle. (For the sake of illustration, these steps are shown to occur sequentially; actually, they occur simultaneously and continuously. Also, we limit the description here to thick ascending limbs; while a similar process may occur in thin ascending limbs, that is a special case which will be discussed later, under Countercurrent Multiplication in the Inner Medulla.)

    1.   The loop of Henle is filled with fluid coming out of the proximal tubule. Although the osmolality of this fluid may be slightly hyposmotic to plasma (Fig. 8-2A), we use 300 mOsm/kg here for the sake of arithmetic simplicity.

    2.   NaCl is reabsorbed actively from the thick ascending limb of Henle (Table 7-1). Since this part of the nephron has a very low permeability for water (Table 7-1), NaCl is reabsorbed virtually without water; this separation of solute transport from water transport—known as the *single effect* of the countercurrent multiplier—renders the osmolality of the interstitium hypertonic to the fluid within the ascending limb and to plasma. In the present example, the ascending limb can pump NaCl actively until a difference of 200 mOsm/kg has been established at each horizontal level. Since the thin descending limb is highly permeable to water (Table 7-1), fluid in that limb comes into osmotic equilibrium with the interstitium. This last process does not dissipate the high osmolality of the interstitium because the ascending limb continues to pump NaCl until the steady-state differences shown in step 2 have been established.

    3.   More fluid comes out of the proximal tubule into the descending limb (in this example, four 'units' at an osmolality of 300 mOsm/kg), pushing the column of fluid ahead of itself. This push has two consequences: (a) hyposmotic fluid leaves the ascending limb and enters the early distal tubule, and (b) more importantly, for understanding the 'trick' of countercurrent multiplication, four units of hyperosmotic fluid (400 mOsm/kg) traverse the bend of the

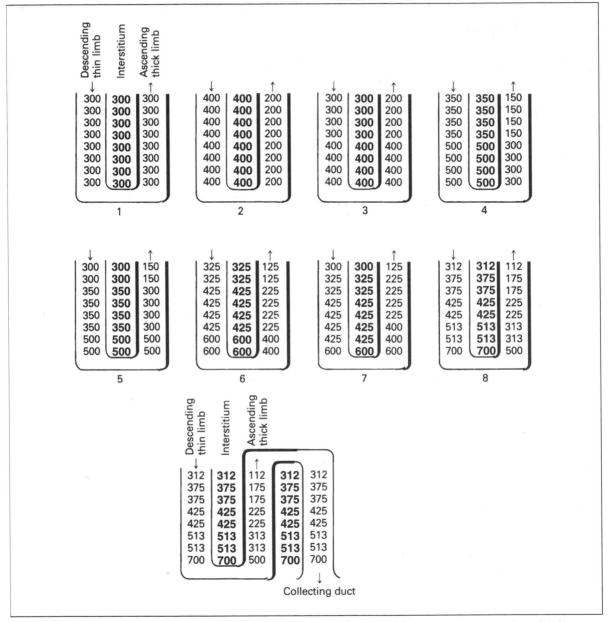

Figure 8-3. Schematic, stepwise operation by which a countercurrent multiplier system in the loops of Henle increases the osmolality of the medullary interstitium. The red boundaries of the ascending limb and early distal tubule indicate that these parts of the nephron are impermeable to water, even in the presence of ADH (see Table 7-1). Numbers refer to osmolalities (mOsm/kg) of tubular fluid and interstitium. Detailed description in text. Adapted from Pitts, R. F. *Physiology of the Kidney and Body Fluids* (3rd ed.). Chicago: Year Book, 1974.

loops of Henle and enter the ascending limb. (In the stepwise schema shown in Figure 8-3, step 3 dilutes part of the interstitium; in reality, this much dilution probably does not occur because reabsorption of more solute from the ascending limb, shown in step 4, takes place simultaneously.)

4.   The process described in step 2 is repeated, again building up a difference of 200 mOsm/kg between the descending limb and interstitium, on the one hand, and fluid in the ascending limb, on the other. Note that now the interstitial osmolality has been raised to 500 mOsm/kg (not to 400 as in step 2) because the active pumping of NaCl started from an osmolality of 400 mOsm/kg (step 3), not from 300 (step 1); next—

5.   More fluid (now two units at 300 mOsm/kg) enters the descending limb, pushing further hyposmotic fluid into the distal tubule and pushing fluid at 500 mOsm/kg into the ascending limb (and so on through steps 6, 7, and 8).

Note the following points. (1) By step 8, the interstitial concentration near the bend of the loop is nearly 400 mOsm/kg higher than that near the beginning of the descending limb, and this increase is much greater than that of 200 mOsm/kg which can be generated at any horizontal level through the active reabsorption of NaCl. That is, the 'single effect' of pumping NaCl to an osmotic difference of 200 mOsm/kg by separating solute from water transport gets multiplied—in the present example, by a factor of 2. Or, to state it differently, the countercurrent system multiplies small transverse gradients (the single effect) into large longitudinal gradients (the corticopapillary interstitial osmotic gradient). The reason why the single effect can be multiplied is that NaCl is pumped out of the ascending limb from a fluid of ever increasing osmolality (from 300 mOsm/kg in step 2, from 400 in step 4, from 500 in step 6, and from 600 in step 8). (2) The longer the loops of Henle, the greater will be the concentration of the interstitium—and hence of the tubular fluid—at the bend of the loop. (3) By themselves, the two limbs of Henle actually dilute the tubular fluid. It is only when a collecting duct is added to the system (lowest panel of Fig. 8-3), thereby giving the tubular fluid a second chance, so to speak, to flow past the hyperosmotic interstitium, that the urine can be rendered hyperosmotic.

COUNTERCURRENT EXCHANGE IN VASA RECTA

Only about 5% of the total renal blood flow (RBF), and hence of the total renal plasma flow (RPF), courses through the outer and inner medulla (see box on p. 97). Nevertheless, because of the very high

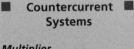

Countercurrent Systems

Multiplier
— creates osmotic gradient in medullary interstitium
— located in loops of Henle

Exchanger
— maintains medullary osmotic gradient
— located in vasa recta

renal blood flow, the amount of plasma that flows in descending vasa recta at the beginning of the outer medulla (Fig. 1-2A,B) exceeds the flow of tubular fluid at the beginning of outer medullary collecting ducts (Figs. 1-2A,B and 8-2A) by a factor of about 10; i.e., approximately 10 times more plasma than tubular fluid enters the area of interstitial hyperosmolality (Fig. 8-2A). Since the vasa recta are highly permeable to water and solutes, and, like the collecting ducts, are also surrounded by hyperosmotic interstitium, it would seem at first glance that the countercurrent mechanism might concentrate about 10 mL of plasma for every 1 mL of collecting duct fluid. In fact, excessive concentration of the blood as it flows through the medulla is prevented by the hairpin (countercurrent) configuration of the vasa recta (Fig. 1-2).

Countercurrent exchange in the vasa recta is illustrated in Figure 8-4. The system prevents undue concentration of plasma as it leaves the kidney, in the following manner:

1. Blood enters the vasa recta at a concentration of about 291 mOsm/kg, having equilibrated with a cortical interstitial osmolality of approximately the same value (Fig. 8-2).

2. As this blood flows through medullary interstitium of increasing osmolality, solute diffuses passively down its concentration gradient into the descending limb of the vasa recta, and water diffuses passively out of this limb in response to the osmotic gradient. This process results in increasing osmolality of plasma within the vasa recta as the bend is approached.

3. As the blood rises in the ascending limb of the vasa recta, it encounters less and less concentrated medullary interstitium. Hence solutes diffuse passively into the interstitium and water diffuses back into the vasa recta.

As a result of this passive countercurrent exchange, blood leaves the kidneys not at 1,200 mOsm/kg (as it would if blood exited at the papilla; i.e., if vasa recta did not exist in a countercurrent configuration) but at about 325 mOsm/kg. Thus, concentration of blood, and hence depletion of medullary solutes by the blood flow, is greatly minimized although not wholly prevented. Note that any blood flow would tend to deplete the medullary interstitium of solute unless countercurrent exchange were 100% efficient; but the lower the blood flow through this area, the less the depletion, and vice versa.

It might be asked why, if blood flow is such a threat to the renal concentrating mechanism, blood must course through the outer and inner medulla at all. There are at least two reasons: (1) There must be nutrient blood flow to the medullary tissues. (2) The water that is reabsorbed from the descending limbs of Henle and the collecting

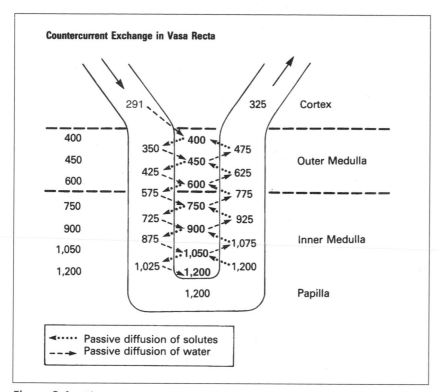

Figure 8-4. The countercurrent exchange system in the vasa recta. Arrows with dotted lines denote passive transport of solutes; arrows with dashed lines denote passive movement of water. The numbers refer to osmolalities (mOsm/kg) in the blood or interstitial fluid. Adapted from Berliner, R. W., Levinsky, N. G., Davidson, D. G., and Eden, M. *Am. J. Med.* 24:730, 1958.

ducts must be removed from the inner regions of the kidney by the vasa recta, lest these regions swell uncontrollably. This necessity is reflected in the finding that blood flow is approximately twice as great in the ascending vasa recta as in the descending vasa recta.

EXPERIMENTAL EVIDENCE FOR THE COUNTERCURRENT SYSTEM

Table 8-1 lists some conditions that must obtain if the countercurrent mechanism is correct, and the experimental proof that the conditions are met.

Table 8-1.   Experimental proof for the countercurrent mechanism.

Condition	Proof
1. The osmolality of the interstitium must increase as the renal papilla is approached; i.e., there must be a so-called corticopapillary osmotic gradient	Cryoscopic measurements of renal tissue slices, and chemical analysis of tissue homogenates. These data constituted the first experimental support for the hypothesis; they were published by Wirz, Hargitay, and Kuhn in 1951
2. Osmolalities of the tubular fluid along the nephron are as follows:	
During formation of hyperosmotic urine (antidiuresis):	
Isosmotic in Bowman's space	Micropuncture (Fig. 8-2A)
Very slightly hyposmotic at end of proximal tubule	Micropuncture (Fig. 8-2A)
Hyperosmotic at bend of loop of Henle	Micropuncture (Fig. 8-2A)
Hyposmotic at beginning of distal tubule	Micropuncture (Fig. 8-2A)
Isosmotic at end of distal tubule	Micropuncture (Fig. 8-2A)
Hyperosmotic at end of collecting duct	Micropuncture (Fig. 8-2A)
During formation of hyposmotic urine (water diuresis):	
Same as above through beginning of distal tubule; however, note quantitative differences (point 4 in this table)	Micropuncture (Fig. 8-2B)
Hyposmotic at end of distal tubule	Micropuncture (Fig. 8-2B)
Hyposmotic at end of collecting duct	Micropuncture (Fig. 8-2B)
3. During antidiuresis, osmolalities at any given level perpendicular to the corticopapillary axis should be about equal	Micropuncture, and cryoscopy of renal tissue slices. At any given horizontal level, the osmolality is about the same in the descending limbs of Henle, collecting ducts, interstitium, and vasa recta; the only exceptions are the ascending limbs of Henle and early distal tubules, where osmolalities are lower than in the interstitium. During water diuresis (formation of hyposmotic urine), fluid in distal tubules and collecting ducts is hyposmotic to plasma and to fluid in the other structures

Table 8-1. Continued

Condition	Proof
4. If the major change in the system between forming hyperosmotic rather than hyposmotic urine is the water permeability of the late distal tubules and collecting ducts, the medullary and papillary interstitium should be hyperosmotic even during water diuresis	Micropuncture, cryoscopy of renal tissue slices, and chemical analysis of tissue homogenates. The condition is met, but the degree of interstitial hyperosmolality is much less in water diuresis than in antidiuresis. For example, in water diuresis the inner medullary interstitium has an osmolality of 500 to 600 mOsm/kg (Fig. 8-2B). Not all the reasons for the difference have been identified; they include decreased reabsorption of urea into the medullary and papillary interstitium (see below), and probably depletion of interstitial solutes (called washout) by increased blood flow through the outer and inner medulla

ROLE OF UREA IN THE COUNTERCURRENT SYSTEM

The principles of the countercurrent mechanism can be understood by considering the transport merely of Na$^+$, Cl$^-$, and water, as we have done. Urea, however, plays an additional and important role.

Deposition of Urea in the Medullary Interstitium

The medullary interstitial osmolality is higher in antidiuresis than in water diuresis (Fig. 8-2). The difference is due largely to urea (see proof for item 4 in Table 8-1), which is deposited in the inner medullary interstitium by the following mechanisms.

- In conjunction with Figure 4-5, we presented the fact that more urea is reabsorbed from the collecting ducts at low urine flows than at high flows, and we described the reasons for this fact.
- Urea deposition into the medullary interstitium is also aided by the process of medullary recycling of urea (Fig. 4-6), which delivers more urea to the collecting ducts than would be the case if recycling did not occur.
- Finally, urea reabsorption from collecting ducts is abetted at low urine flows (antidiuresis) by a differential effect of ADH on the urea and water permeabilities of the distal tubules and collecting ducts (Fig. 8-5).

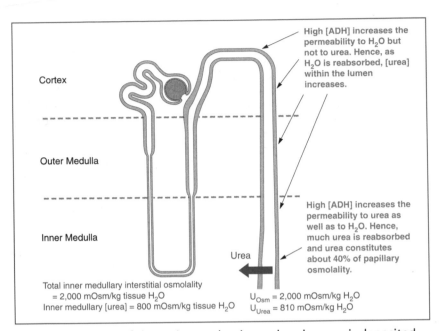

High [ADH] increases the permeability to H$_2$O but not to urea. Hence, as H$_2$O is reabsorbed, [urea] within the lumen increases.

Cortex

Outer Medulla

Inner Medulla

Urea

High [ADH] increases the permeability to urea as well as to H$_2$O. Hence, much urea is reabsorbed and urea constitutes about 40% of papillary osmolality.

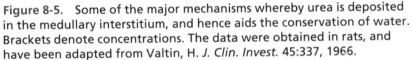

Total inner medullary interstitial osmolality
= 2,000 mOsm/kg tissue H$_2$O
Inner medullary [urea] = 800 mOsm/kg tissue H$_2$O

U_{Osm} = 2,000 mOsm/kg H$_2$O
U_{Urea} = 810 mOsm/kg H$_2$O

Figure 8-5. Some of the major mechanisms whereby urea is deposited in the medullary interstitium, and hence aids the conservation of water. Brackets denote concentrations. The data were obtained in rats, and have been adapted from Valtin, H. *J. Clin. Invest.* 45:337, 1966.

ADH increases the *water* permeability of the late distal tubule and the *entire* collecting duct (Table 7-1); however, it increases the *urea* permeability only of the terminal portion of the inner medullary collecting duct. Even in the presence of ADH, the distal tubule, as well as the cortical outer medullary, and early inner medullary collecting duct have a very low permeability for urea. Consequently, as water is withdrawn from these structures during the formation of hyperosmotic urine, the urea, unable to diffuse out of the lumen as readily as water, is progressively concentrated. When the fluid reaches the final part of the inner medullary collecting duct, the concentrated urea diffuses into the inner medullary interstitium until its concentration at any given level in the interstitium is equal to its concentration at the same level in the collecting duct.

As a result of the processes that promote its reabsorption, urea constitutes about 40% of the total inner medullary solute concentration during antidiuresis, whereas it contributes less than 10% to the interstitial osmolality during water diuresis.

Dissipation of Urea from the Inner Medulla

With a high concentration of urea within the inner medullary interstitium (Fig. 8-5), there is a constant tendency for this compound to be lost from this region—mostly by entering the ascending vasa recta, but also by simple diffusion through the interstitium towards the cortex. Yet, a high urea concentration within the interstitium is essential to full concentration of urine. Even though loss of urea from the inner medulla is minimized by countercurrent exchange in the vasa recta (Fig. 8-4), quite a bit is carried into the outer medulla. This urea is restored to the inner medulla through *medullary recycling of urea,* which was described earlier in conjunction with Figure 4-6 (p. 77); another version of that figure, which stresses the return of urea to the inner medulla utilizing the phenomenon of nephron heterogeneity, is reproduced here as Figure 8-6.

As urea is reabsorbed from the last part of the inner medullary collecting duct (*step 6* in Fig. 8-6), much of it is deposited in the inner medullary interstitium, although a considerable amount enters the ascending vasa recta and is dissipated toward the outer medulla (*step 1*). As these vessels enter the outer medulla, they come into close apposition with the pars recta and descending limbs of short loops of Henle, but not of long loops. Consequently, urea can more readily enter these segments of superficial nephrons (*step 2*) than the corresponding segments of juxtamedullary nephrons. Thereafter, the recycled urea encounters nothing but urea-impermeable segments until it again reaches the terminal inner medullary collecting duct— consecutively, thick ascending limb of Henle (*step 3*), distal tubule (*step 4*), and cortical, outer medullary, and first part of inner medullary collecting duct (*step 5*). The dissipated urea is then returned to the inner medullary interstitium by being reabsorbed from the terminal portion of the inner medullary collecting duct (*step 6*).

Long loops of Henle are quite permeable to urea, and therefore urea probably moves from the inner medullary interstitium into both the descending and ascending limbs of long loops. Net dissipation of urea from the inner medulla by long loops might be prevented, however, by the reabsorption of urea from inner medullary collecting ducts (*step 6*) counterbalancing the urea that is secreted into long loops of Henle—i.e., by descending and ascending long limbs of Henle combining functionally with late inner medullary collecting ducts to constitute a countercurrent exchange system for urea (*step 7*).

Note that the system for returning dissipated urea to the inner medulla 'takes advantage' of nephron heterogeneity (in this case, differences between long and short loops of Henle), and that it il-

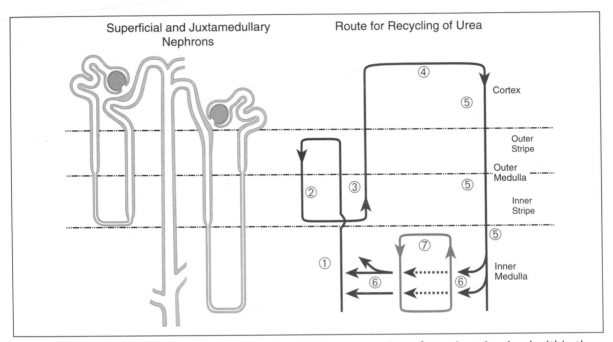

Figure 8-6. Means whereby a high concentration of urea is maintained within the inner medullary interstitium: (a) return of urea that leaves the inner medulla in ascending vasa recta, through medullary recycling of urea via short loops of Henle (*steps 1* through *6*); and (b) possible countercurrent exchange of urea in descending and ascending long limbs of Henle acting in consort with inner medullary collecting ducts (*step 7*). Not shown is countercurrent exchange of urea by vasa recta (Fig. 8-4), which minimizes the amount of urea that is lost from the inner medulla in step 1. Note that not all of the elements shown on the right correspond to structures on the left; thus, ascending vasa recta (*step 1*) are not shown on the left. Details are described in the text.

lustrates the principle of anatomical/functional correlation (the apposition of ascending vasa recta with descending *short* limbs of Henle but not with descending *long* limbs). In fact, thin ascending long limbs lie close to inner medullary collecting ducts, an anatomical juxtaposition that could facilitate countercurrent exchange.

Excretion of Urea with Minimal Water

It is of considerable interest, from an evolutionary point of view, that urea is the only endogenous solute that is handled by the kidneys in the manner described in the above two sections. As the major end product of protein catabolism in mammals, urea must be excreted by the kidneys in order to preserve urea balance. Usually when a solute is excreted in the urine, it obligates the simultaneous excretion of water. This is so because the solute contributes to the osmolality of the tubular fluid and thereby decreases the osmotic gradient (which governs the passive reabsorption of water) between tubular lumen and interstitium. The classic example, used in clinical situations, is osmotic diuresis induced by mannitol. Mannitol is a six-carbon sugar (i.e., a small, freely filterable solute) that is not reabsorbed by the tubules. When mannitol is given intravenously, and thence filtered, it raises the osmolality of tubular fluid and decreases the reabsorption of water, so that a diuresis ensues.

In the case of urea, however, that portion of the osmolality within late collecting ducts that is due to urea is balanced by an equal concentration of urea in the interstitium surrounding the collecting ducts (Fig. 8-5). Hence, urea can be excreted in the urine without entailing the simultaneous excretion of large amounts of water; in other words, urea within collecting duct fluid does not set up an osmotic gradient that obligates water to stay within the tubular lumen. This fact was described in 1934 by J. L. Gamble and his associates as a feature that is unique to urea. They noticed that rats had a much lower rate of urinary flow if they excreted urea than if they had to excrete any other solute in equimolar amounts. Such 'economy of water', as they called it, is of obvious advantage for organisms that must avidly conserve water in order to survive.

> ■ **Special Properties** ■
> **of Urea**
>
> As end product of protein catabolism, urea must be excreted by kidneys
>
> Yet, terrestrial mammals must conserve water
>
> Urea can be excreted in less urine than can any other solute, because—
>
> Unlike any other solute, urea does not set up an osmotic gradient between collecting duct and interstitium

Countercurrent Multiplication in the Inner Medulla

There is an old problem, still unresolved: The corticopapillary interstitial osmotic gradient rises steadily all the way to the papilla (Fig. 8-2A)—not only within the outer medulla, where active reabsorption of NaCl from thick ascending limbs of Henle produces the single effect of a countercurrent multiplier (Fig. 8-3), but also within the inner medulla, where thin limbs of Henle are largely or wholly incapable of active transport (Table 7-1). (Note, in Fig. 1-3, that thin descending limbs of Henle within the inner medulla and thin ascending limbs have virtually no mitochondria, which are considered essential organelles for active transport.) Thus, the problem is: Where is the single effect, and what mechanisms are involved, for countercurrent multiplication within the inner medulla?

Many possible answers have been and continue to be considered, but the solution to the problem remains elusive. We do know that countercurrent multiplication continues within the inner medulla, but we do not know how it comes about. Until the answer is known, it remains possible that urea plays an essential role in the process; that is the reason why this question is grouped here, under the topic Role of Urea in the Countercurrent System.

WATER BALANCE

There are two major mechanisms by which total body water is maintained at a normal level: (a) alteration in the rate of secretion of ADH and (b) regulation of thirst.

Secretion of ADH
Osmoreceptors

The classic experiments of E. B. Verney in the early 1940s elucidated the principal means by which the secretion of ADH from the posterior pituitary gland is regulated. These experiments are diagrammed in Figure 8-7A. Verney worked with trained, unanesthetized dogs in which he had exteriorized loops of both common carotid arteries, prior to carrying out the experiments. He observed that within 30 to 60 minutes after receiving a large oral load of tap water, these dogs excreted large amounts of hyposmotic urine. This water diuresis could be abruptly interrupted by infusing a bolus of hyperosmotic solution into the exteriorized carotid loop, but not if the posterior pituitary gland had been removed. If posterior pituitary extract was given to an hypophysectomized animal, the water diuresis was also interrupted.

On the basis of these results, Verney proposed the schema outlined in Figure 8-7B. When an individual is deprived of water, continued obligatory loss of water—not only as urine but especially as evaporation from the skin and breath, called *insensible water loss* (see Table A-4 in the Appendix)—renders the plasma hyperosmotic. This change stimulates osmoreceptors that generate afferent signals calling for the secretion of ADH. The resulting high concentration of ADH in the blood then leads to antidiuresis, which is mediated mainly through increased water permeability of the late distal tubules and collecting ducts.

Conversely, when an individual drinks a large amount of dilute fluid, the plasma becomes hyposmotic. This, Verney proposed, sets off the opposite chain of events, leading to a decreased concentration of ADH in the blood, decreased water permeability of the late distal tubules and collecting ducts, and water diuresis.

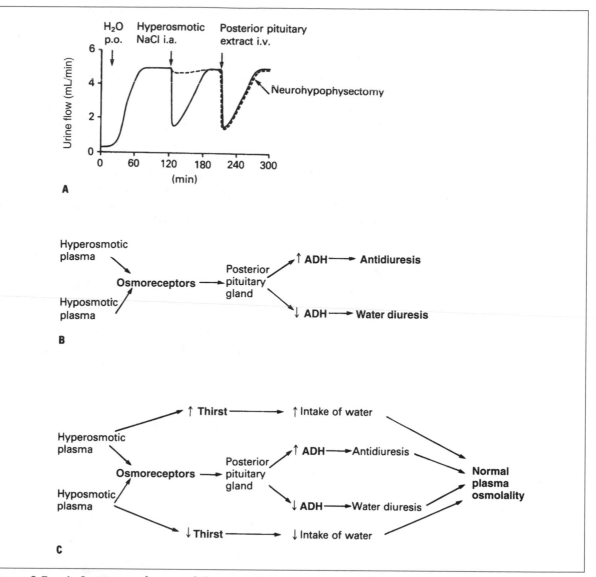

Figure 8-7. A. Summary of some of the important results obtained on unanesthetized dogs by E. B. Verney. *Proc. Roy. Soc. London,* Series B. 135:25, 1947. Solid
line graph represents results on a dog prior to removal of the neurohypophysis; the
dashed line represents results on the same dog after neurohypophysectomy. p.o. =
per os (by mouth); i.a. = intra-arterially (into the exteriorized loop of the common
carotid artery); i.v. = intravenously.

B. Chain of events whereby changes in plasma osmolality regulate the secretion of
antidiuretic hormone (ADH) and hence urine flow. Although many other factors can
also affect ADH secretion (see text, Volume Receptors; Other Influences), the osmoreceptor system is the major mechanism that regulates water balance from moment to moment.

C. Interplay of thirst and of the osmoreceptor system for release of ADH, in the
maintenance of water balance as reflected in a normal plasma osmolality.

Since prior removal of the pars nervosa abolished the response to hyperosmotic solutions, Verney surmised that ADH came from the posterior pituitary gland. This suspicion was supported by the antidiuretic response to posterior pituitary extract. The osmoreceptors have not been identified anatomically; they presumably lie within the distribution of the internal carotid artery.

As is shown in Figure 8-7A, modulations in ADH secretion, and hence in urine flow, occur very rapidly—within a few minutes. Thus, both the pituitary and the renal components of this system constitute a sensitive and precise mechanism for maintaining water balance.

Volume Receptors

Although the osmoreceptor system (Fig. 8-7B) is the main factor that regulates ADH secretion from moment to moment, there are other influences that modulate this rate, chief among which is the status of the extracellular fluid volume. This effect is shown in Figure 8-8. When the extracellular fluid volume is contracted, a state

Figure 8-8.   Regulation of water balance by osmotic, volume, and hemodynamic factors through their influence on the plasma concentration of the antidiuretic hormone (ADH or vasopressin) and on thirst.

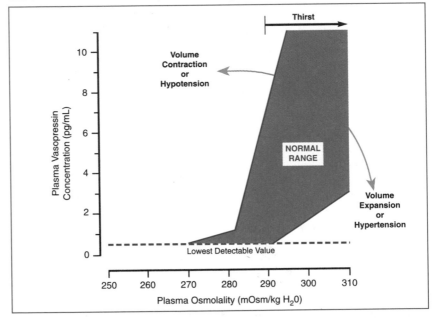

that is usually accompanied by some decrease in systemic blood pressure, the relationship between plasma osmolality and the plasma concentration of ADH becomes steeper so that, at any given plasma osmolality, more ADH is secreted in the presence of volume contraction than when extracellular volume is normal. Simultaneously, there is a slight shift of the relationship to the left, so that the threshold for ADH release from the posterior pituitary gland occurs at a lower plasma osmolality than normally. The reverse changes hold when the extracellular fluid volume is expanded, a state that leads to a rise in systemic blood pressure.

The receptors that perceive the status of the extracellular volume, known as *volume receptors* or *low-pressure receptors,* are thought to be located chiefly in the cardiac atria and pulmonary veins (Fig. 7-11). Those that sense changes in systemic pressure, called *baroreceptors,* are mainly the carotid sinus and aortic arch, as well as the juxtaglomerular apparatus (Figs. 7-9 and 7-11). The osmoreceptor system is more sensitive than the volume receptor system: A very small change in plasma osmolality, as little as 1 or 2%, will alter ADH secretion, whereas a change of 10 to 15% in the extracellular fluid volume is required before a difference in ADH secretion can be perceived.

Other Influences

Numerous factors, in addition to those discussed above, can alter the secretion of ADH. Among these are: nausea, stress, body temperature, acid-base balance, and most importantly, a host of drugs and hormones.

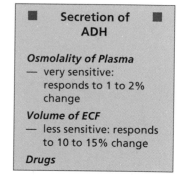

■   **Secretion of**   ■
ADH

Osmolality of Plasma
— very sensitive: responds to 1 to 2% change

Volume of ECF
— less sensitive: responds to 10 to 15% change

Drugs

Thirst

Even though ADH is highly effective in regulating water balance, it alone does not suffice to maintain balance. For example, even in the face of maximal renal conservation of water, an obligatory loss of water (both renal and extrarenal or insensible, referred to above) continues. This persistent loss will lead to dehydration—even in the face of maximal ADH—unless the loss of water is replaced by acquisition of water. How thirst governs that acquisition, and how it is integrated with ADH, is shown in Figures 8-7C and 8-8. Hyperosmotic plasma stimulates not only the release of ADH but also thirst; and together—the first by renal conservation of water, the second by increased intake of water—they normalize the osmolality of plasma. The opposite chain of events sets in when the plasma is hyposmotic. Like the mechanism for ADH, that for thirst is prompt, sensitive, and precise. For example, acute hemorrhage—as in a patient with trauma—leads to immediate thirst.

FREE WATER

'Free water' refers to water that is free of solutes. In the kidney, free water is produced or 'generated' in the ascending limbs of Henle and early distal tubules, where relatively more Na$^+$ and Cl$^-$ than water are reabsorbed (see Fig. 8-2). Whether or not free water is excreted in the urine depends on ADH and the water permeability of the late distal tubules and collecting ducts. If the concentration of ADH in blood is low (Fig. 8-2B), much of the free water that was generated in the ascending limbs will not be reabsorbed, and hyposmotic urine will be excreted. Relative to the isosmotic plasma that was filtered, more water than solute will have been excreted, and in this sense the net result will be that free water has been removed or cleared from the plasma. When the concentration of ADH is high (Fig. 8-2A), all the generated free water, and more, will be reabsorbed and hyperosmotic urine will be excreted. The excretion of hyperosmotic urine reflects a net process in which relatively more solute than water was removed from isosmotic plasma. In this sense, no free water will have been removed or cleared from the plasma; in fact, a negative quantity of free water will have been cleared.

Free-Water Clearance

The view that the excretion of hyposmotic or hyperosmotic urine represents the clearance of a positive and negative quantity of free water, respectively, from isosmotic plasma, led to the expression 'free-water clearance' (C_{H_2O}). This is unfortunate, for unlike all other renal clearances, C_{H_2O} is *not* equal to $U_{H_2O} \times \dot{V}/P_{H_2O}$. However, the term is so well established in renal physiology that any attempt to change it is likely to cause more confusion than enlightenment. Hence, the term will be used in this book, but with the admonition that C_{H_2O} *is not a classic renal clearance.*

Free-water clearance may be defined as the amount of distilled water that must be subtracted from the urine (during water diuresis) or added to the urine (during antidiuresis) in order to render that urine isosmotic with plasma. The formula for calculating this amount of distilled water is as follows:

> ■   **Free-Water**   ■
> **Clearance**
>
> *Not Calculated as U $\times$ $\dot{V}$/P*
>
> **Negative**
> when urine is hyperosmotic
>
> **Positive**
> when urine is hyposmotic
>
> **Zero**
> when urine is isosmotic

$$C_{H_2O} = \dot{V} - C_{Osm} \tag{8-1}$$

where: C_{Osm} = the osmolal clearance, or $U_{Osm} \times \dot{V}/P_{Osm}$.

When a hyposmotic urine of 100 mOsm/kg is formed, the urine flow is 10 mL per minute, and plasma osmolality is 300 mOsm/kg, then

$$C_{H_2O} = \frac{10 \text{ mL}}{\text{min}} - \left(\frac{100 \text{ mOsmols}}{1,000 \text{ mL}} \times \frac{10 \text{ mL}}{\text{min}} \times \frac{1,000 \text{ mL}}{300 \text{ mOsmols}} \right)$$

$$C_{H_2O} = 6.7 \text{ mL/min}$$

When a hyperosmotic urine of 1,000 mOsm/kg is formed, and the urine flow is 0.5 mL per minute, then

$$C_{H_2O} = \frac{0.5 \text{ mL}}{\text{min}} - \left(\frac{1,000 \text{ mOsmols}}{1,000 \text{ mL}} \times \frac{0.5 \text{ mL}}{\text{min}} \times \frac{1,000 \text{ mL}}{300 \text{ mOsmols}} \right)$$

$$C_{H_2O} = -1.2 \text{ mL/min}$$

That is, when hyposmotic urine is formed, the free-water clearance has a positive value, and when hyperosmotic urine is formed, this clearance has a negative value. Obviously, when the urine is isosmotic with plasma, C_{H_2O} will be zero.

SUMMARY

Water balance is maintained mainly through the regulation of thirst and of the secretion of antidiuretic hormone (ADH). When a subject is deprived of drinking water, the plasma becomes hyperosmotic, and this change stimulates thirst and increases the secretion of ADH from the posterior pituitary gland (Fig. 8-7C). Both effects tend to raise the total water content of the body—thirst by raising the intake of water, and ADH by increasing the water permeability of the late distal tubules and collecting ducts, which promotes renal conservation of water. Conversely, when a subject imbibes a large amount of water, the consequent dilution of the plasma inhibits both thirst and the secretion of ADH; and these changes tend to decrease the total water content of the body by decreasing the acquisition and increasing the excretion of water, respectively.

ADH changes water permeability through a mechanism that shuttles specific water channels in and out of the apical membrane of late distal tubules and collecting ducts. Other, structurally related channels that are not modulated by ADH impart continuously high water permeability to other parts of the nephron, especially the proximal tubules, descending limbs of Henle, and the basolateral membranes of late distal tubules and collecting ducts. In contrast, those segments of the nephron that are continuously impermeable to water appear to have no water channels, namely, the thin and thick ascending limbs of Henle.

From moment to moment, the secretion of ADH is regulated by the osmoreceptor system, which is exquisitely sensitive; a change in plasma osmolality of just 2 to 5 mOsm/kg suffices to alter the release of ADH. This sensitivity—both in slope and in threshold—can be modulated by the size of the extracellular fluid volume, but only if this volume is altered by at least 10 to 15% (Fig. 8-8). Many other factors can influence the secretion of ADH, among them the systemic blood pressure, certain hormones, and drugs.

Concentrated (or hyperosmotic) urine is formed through passive reabsorption of water by means of the countercurrent mechanism. Countercurrent multiplication of the single effect of reabsorbing Na^+ and Cl^-, virtually without water, from ascending limbs of Henle results in progressive hyperosmolality of the medullary interstitium, called the corticopapillary osmotic gradient. Dissipation of the gradient by the medullary blood flow is minimized by the countercurrent configuration of the vasa recta, which enables them to function as countercurrent exchangers. In the presence of high concentrations of ADH and resultant high water permeability, water is reabsorbed passively in response to the osmotic gradient between late distal tubules and collecting ducts and the surrounding interstitium, and hyperosmotic urine is formed.

During formation of dilute urine, the countercurrent mechanism continues to function qualitatively in the same manner. But now, in the absence of ADH, water reabsorption from distal tubules and collecting ducts is minimized despite the existence of osmotic gradients. Consequently, hyposmotic urine is excreted.

Urea, the main end product of protein catabolism in mammals, serves a unique role in water conservation by this class of vertebrates. A high concentration of urea within the inner medullary interstitium is maintained by a series of processes acting in an integrated manner: (a) by a differential effect of ADH on the water and urea permeabilities of late distal tubules and collecting ducts; (b) by medullary recycling of urea via short descending limbs of Henle; (c) by countercurrent exchange of urea in vasa recta; and, possibly, (d) by countercurrent exchange in long loops of Henle acting in concert with inner medullary collecting ducts. As a result of this high interstitial concentration, urea within the collecting duct lumen does not set up an osmotic gradient that obligates water to stay in the lumen; consequently, urea can be excreted at a lesser cost of water than can other urinary solutes.

The excretion of solute-free water is gauged in relation to the isosmotic plasma that is filtered. When urine is hyposmotic to plasma, relatively more water than solute must have been removed or cleared from the plasma. Hence, under these circumstances the free-water clearance (C$_{H_2O}$)—a misnomer—has a positive sign. When urine is hyperosmotic to plasma, relatively less water than solute must have been removed (or cleared) from the filtered plasma; therefore, under these conditions C$_{H_2O}$ is negative. Finally, when the urine is isosmotic with plasma, solute and water were cleared from the glomerular filtrate in proportion to their concentrations in plasma, and C$_{H_2O}$ is zero.

SUGGESTED READINGS

Agre, P., Preston, G. M., Smith, B. L., Jung, J. S., Raina, S., Moon, C., Guggino, W. B., and Nielsen, S. Aquaporin CHIP: the archetypal molecular water channel. *Am. J. Physiol.* 265 (*Renal Fluid Electrolyte Physiol.* 34):F463, 1993.

Berliner, R. W. Formation of Concentrated Urine. In C. W. Gottschalk, R. W. Berliner, and G. H. Giebisch (Eds.), *Renal Physiology. People and Ideas.* Bethesda: American Physiological Society, 1987. Chap. III.

Fitzsimons, J. T. Physiology and Pathophysiology of Thirst and Sodium Appetite. In D. W. Seldin and G. Giebisch (Eds.), *The Kidney. Physiology and Pathophysiology* (2nd ed.). New York: Raven, 1992. Chap. 44.

Gross, P., Richter, D., and Robertson, G. L. (Eds.). *Vasopressin.* Paris: John Libbey Eurotext, 1993.
This volume represents the proceedings of the 4th International Conference on Vasopressin. The conferences are held regularly, and the proceedings are published promptly after each meeting.

Harris, H. W., Jr., Strange, K., and Zeidel, M. L. Current understanding of the cellular biology and molecular structure of the antidiuretic hormone-stimulated water transport pathway. *J. Clin. Invest.* 88:1, 1991.

Hays, R. M. Cell Biology of Vasopressin. In B. M. Brenner and F. C. Rector, Jr. (Eds.), *The Kidney* (4th ed.). Philadelphia: Saunders, 1991. Chap. 11.

Kirk, K. L., and Schafer, J. A. Water transport and osmoregulation by antidiuretic hormone in terminal nephron segments. In D. W. Seldin and G. Giebisch (Eds.), *The Kidney: Physiology and Pathophysiology* (2nd ed.). New York: Raven, 1992. Chap. 48.

Knepper, M. A., and Rector, F. C., Jr. Urinary Concentration and Dilution. In B. M. Brenner and F. C. Rector, Jr. (Eds.), *The Kidney* (4th ed.). Philadelphia: Saunders, 1991. Chap. 12.

North, W. G., Moses, A. M., and Share, L. (Eds.), Neurohypophysis: A Window on Brain Function. *Ann. N.Y. Acad. Sci.* 689, 1993.
This volume represents the proceedings of the 5th International Conference on the Neurohypophysis. Like those on Vasopressin *(see Gross, above), these meetings are held and published at regular intervals.*

Robertson, G. L. Regulation of Vasopressin Secretion. In D. W. Seldin and G. Giebisch (Eds.), *The Kidney: Physiology and Pathophysiology* (2nd ed.). New York: Raven, 1992. Chap. 43.

Schmidt-Nielsen, K. Desert Animals: Physiological Problems of Heat and Water. London: Oxford University Press, 1964.

Valtin, H. Structural and functional heterogeneity of mammalian nephrons. *Am. J. Physiol.* 233 (*Renal Fluid Electrolyte Physiol.* 2):F491, 1977.

Valtin, H. Genetic models of diabetes insipidus. In E. E. Windhager (Ed.), *Handbook of Physiology,* vol. II, section 8: *Renal Physiology.* New York: Oxford University Press, 1992. Chap. 28.

Verkman, A. S. *Water Channels.* Austin: Landes, 1993.

Problem 8-1. Renal handling of salt, water, and urea in varying states of water intake. The following data were obtained on a healthy medical student, under three conditions: (a) while drinking ad libitum; (b) after 12 hours of thirsting; and (c) within 90 minutes after drinking 1 liter of tap water. Fill in the blanks, and be sure to specify units. Neglect corrections for plasma water and for Donnan distribution.

	$\dot{V}$ (mL/min)	U_{In} (mg/mL)	P_{In} (mg/mL)	GFR ( )	U/P inulin	Proportion of filtered water (i.e., of GFR) reabsorbed (%)
While drinking ad libitum	1.2	15.8	0.151			
After 12 hours of thirsting	0.75	25.2	0.155			
Within 90 minutes after drinking 1 liter water	15.0	1.23	0.154			

	P_{Na} (mmol/L)	Filtered load of Na ( )	U_{Na} (mmol/L)	Urinary Na excretion ( )	Proportion of filtered Na reabsorbed (%)
While drinking ad libitum	136		128		
After 12 hours of thirsting	144		192		
Within 90 minutes after drinking 1 liter water	134		10.2		

	U_{Osm} (mOsm/kg)	P_{Osm} (mOsm/kg)	C_{H_2O} ( )	$U_{Urea\,N}$[a] (mg/dL)	$P_{Urea\,N}$[a] (mg/dL)	C_{Urea} ( )	Proportion of filtered urea reabsorbed (%)
While drinking ad libitum	663	290		480	12		
After 12 hours of thirsting	1,000	300		720	15		
Within 90 minutes after drinking 1 liter water	100	287		48	10		

[a]Concentrations of urea are usually determined by measuring the amount of nitrogen in urea; hence, the expression *urea nitrogen*. The two nitrogen atoms constitute 28/60 of the urea molecule: $CO(NH_2)_2$; i.e., 28 g of the 60 g molecular weight of urea is due to the nitrogens. The clearance of urea (C_{Urea}) can be calculated without converting 'Urea N' to 'Urea,' since the conversion factors for $U_{Urea\,N}$ and $P_{Urea\,N}$ cancel out.

PROBLEM 8-2

Normally, in an adult man, about 125 mL of plasma H$_2$O is filtered into Bowman's space each minute. Of this amount, approximately 124 mL per minute is reabsorbed. (a) In which parts of the nephron is the H$_2$O reabsorbed, and (b) what happens to the H$_2$O once it has been reabsorbed? (c) In the same person, 660 mL of plasma enters the kidneys at an osmolality of 290 mOsm/kg, and 1 mL of urine leaves the kidneys at an osmolality of 700 mOsm/kg. What, then, is the osmolality of plasma that leaves the kidneys via the renal veins?

H$^+$ Balance

9

■   ■   ■   ■   ■

THE PROBLEM OF MAMMALIAN H+ BALANCE

The pH of the blood is normally maintained within the alkaline range of about 7.38 to 7.42. This narrow range of pH is essential to normal metabolic function, probably because the activities of protein macromolecules such as enzymes and of elements required for blood clotting and muscle contraction are importantly influenced by pH. The extreme range of plasma pH that is compatible with life is approximately 6.8 to 7.8.

The pH of the body fluids is maintained alkaline even though the mammalian body normally produces large amounts of acid, from two major sources: (1) The volatile acid H_2CO_3 (see below) is produced from CO_2, the end product of oxidative metabolism, and (2) a variety of nonvolatile acids are produced from dietary substances. As outlined next, the first source is by far the larger.

Some 13,000 to 20,000 mmol of CO_2 are produced daily as the result of oxidative metabolism; when processed, this CO_2 yields H^+ according to either or both of the following reactions:

$$CO_2 + H_2O \rightleftharpoons H_2CO_3 \rightleftharpoons H^+ + HCO_3^- \tag{9-1}$$

and/or

$$HOH \rightleftharpoons OH^- + H^+$$
$$+ CO_2 \underset{\text{C.A.}}{\rightleftharpoons} HCO_3^- \tag{9-2}$$

Note that the final products are H^+ and HCO_3^-, whether the hydration of CO_2 is involved (Eq. 9-1) or the splitting of H_2O and subsequent hydroxylation of CO_2 (Eq. 9-2). There is evidence that carbonic anhydrase (C.A.) catalyzes reaction 9-2 but not 9-1. Because when either of these reactions moves to the left, the CO_2 formed is rapidly dissipated by the lungs, H_2CO_3 is referred to as a *volatile acid*.

In most western countries, where meat constitutes a large part of the diet, there is also a net daily production of some 40 to 60 mmol of inorganic and organic acids that are not derived from CO_2. Sulfuric acid is produced from protein catabolism through the conversion of sulfur in the amino acid residues, cysteine, cystine, and methionine, as exemplified by the following reaction for methionine:

$$2\ C_5H_{11}NO_2S + 15\ O_2 \rightarrow 4\ H^+ + 2\ SO_4^{2-} + CO(NH_2)_2 + 7\ H_2O + 9\ CO_2 \tag{9-3}$$
methionine   urea

Formation of phosphoric acid during the catabolism of phospholipids makes a minor contribution, as does partial metabolism of

■ Daily Loads of ■ Acids (H+)

Volatile
  CO_2 (Eqs. 9-1 and 9-2)
  13,000 to 20,000 mmols

Nonvolatile, or Fixed
  e.g., H_2SO_4
  40 to 60 mmols

carbohydrates and fats, which yields a variety of organic acids. Because all these acids, unlike CO_2, are not volatile or in equilibrium with a volatile component, they are known as *nonvolatile,* or *fixed,* acids. Finally, normal digestive processes result in the loss of some 20 to 40 mmol of alkali in the stool. In net balance this loss is equivalent to the addition of nonvolatile acid to the body. (When the diet consists mainly of vegetables and fruits, the net production of nonvolatile constituents consists of alkalis, such as K^+ or Na^+ carbonate or hydroxide resulting from the metabolism of organic anions.)

In certain physiological and pathological states, the production of nonvolatile acids may rise as much as tenfold. Examples include the production of lactic acid during muscular exercise and states of hypoxia, and the production of acetoacetic acid and 3-hydroxybutyric (β-OH butyric) acid during uncontrolled diabetes mellitus.

Thus, the problem of H^+ balance in most mammals is the defense of normal alkalinity in the face of a constant onslaught of acid.

pH VERSUS [H⁺]

Some experts advocate the substitution of the hydrogen ion concentration, [H⁺], for pH. One can switch from one system to the other through the expression:

$$pH \equiv -\log[H^+] \tag{9-4}$$

For the sake of simplicity, we shall use only pH in this book.

BUFFERING OF NONVOLATILE (FIXED) ACIDS

The very effective defense of alkalinity in a normal dog is illustrated in Figure 9-1. It compares the change in the pH of arterial plasma when 156 mL of a 1 N HCl solution was infused intravenously with the drop in pH when the same amount of acid was gradually added to 11.4 liters of distilled water. This volume of distilled water is about equal to the total body water of the dog.

In the dog the pH dropped from 7.44 to 7.14, a state of severe acidosis but one compatible with survival. In contrast, the addition of just a few millimol of H^+ to unbuffered distilled water sharply lowered the pH to a value that would have been fatal to the animal, and the final level was 1.84. This section deals with the mechanisms that permit such effective buffering in vivo.

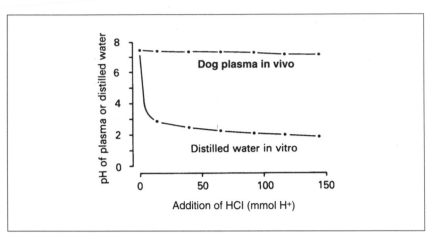

Figure 9-1. An experiment contrasting the effective buffering of HCl in a dog with the lack of buffering when the same amount of acid is added to distilled water. The pH of the dog's arterial plasma decreased gradually from 7.44 to 7.14; that of unbuffered distilled water dropped precipitously to a level that would be fatal if it occurred in vivo. Redrawn from Pitts, R. F., *Harvey Lect.* 48:172, 1953.

First Line of Defense—Instantaneous Physicochemical Buffering

The following reaction is the prototype for physicochemical buffering:

$$\text{Strong acid} + \text{Buffer salt} \rightleftharpoons \text{Neutral salt} + \text{Weak acid} \tag{9-5}$$

If hydrochloric acid is buffered by the bicarbonate buffer system, the reaction is:

$$H^+ + Cl^- + Na^+ + HCO_3^- \rightleftharpoons Na^+ + Cl^- + H_2CO_3 \tag{9-6}$$

Insofar as physicochemical buffering reduces the amount of buffer salt and increases the amount of weak acid, this type of reaction only minimizes, but by no means prevents, a decrease in pH. This point can be illustrated by simple calculations that utilize the derivation of the Henderson-Hasselbalch equation as it applies to the bicarbonate system:

$$pH = pK' + \log \frac{[HCO_3^-]}{[\text{Dissolved } CO_2]} \tag{9-7}$$

In this equation the pK' (negative logarithm of the apparent dissociation constant) has a value of 6.1. In the sense that the denominator of Equation 9-7 consists overwhelmingly of CO_2 and not of H_2CO_3, the acid moiety of the bicarbonate buffer system is CO_2, even though it cannot donate H^+ (also called *protons*); in fact, many authorities speak of the 'HCO_3^-/CO_2' buffer system rather than of the 'HCO_3^-/H_2CO_3' system, and we shall use the former expression from now on. [Note that while CO_2 is not itself a donor of protons, it either leads to the production of H^+ (Eq. 9-1) or accepts OH^- (Eq. 9-2), and it therefore acidifies the medium.]

The concentration of dissolved CO_2 in plasma is proportional to the partial pressure of CO_2 (P_{CO_2}) in the plasma, which is relatively easy to determine. The proportionality constant for plasma at 37°C, which converts P_{CO_2} in millimeters of mercury (mm Hg) to concentration of dissolved CO_2 expressed as mmol/L, is 0.03. Thus, the denominator in Equation 9-7 can be very closely approximated as $0.03 \times P_{CO_2}$, and this equation may be rewritten in a form that is most useful in physiological and clinical practice:

$$pH = 6.1 + \log \frac{[HCO_3^-]}{0.03 \times P_{CO_2}} \tag{9-8}$$

In this equation, $[HCO_3^-]$ is expressed as mmol/L and P_{CO_2} in mm Hg. Substituting normal values for arterial plasma of humans (see Table A-1 in the Appendix):

$$pH = 6.1 + \log \frac{24 \text{ mmol/L}}{0.03 \times 40 \text{ mm Hg}}$$

$$pH = 6.1 + \log \frac{24 \text{ mmol/L}}{1.2 \text{ mmol/L}} \tag{9-9}$$

$$pH = 6.1 + \log 20$$

$$pH = 7.40$$

If 12 mmol of HCl were added to each liter of extracellular fluid— and if, for the moment, we say that all the acid is buffered by HCO_3^-—then physicochemical buffering would decrease the numerator and increase the denominator by 12 mmol/L each, according to the following reaction:

$$12 \text{ H}^+ + 12 \text{ Cl}^- + 24 \text{ Na}^+ + 24 \text{ HCO}_3^- \rightleftharpoons 12 \text{ Na}^+ + 12 \text{ Cl}^- + 12 \text{ Na}^+$$
$$+ 12 \text{ HCO}_3^- + 12 \text{ H}_2\text{CO}_3$$
$$\Updownarrow \tag{9-10}$$
$$12 \text{ CO}_2 + 12 \text{ H}_2\text{O}$$

If this reaction were to occur in a 'closed system'—i.e., without a ventilatory system to eliminate the newly generated CO_2—the pH would drop to the fatal level of 6.06:

$$pH = 6.1 + \log \frac{12 \text{ mmol/L}}{1.2 + 12 \text{ mmol/L}}$$

$$pH = 6.1 + \log \frac{12 \text{ mmol/L}}{13.2 \text{ mmol/L}}$$

$$pH = 6.06$$

This dire consequence is prevented by the second line of defense, which, like physicochemical buffering, comes into play within seconds or minutes after the administration of HCl.

Second Line of Defense—Fast Respiratory Component

Because of the equilibrium in Equation 9-1, virtually all the H_2CO_3 that was produced through physicochemical buffering is converted to CO_2 and H_2O (Eq. 9-10), and the CO_2 is excreted by the lungs. If all the extra CO_2 were excreted, returning the denominator to 1.2 mmol/L, the resulting pH would fall into the range that is compatible with survival.

$$pH = 6.1 + \log \frac{12 \text{ mmol/L}}{1.2 \text{ mmol/L}}$$

$$pH = 6.1 + \log 10$$

$$pH = 7.10$$

Respiratory compensation goes further, however. As a result of the lower pH of the blood, alveolar ventilation is increased, so that alveolar and hence arterial P_{CO_2} are decreased. Consequently the pH is returned toward, but not quite to, the normal value.

$$pH = 6.1 + \log \frac{12 \text{ mmol/L}}{0.03 \times 23 \text{ mm Hg}}$$

$$pH = 6.1 + \log \frac{12 \text{ mmol/L}}{0.69 \text{ mmol/L}}$$

$$pH = 7.34$$

Third Line of Defense—Slow Renal Component

Although respiratory compensation has, within minutes, restored the pH almost to normal, the body stores of the main extracellular buffer have been depleted. This fact is reflected in the decrease of the HCO_3^- concentration from 24 to 12 mmol/L. Furthermore, some of the added H⁺, although admittedly no longer in free solution, still remains within the body as weak acid. Both of these remaining abnormalities are corrected by the kidneys, which excrete H^+ and simultaneously replenish the depleted HCO_3^- stores. This process is a much slower one than the first two lines of defense, requiring hours to days rather than seconds or minutes. How the kidneys accomplish this task, which finally restores H^+ balance, is discussed in Chapter 10.

The above is a dramatic example that occurs only under artificial experimental conditions or in disease states. Nevertheless, these are the pathways by which the daily loads of nonvolatile acids are handled. The following quantitative comparison may put the normal daily challenge from these fixed acids into perspective. An adult weighing 70 kg has about 14 liters of extracellular fluid (about 20% of body weight; Fig. 2-1). Hence the addition of 12 mmol of HCl to each liter of extracellular fluid, as in the example described above, would be a total acid load to an adult human of 168 mmol (12 mmol/L × 14 liters). The normal daily load of 40 to 60 mmol of fixed acids is only about one-third of that amount, and it is released relatively slowly over a 24-hour period, rather than in 1 to 2 hours, as in the above example. If, for the sake of illustration, about one-third of a total load of 48 mmol were released after each meal, 16 mmol (48 ÷ 3) would be added to 14 liters of extracellular fluid, i.e., an addition of about 1 mmol per liter of extracellular fluid. Since sulfuric acid is normally the major fixed acid (Eq. 9-3), the quantitative reaction would be as follows:

$$2\,H^+ + SO_4^{2-} + 24\,Na^+ + 24\,HCO_3^- \rightleftharpoons 2\,Na^+ + SO_4^{2-} + 22\,Na^+ \\ + 22\,HCO_3^- + 2\,H_2CO_3 \\ \Updownarrow \qquad\qquad (9\text{-}11) \\ 2\,CO_2 + 2\,H_2O$$

Despite the apparent lowering of $[HCO_3^-]$ from even this small addition of acid, the arterial pH actually does not change. This is so because, in a normal individual in the steady state, the processes described above as the first and second lines of defense are accompanied by the renal excretion of H^+ and the reabsorption of HCO_3^- (the third line of defense, described in Chap. 10).

BUFFERING OF THE VOLATILE 'ACID' CO_2

At the beginning of this chapter, we cited the fact that some 13,000 to 20,000 mmol of CO_2 is produced daily by an adult person, as the result of metabolic events. As shown in Equations 9-1 and 9-2, the

■ **Buffering of Fixed Acids** ■

First Line of Defense
— physicochemical; instantaneous

Second Line of Defense
— respiratory; fast

Third Line of Defense
— renal; slow

processing of this CO_2 can generate H^+, and the production of CO_2 therefore potentially disturbs H^+ balance. Ultimately, elimination of all the extra CO_2 by the lungs prevents acidosis (Eq. 9-8); but before that elimination can occur, defense of alkalinity is threatened as the CO_2 is carried in the blood from the cells, where it is produced, to the lungs, where it is excreted. The extremely effective buffering in the blood is reflected in the fact that the difference in pH between venous blood, which goes to the lungs, and arterial blood, which leaves them, seldom exceeds 0.04 of a pH unit. This section deals with the mechanisms by which H^+ is buffered as CO_2 is transported in the blood.

Transport of CO_2 in Blood

The plasma P_{CO_2} at the arterial end of tissue capillaries is about 40 mm Hg. Since the P_{CO_2} is higher in tissue cells that produce CO_2, the gas will diffuse from the tissue cells into the capillary. The chain of events that then occurs, shown in Figure 9-2, is as follows:

1.   There is still no agreement whether CO_2 is processed mainly by hydration (Eq. 9-1) or by hydroxylation (Eq. 9-2). Because it is the latter reaction that is probably catalyzed by carbonic anhydrase (C.A.), we will use Equation 9-2 to show the processing of CO_2 within cells where C.A. is present, and Equation 9-1 for extracellular fluids where C.A. is absent.

Most cell membranes, including those of red blood cells (erythrocytes), are highly permeable to CO_2. Hence CO_2 diffuses not only into the plasma but also into the erythrocytes. Because there is much carbonic anhydrase in erythrocytes but none in plasma, CO_2 is processed much more rapidly within these cells than in the plasma. In fact, the processing is negligible in plasma; the small amount of H^+ that is formed from this reaction is buffered by the nonbicarbonate buffer anions of plasma, the proteins (Pr^{n-}) and inorganic phosphate (HPO_4^{2-}).

2.   The rapid combination of CO_2 with OH^- within the erythrocytes yields HCO_3^-. Most of the newly formed HCO_3^- diffuses into the plasma, and Cl^- shifts into the erythrocytes. In this way, most of the CO_2 that is added to venous capillary blood is carried to the lungs as HCO_3^- in the plasma. A portion combines with hemoglobin to form carbamino hemoglobin, and an even smaller amount is carried as dissolved CO_2 within the erythrocytes. The H^+ formed when water is split is buffered primarily by hemoglobin. The same is true of the H^+ that is released during the formation of carbamino hemoglobin.

■   **Buffering of**   ■
Volatile Acid

Hydroxylated CO_2 (Eq. 9-2) *carried as HCO_3^-* (Fig. 9-2)

H^+ buffered by deoxygenated hemoglobin (Fig. 9-2)

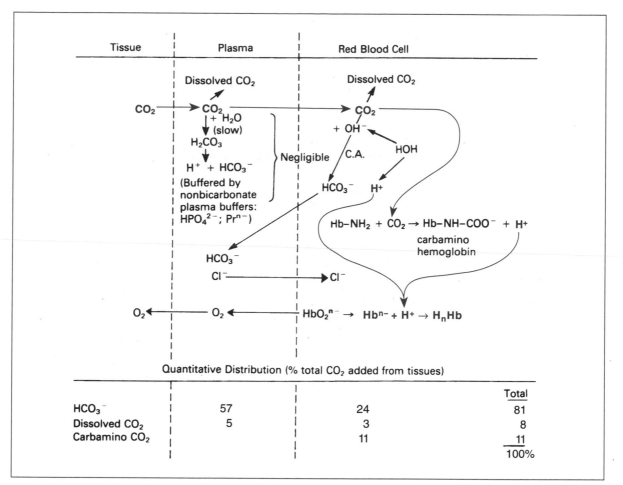

Figure 9-2. Transport of CO_2 and buffering of H^+ by the blood. Adapted from Davenport, H. W., *The ABC of Acid-Base Chemistry* (6th ed.). Chicago: University of Chicago Press, 1974; and Masoro, E. J., and Siegel, P. D., *Acid-Base Regulation: Its Physiology, Pathophysiology and the Interpretation of Blood-Gas Analysis* (2nd ed.). Philadelphia: Saunders, 1977.

3. In a normal, resting adult human, every liter of venous blood that goes to the lungs carries about 1.68 mmol of extra CO_2 for excretion. The quantitative distribution of the various forms in which the added CO_2 is carried is shown at the bottom of Figure 9-2. Approximately 81% of the 1.68 mmol is carried as HCO_3^-, most of which is carried in the plasma, even though virtually all of it was generated within the erythrocytes. The remainder is divided between dissolved CO_2 and carbamino CO_2. Of these, the major

portion of dissolved CO_2 is carried in the plasma, whereas practically all the carbamino CO_2 is found in the erythrocytes.

CONCEPT OF METABOLIC AND RESPIRATORY DISTURBANCES

Primary Disturbances

Inspection of the Henderson-Hasselbalch equation, as represented in Equation 9-8, makes clear that an abnormality of plasma pH can result from a primary deviation of either the $[HCO_3^-]$ or the P_{CO_2}. Since the latter is regulated by the rate of alveolar ventilation, any disturbance in pH that results from a primary change in P_{CO_2} is called a *respiratory acid-base disorder*. Hypoventilation and retention of CO_2 (as in chronic pulmonary disease, attempted suicide with sedatives, or bronchial obstruction) lead to a reduction in pH that is called *respiratory acidosis*. Hyperventilation and a fall in P_{CO_2} (as during ascent to high altitude, anxiety attacks, or gram-negative sepsis) lead to a rise in pH that is called *respiratory alkalosis*. Changes in the concentration of HCO_3^- are brought about most commonly by the addition or loss of nonvolatile (fixed) acids or bases, which are derived mainly from metabolic processes. Hence, any abnormality of pH resulting from a change in $[HCO_3^-]$ is called a *metabolic acid-base disorder*. A primary reduction in $[HCO_3^-]$, termed *metabolic acidosis,* can occur when endogenous acids are produced faster than they can be excreted (as in uncontrolled diabetes mellitus or renal failure), when HCO_3^- is lost from the body (as in severe diarrhea), or when exogenous acid is administered [e.g., oxalic acid during poisoning with ethylene glycol (antifreeze)]. A primary increase in $[HCO_3^-]$, termed *metabolic alkalosis,* can occur when endogenous HCl is lost from the body (as in vomiting), when excess HCO_3^- is retained (as with diuretics), or when exogenous HCO_3^- is administered under certain circumstances (e.g., during volume contraction).

Thus, there are four primary disturbances of H⁺ balance (often called acid-base balance): (1) respiratory acidosis, (2) respiratory alkalosis, (3) metabolic acidosis, and (4) metabolic alkalosis. Some examples of these disorders are listed in the marginal box.

Mixed Disturbances

Not infrequently, two primary disturbances, usually one respiratory and the other metabolic, occur simultaneously in the same

---

■ **Examples of** ■
Primary Acid-Base Disturbances

Metabolic Acidosis
  uncontrolled diabetes
    mellitus
  renal failure
  severe diarrhea
  ingestion of antifreeze

Metabolic Alkalosis
  vomiting
  nasogastric drainage
  use of diuretics
  giving HCO_3^-

Respiratory Acidosis
  chronic pulmonary disease
  sedative overdosage
  obstruction of airway

Respiratory Alkalosis
  high altitude
  anxiety hyperventilation
  gram-negative sepsis

individual. Such patients are said to have 'mixed' acid-base disturbances. For example, a patient who manifests alveolar hypoventilation from emphysema may also have an obstructed duodenal ul-
cer leading to loss of HCl through vomiting. This patient would
have a mixed disturbance of respiratory acidosis and metabolic alkalosis. Another patient may have both emphysema, with retention of CO_2, and renal failure, which leads to the retention of fixed
acids. This patient would have a mixed disturbance of respiratory
acidosis and metabolic acidosis. There even can be triple disturbances, as in a patient receiving chemotherapy for cancer, who has
metabolic alkalosis from nausea and vomiting, respiratory alkalosis from a concurrent gram-negative sepsis, and lactic acidosis
from associated low blood pressure and underperfusion of tissues.

Compensatory Responses

Primary disturbances in H⁺ balance elicit a secondary response
that partially corrects the pH. In the example cited earlier in this
chapter, the addition of HCl led to a decrease in $[HCO_3^-]$ and hence
to metabolic acidosis. This disturbance was largely compensated
for by the second line of defense (see marginal box, p. 189), in
which alveolar hyperventilation lowered the PCO_2 and thereby adjusted the pH to a near normal value.

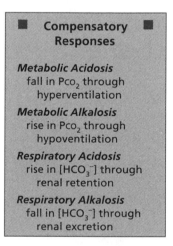

■ **Compensatory** ■
Responses

Metabolic Acidosis
fall in PCO_2 through
hyperventilation

Metabolic Alkalosis
rise in PCO_2 through
hypoventilation

Respiratory Acidosis
rise in $[HCO_3^-]$ through
renal retention

Respiratory Alkalosis
fall in $[HCO_3^-]$ through
renal excretion

This example illustrates two points: (1) that a compensatory response involves the system opposite to the one that caused the primary disturbance (e.g., *metabolic* alkalosis is compensated for by a
respiratory response, and vice versa) and (2) that compensation
shifts the pH *toward* but not to the normal value. Regarding the
second point, in the example given earlier in this chapter (p. 188),
respiratory compensation moved the pH to 7.34 but not entirely
into the normal range.

One can predict the direction of the compensatory response by
utilizing Equation 9-8:

$$pH = 6.1 + \log \frac{[HCO_3^-]}{0.03 \times PCO_2}$$

Following a primary disturbance, return toward a normal pH will
result if the ratio $[HCO_3^-]/0.03 \times PCO_2$ is restored toward its normal
value of 20 (i.e., 24/1.2 = 20). Thus, if a primary metabolic acidosis
has lowered the $[HCO_3^-]$, then the compensatory response must be
in the opposite system, i.e., in the PCO_2, and the PCO_2 must be lowered if the ratio is again to approach 20; or, if a primary disturbance
of respiratory acidosis has raised the PCO_2, then the compensatory
response must be one that raises the numerator, $[HCO_3^-]$; etc.

Since primary disturbances may be either metabolic or respiratory in origin, and may cause either acidosis or alkalosis, there are four general types of compensatory responses: (1) Metabolic acidosis is compensated by alveolar hyperventilation. (2) Metabolic alkalosis is compensated by a reduction in alveolar ventilation. (3) Respiratory acidosis is compensated by increased renal excretion of H$^+$ and increased renal reabsorption of HCO$_3^-$ (see Chap. 10 for mechanisms by which this response is accomplished). (4) Respiratory alkalosis is compensated by decreased renal excretion of H$^+$ and decreased renal reabsorption of HCO$_3^-$.

Acute and Chronic Respiratory Disturbances

Compensations for primary metabolic disturbances occur virtually immediately, whereas those for primary respiratory disturbances are fully manifested only after several days. The reason is that changes in alveolar ventilation alter the level of P$_{CO_2}$ very quickly, while changes in renal function that alter the plasma [HCO$_3^-$] take much longer. It is because of this difference in the time course of compensatory responses that primary respiratory disturbances—but not primary metabolic disturbances—are subdivided into acute (up to 8 hours) and chronic (present for 2 to 3 days or longer) phases. Between these time intervals a transitional phase is present, reflecting the gradual development of the renal response. During acute respiratory acidosis or alkalosis there will be a very slight rise or fall, respectively, of the plasma [HCO$_3^-$] resulting from the chemical reactions shown in Equations 9-1 and 9-2, as well as from the H$^+$ involved in these reactions interacting with nonbicarbonate buffers, Buf$^-$ (Eq. 9-14). In chronic respiratory disturbances the changes in plasma [HCO$_3^-$] are much greater because the kidneys have compensated by altering the reabsorptive rate for HCO$_3^-$ (described further in Chap. 10).

THE IMPORTANT BUFFERS OF MAMMALS

Thus far we have spoken almost exclusively about the bicarbonate and the hemoglobin buffer systems. In this section we shall emphasize that the body contains other important buffers, and that all these participate in the regulation of pH.

A buffer is a mixture either of a weak acid and its conjugate base or of a weak base and its conjugate acid. (Acid is here defined as an H$^+$ donor and base as an H$^+$ acceptor.) The buffers of physiological importance in mammals are all of the first type. They have been listed in Figure 9-3. These buffer systems are by no means limited

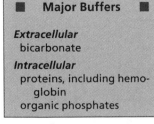

■   **Major Buffers**   ■

Extracellular
bicarbonate

Intracellular
proteins, including hemo-
  globin
organic phosphates

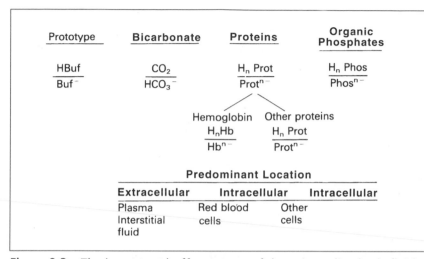

Figure 9-3. The important buffer systems of the mammalian body fluid compartments. Note that CO_2 is denoted as the acid moiety of the bicarbonate buffer system, even though CO_2 is not a H⁺ donor (see text discussion of Eq. 9-7). The locations refer to quantitative predominance and are not exclusive except for hemoglobin in erythrocytes. The valence of phosphate is designated as indefinite because it is quantitatively an important chemical buffer mainly within the intracellular fluid, where its valence as organic phosphate is not known.

to the plasma. They are found in all phases of the body fluids—plasma, interstitial fluid, intracellular fluid—and bone. The bicarbonate system predominates in plasma and interstitial fluid, while organic phosphates and proteins (especially hemoglobin) predominate in the intracellular space.

Isohydric Principle

When several buffers exist in a common solution, as in a beaker, all the buffer pairs are in equilibrium with the same concentration of H⁺. Expressed in the terminology of the Henderson-Hasselbalch equation, and for plasma—which is a common solution containing the bicarbonate, protein, and inorganic phosphate buffer systems—the isohydric principle can be stated as follows:

$$pH = pK'_1 + \log \frac{[HCO_3^-]}{[CO_2]} = pK_2 + \log \frac{[HPO_4^{2-}]}{[H_2PO_4^-]} = pK_3 + \log \frac{[Prot^{n-}]}{[H_nProt]}$$

$$(9\text{-}12)$$

This principle has an important application in the analysis of acid-base disturbances, because one can infer the status of most of the body buffer pairs by determining the status of just one of them. In practice, one usually measures two of the three variables of the bicarbonate system, so that the third can easily be calculated (Eq. 9-8). For plasma, which is a homogeneous solution, knowledge of the bicarbonate system can thus be extended precisely to the phosphate and protein buffer pairs without actually measuring their concentrations.

Precise extension to the buffers in the other major fluid compartments is not possible because these compartments are not part of a homogeneous solution, in which all the buffers are evenly distributed. For example, the pH of the intracellular compartment is considerably lower (perhaps 7.00) than that of the extracellular compartment, because of three influences: (1) metabolic production of acids within cells, which is modified by (2) active transport of H⁺ out of cells, and (3) the Gibbs-Donnan effect, which results in a slightly unequal distribution of diffusible electrolytes on two sides of a semipermeable membrane (see Chap. 2, under Gibbs-Donnan Equilibrium, p. 27). The Gibbs-Donnan effect accounts for the approximately 5% difference in buffer concentrations between the plasma and interstitial fluid. Despite these differences among compartments, however, the isohydric principle can be applied in many conditions of H⁺ imbalance to infer qualitative changes in all or most of the body buffers from knowledge of the bicarbonate system alone. This is permissible because many acid-base disturbances represent relatively chronic situations in which the change in H⁺ balance within one fluid compartment has been accompanied by qualitatively similar changes in the other compartments.

Special Attributes of the Bicarbonate System

Titration curves for the bicarbonate and inorganic phosphate buffers, which are found in plasma and interstitial fluid, are shown in Figure 9-4A. Several points, which are characteristic of all buffers, should be noted:

1. the pK is numerically equal to the pH existing when the weak acid and its conjugate base each comprise 50% of the total concentration of that particular buffer;
2. the change in pH per quantum of H⁺ or OH⁻ added is least in the steep, linear portion of each titration curve; and
3. this linear portion of most effective chemical buffering extends roughly 1.0 pH unit to either side of the pK—from pH of about

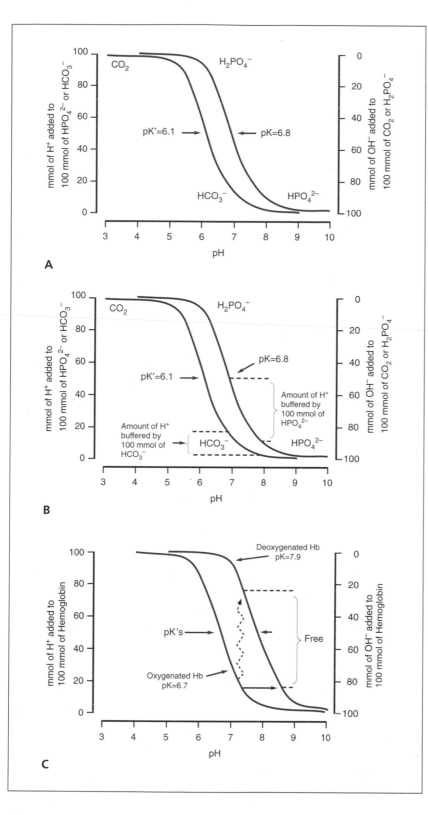

Figure 9-4. A. Titration curves for the bicarbonate and inorganic phosphate buffers in a closed system, when the CO_2 cannot be eliminated through diffusion to the outside.

B. Under these conditions, and in the range of pH for plasma (6.8–7.8), phosphate is actually a more effective buffer than is HCO_3^-. The fact, however, that ordinarily CO_2 can be excreted by the lungs, and the further fact that the plasma concentration is considerably higher for HCO_3^- than for HPO^{2-}, makes bicarbonate the major buffer in extracellular fluid.

C. Titration curves for oxygenated and deoxygenated hemoglobin (Hb). The fact that deoxygenated hemoglobin has a higher pK than does oxygenated hemoglobin makes it possible to carry large quantities of CO_2—and hence of H^+ (Eqs. 9-1 and 9-2)—in the blood with only a very slight decrease in pH. Zigzag arrow indicates actual path as CO_2 produced in tissues is added to venous blood.

197

5.1 to 7.1 for the bicarbonate system, and from about 5.8 to 7.8 for inorganic phosphate.

In other words, in the range of plasma pH that is compatible with survival (about 6.8 to 7.8), each quantum of phosphate can buffer more H^+ than can an equal quantum of bicarbonate (Fig. 9-4B). Nevertheless, bicarbonate plays a much more important physiological role as an extracellular buffer than does phosphate.

The reason for the seeming paradox is not only that the extracellular concentration of bicarbonate (about 24 mmol/L) is so much higher than that of phosphate (1 to 2 mmol/L; see Table A-1 in the Appendix) but also, and more importantly, that bicarbonate has certain physiological properties that make it a uniquely effective buffer. The central property is that carbonic acid is in equilibrium with volatile CO_2 (Eqs. 9-1 and 9-2), which can be rapidly excreted or retained by the lungs (see Second Line of Defense, p. 188). Furthermore, both the acid moiety, CO_2, and the conjugate base, HCO_3^-, of the bicarbonate buffer system are more abundantly available from daily metabolic processes than are those of any other buffer system.

Special Attributes of the Hemoglobin System

Like the bicarbonate system, so the hemoglobin buffer system has special properties that make it uniquely suited to carrying CO_2 from the tissues to the lungs. The explanation is shown diagrammatically in Figure 9-4C, which depicts the titration curve for oxygenated hemoglobin with a pK of 6.7 on the left, and that for deoxygenated hemoglobin with a pK of 7.9 on the right. As CO_2 is added from the tissues to capillary blood, H^+ is generated and this H^+ is buffered mainly by hemoglobin (Fig. 9-2). Were it not for the difference in pKs of the two hemoglobins, the H^+ would be buffered by oxygenated hemoglobin and in the process, the plasma pH would immediately decrease from its normal value of 7.40. What happens, however, is that the moment the arterial blood gives up oxygen to the tissues, the hemoglobin shifts from being oxygenated to being deoxygenated (long arrow at the bottom of Fig. 9-4C, pointing to the right). Consequently, as H^+ is added, the titration curve being followed is that of deoxygenated hemoglobin, and a great deal of H^+ can be added to capillary blood 'free,' in the sense that the pH does not drop below 7.40. In fact, more than 80% of the H^+ that is generated from CO_2 is added free, so that, despite the enormous quantities of CO_2 being carried to the lungs, the pH of venous blood is only approximately 0.03 of a pH unit lower than that of arterial blood. (Of course, the shift from oxygenated to deoxygenated hemoglobin does not cause the alkalinization of plasma as shown in the diagram; rather, the simultaneous exchange of O_2 for CO_2 in plasma causes almost imperceptible changes in pH, as indicated by the zigzag arrow.)

UTILIZATION OF THE VARIOUS BUFFERS

Addition of Strong Acid

Earlier in this chapter, when we described the buffering of nonvolatile (fixed) acids—i.e., of H⁺ other than that generated by CO_2 (Eqs. 9-1 and 9-2)—we limited the analysis to the bicarbonate buffer system in plasma. This simplification was not seriously inaccurate, since an acid that is infused intravenously will initially have its impact on the plasma. The description, however, did not include the participation of the other buffer systems of the body. The total picture is presented in Figure 9-5, which indicates not only the time course for distribution of a fixed acid throughout the body fluid compartments but also the quantitative contribution of the major buffers. (The figure refers to the addition of an inorganic, or mineral, acid; details may be slightly different when the same amount of H⁺ is added in the form of an organic acid, such as lactic acid.)

Figure 9-5 is based on experimental work in dogs that were given intravenous infusions of hydrochloric acid over periods of 1.5 to 3 hours. Within seconds to minutes, the acid was being handled by the various buffers of the blood. In the plasma, this process involves mainly the bicarbonate system (see marginal box, p. 194), because its ionic concentration in plasma is so much greater than that of the proteins and inorganic phosphate (Table A-1), and because CO_2, which is formed in the buffering reaction, is quickly eliminated via the lungs. The acid also quickly enters the erythrocytes, where it is buffered primarily by hemoglobin; bicarbonate, and to an even lesser extent organic phosphates, within erythrocytes contribute a little bit to the buffering. A small amount of the acid is buffered in the plasma, by bicarbonate that was derived from the erythrocytes through an exchange of Cl⁻ for HCO_3^-.

As soon as the HCl is infused into the plasma, it begins to enter the interstitial compartment. Although it takes about one-half hour for the acid to be evenly distributed between the plasma and interstitial fluid, the latter actually contributes more to the total buffering because its volume is about four times greater than that of plasma (Fig. 2-1). Again, inorganic phosphate in the interstitium also participates, but to a negligible extent, because its concentration in interstitial fluid, as in plasma, is very low.

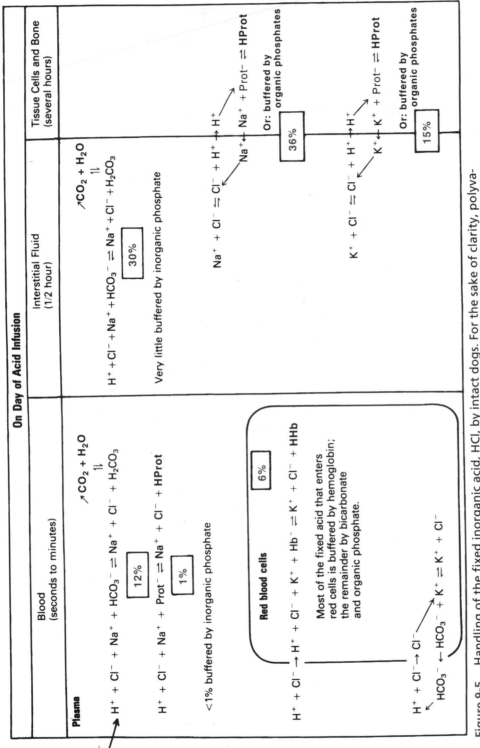

Figure 9-5. Handling of the fixed inorganic acid, HCl, by intact dogs. For the sake of clarity, polyvalent anions such as proteins and hemoglobin have been drawn with a single negative sign. A slanted arrow next to CO_2 indicates that the CO_2 is quickly excreted through the lungs. The percentages enclosed in rectangles indicate the approximate proportion of the total acid load that is buffered by each mechanism. Data from Swan, R. C., and Pitts, R. F., *J. Clin. Invest.* 34:205, 1955; Yoshimura, H., et al., *Jpn. J. Physiol.* 11:109, 1961; Pitts, R. F., *Physiology of the Kidney and Body Fluids* (3rd ed.). Chicago: Year Book, 1974; and Masoro, E. J., and Siegel, P. D., *Acid-Base Regulation: Its Physiology, Pathophysiology and the Interpretation of Blood-Gas Analysis* (2nd ed.). Philadelphia: Saunders, 1977.

Several hours elapse before the acid is evenly distributed throughout the intracellular compartment. Nevertheless, the contribution of the intracellular buffers is great. Utilization of these buffers—mainly proteins and organic phosphates (see marginal box, p. 194)—is accomplished by exchange of extracellular H^+ for either intracellular Na^+ or intracellular K^+. Some of the Na^+ probably comes from the apatite of bone, and the H^+ that is exchanged for this Na^+ enters into a chemical reaction with the apatite, finally being incorporated into HCO_3^-. The involvement of bone in buffering is probably much more important during chronic disturbances of acid-base balance (as in chronic renal failure) than during the relatively acute disturbance illustrated in Figure 9-5.

The relative quantitative contributions of the various buffers are indicated by the boxes in Figure 9-5, which give the percentage of the total acid load that is handled by each mechanism. It is clear that less than 15% is buffered in the plasma, and less than 20% by whole blood. To be emphasized is the fact that about one-half of the administered acid is buffered in the intracellular compartment.

Although buffering of the acid has minimized changes in pH, restoration of external balance must await excretion of the acid load in the urine. This occurs during the following several days. By the second day after the infusion, about 25% of the acid has been excreted, and both the pH and ionic composition of the extracellular fluids have returned to near normal values. It follows that 75% of the acid load must now reside within the cells and bone, where it is buffered. This remaining acid is slowly released into the extracellular fluids and is excreted by the kidneys during the second to sixth days after the acid was given.

Addition of Strong Alkali

When base is infused intravenously, or HCl is eliminated, as by vomiting, the chain of events is similar to that discussed above, except that the reactions go in the opposite direction. There is a marked participation by the intracellular buffers, and the time course for the utilization of the various buffers is similar to that shown in Figure 9-5. Three differences should be noted, however: (1) respiratory compensation—i.e., alveolar hypoventilation due to an increase in pH—is less intense in metabolic alkalosis than in metabolic acidosis (in part, perhaps, because the hypoxia that results from hypoventilation tends to stimulate respiration); (2) lactic acid moves out of skeletal muscle cells, to buffer the base in the extracellular fluid; and (3) the renal excretion of base, such as sodium bicarbonate, usually occurs more rapidly than does the renal excretion of H^+. The last two effects occur only when the alkalosis is due to addition of base rather than to loss of acid.

Addition of the Volatile 'Acid' CO_2—Hypercapnia

If excess CO_2 is produced endogenously and there is no disorder of respiration, the surplus is quickly excreted through the lungs by the mechanisms shown in Figure 9-2. If, however, CO_2 is added from an external source, as by breathing a gas mixture containing 5% CO_2, or if CO_2 accumulates because of some disorder of respiration, there is a net addition of acid to the body by the reactions shown in Equations 9-1 and 9-2. The chain of events that is set into motion under these circumstances is shown in Figure 9-6.

The first important point to recognize is that the H^+ produced when CO_2 is added cannot be buffered by the bicarbonate system. The reason is evident from Equation 9-13. When H^+ is buffered by HCO_3^- (as in Eqs. 9-10 and 9-11), carbonic acid is formed momentarily, and the final products are CO_2 and H_2O:

$$H^+ + HCO_3^- \rightleftharpoons H_2CO_3 \rightleftharpoons CO_2 + H_2O \tag{9-13}$$

Since CO_2 and H_2O are the starting substrates when CO_2 is added to the body (Eqs. 9-1 and 9-2), reaction 9-13, under that circumstance, is being driven to the left, and it cannot simultaneously be driven to the right, as would be required if the H^+ were to be buffered by HCO_3^-. Instead, the H^+ must be buffered by the nonbicarbonate buffers (proteins and phosphates), designated by Buf^- in the following reaction:

**■ Distribution of ■
Acid Load**

Fixed Acid
~50% extracellular
~50% intracellular

Volatile Acid
~ 5% extracellular
~95% intracellular

$$HOH \rightleftharpoons OH^- + H^+ \quad \Big\} \quad \rightleftharpoons \begin{array}{c} + Buf^- \\ + Na^+ \end{array} \tag{9-14}$$

$$+ CO_2 \underset{C.A.}{\rightleftharpoons} HCO_3^-$$

$$HBuf + Na^+ + HCO_3^-$$

As is shown in Figure 9-3 and in the marginal box on p. 194, the only buffer of quantitative importance in the extracellular fluid is the bicarbonate system. It follows, then, that very little of the H^+ that is generated when CO_2 is added to the body—in fact, less than 5% (Fig. 9-6)—can be buffered in the extracellular compartment, i.e., in the plasma and interstitial fluid.

A second important distinction between the addition of a fixed acid and the addition of the volatile 'acid' CO_2 lies in the time required for the acid load to be distributed throughout the major fluid compartments. This process takes hours for a fixed acid (Fig. 9-5),

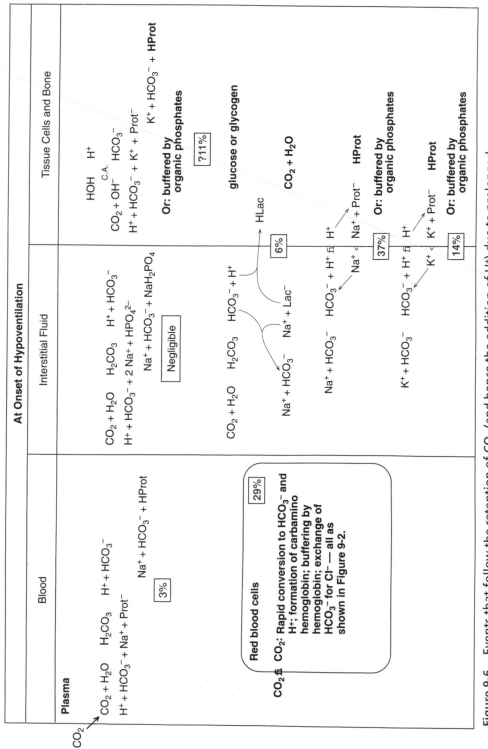

Figure 9-6. Events that follow the retention of CO_2 (and hence the addition of H^+) due to prolonged alveolar hypoventilation. For the sake of clarity, polyvalent protein anions have been written with a single negative sign. The approximate proportion of the total acid load that is buffered by each mechanism is indicated by the percentages in the rectangles; the figure of 11% is uncertain. Data adapted from Giebisch, G., et al. *J. Clin. Invest.* 34:231, 1955; Pitts, R. F. *Physiology of the Kidney and Body Fluids* (3rd ed.). Chicago: Year Book, 1974; and Masoro, E. J., and Siegel, P. D. *Acid-Base Regulation: Its Physiology, Pathophysiology and the Interpretation of Blood-Gas Analysis* (2nd ed.). Philadelphia: Saunders, 1977.

whereas it occurs within minutes for CO_2, which readily diffuses across both the vascular endothelium and the cell membrane.

Hemoglobin, of course, is the most abundant nonbicarbonate buffer in blood (Fig. 9-3). Consequently, a large proportion of the added volatile acid is buffered by the various mechanisms outlined in Figure 9-2. Since CO_2 diffuses so easily across cell membranes, the reactions in erythrocytes occur within seconds after the onset of the disturbance. However, since H$^+$ is simultaneously being formed in the interstitial compartment (where only small amounts of nonbicarbonate buffers are available), the fall in extracellular pH is much greater than would occur if the CO_2 were confined to the blood compartment. The H$^+$ formed in the extracellular compartment is buffered primarily within cells. Entry of H$^+$ into cells is accomplished mainly by exchange of H$^+$ for Na$^+$ across cell membranes, by H$^+$ for K$^+$ exchange in severe disturbances, and to a lesser extent by H$^+$ combining with lactate anions within the interstitial fluid. CO_2 rapidly enters all cells (not just erythrocytes), and the H$^+$ that is formed within cells is also buffered by intracellular nonbicarbonate buffers.

Thus, since the H$^+$ generated when CO_2 is added cannot be buffered by the bicarbonate system, which exists mainly in the extracellular compartment, all but 3% of the added acid load is buffered either within cells (erythrocytes, tissue cells, and bone) or by lactate, which, as lactic acid, is metabolized within cells. These buffer reactions essentially reach equilibrium within 15 minutes after a change in PCO_2 has occurred.

As was the case after the addition of strong acid, so here too the renal response is a relatively slow one, requiring days before a new steady state is reached. In this connection, a third difference between the addition of a fixed acid and the addition of volatile acid should be noted (alluded to earlier, under Acute and Chronic Respiratory Disturbances, p. 194). The events occurring on the day of adding strong acid (Fig. 9-5) include the rapid second line of defense, in which the excretion of CO_2 'adjusts' the denominator of the Henderson-Hasselbalch equation. Consequently, a near normal plasma pH is attained quickly. However, when the primary acid-base disturbance is respiratory (i.e., when the initial change is in the denominator of the Henderson-Hasselbalch equation; Eq. 9-8), the events occurring at the onset are limited to chemical buffering (Fig. 9-6), and compensatory 'adjustment' of the numerator must await the much slower renal process. Hence, primary respiratory disturbances are accompanied by relatively marked deviations of pH during the first few days, and a near normal pH is attained only after a number of days.

Deficit of the Volatile 'Acid' CO_2—Hypocapnia

The responses that set in when alveolar hyperventilation reduces CO_2, and hence H^+ (Eqs. 9-1 and 9-2), are analogous to those depicted in Figure 9-6, except that the reactions proceed in the opposite direction.

SUMMARY

Every day a person produces large quantities of acid. In an adult this amounts to approximately 50 mmol of nonvolatile acid, derived mainly from dietary proteins and phospholipids, and at least 13,000 mmol of CO_2 (approximately 90% of which momentarily generates H^+ as the CO_2 is carried in the blood to the lungs, where it is expired (Fig. 9-2). Despite these large loads of acid the person maintains an alkaline plasma pH, which is crucial to survival.

The concept of CO_2 as an acid is complicated because CO_2 is not a proton donor, nor does H_2CO_3 exist in appreciable amounts in the body fluids. Rather, most of the H^+ that results from the processing of metabolic CO_2 is derived from the dissociation of water (Eq. 9-2 and Fig. 9-2). As metabolic CO_2 enters the blood from tissue cells, this generation of H^+ poses a threat to H^+ balance. The decrease in pH is minimized by a special property of hemoglobin as a buffer, which makes nonoxygenated hemoglobin less acidic than oxygenated hemoglobin. Hence, as arterial capillary blood releases O_2, it can take up a great deal of H^+ without any change in pH (Fig. 9-4C). Simultaneously, the CO_2 coming from the cells combines with the OH^- of dissociated water to yield HCO_3^-, and it is mainly in this form that CO_2 is carried to the lungs for excretion.

Acids other than CO_2 do not have a volatile component; they are therefore known as nonvolatile, or 'fixed,' acids. Normally, such acids are derived from the catabolism primarily of proteins, and to a lesser extent of phospholipids; partial metabolism of carbohydrates and fats as well as loss of HCO_3^- in stool make further contributions. Acid-base balance in the presence of these acids is preserved by three lines of defense: (1) physicochemical buffering, which begins immediately after introduction of the acid; (2) adjustments in alveolar ventilation, which occur within seconds or minutes; and (3) renal excretion of H^+ and renal reabsorption of HCO_3^-, which may take days to reach completion. The bicarbonate buffer system is especially effective in handling excesses or deficits of fixed acids because (1) it involves an equilibrium with a volatile component, CO_2, which can be regulated by changes in alveolar ventilation, and (2) the substrates of this buffer system, namely, CO_2 and HCO_3^-, are readily available from metabolic processes.

Disturbances of H⁺ balance may have either a metabolic origin or a respiratory origin. The first will cause a deviation in the numerator of the Henderson-Hasselbalch equation (Eq. 9-8), which will tend to shift the pH in either an acid or an alkaline direction; the second will lead to a deviation in the denominator, which likewise may shift the pH in either direction. A primary disturbance of one origin (i.e., metabolic or respiratory) is accompanied by a secondary, or compensatory, response of opposite origin (i.e., respiratory or metabolic, respectively), which restores the plasma pH toward normal. Compensations for primary metabolic disturbances are almost instantaneous, whereas those for primary respiratory disturbances become fully effective only after several days. Because of this difference, primary respiratory disturbances (but not primary metabolic disturbances) are divided into an acute phase when virtually no renal compensation has taken place, and a chronic phase when renal compensation is essentially complete. When two or more primary disturbances occur simultaneously in the same individual, the resulting state is known as a mixed disturbance.

A load of acid or alkali calls into play not only the buffers of the plasma but also those of interstitial fluid, cells, and bone. Roughly 50% of fixed acid is buffered within cells. In contrast, the buffering of more than 95% of the H⁺ resulting from an excess or deficit of CO_2 (Eqs. 9-1 and 9-2) involves the intracellular space; this is so

Problem 9-1.   The data below were obtained on each of four patients. Complete the analysis of the acid-base status of each patient by filling in the blank spaces.

Normal arterial values from Table A-1 in the Appendix: pH = 7.38 to 7.42; $[HCO_3^-]$ = 22 to 26 mmol/L; Pco_2 = 37 to 43 mm Hg.

	Arterial plasma			
Cause of the disturbance	pH	Pco_2 (mm Hg)	$[HCO_3^-]$ (mmol/L)	Type of disturbance
Prolonged vomiting	7.50	49		
Ingestion of NH_4Cl[a]		22	10	
Anxiety-hyperventilation syndrome	7.57		21	
Emphysema	7.33	68		

[a]The net effect of ingesting NH_4Cl is the addition of hydrochloric acid, by the following reaction:
$2\ NH_4Cl + CO_2 \rightarrow 2\ H^+ + 2\ Cl^- + H_2O + CO(NH_2)_2$ (Last compound is urea)

because this H⁺ cannot be buffered by the bicarbonate system (Eqs. 9-13 and 9-14), which is overwhelmingly the predominant buffer of extracellular fluid, i.e., the plasma and interstitium.

The isohydric principle states that all buffer pairs in a common solution are in equilibrium with the same H⁺ concentration. The various body fluid compartments do not represent a common solution. Nevertheless, the principle can be applied in most steady states by extending knowledge of the bicarbonate system to assess the approximate status of all buffers in the body.

PROBLEM 9-2

Outline the sequential steps involved in the development of a steady state of: respiratory acidosis; metabolic alkalosis; and respiratory alkalosis.

What will be the pH of arterial plasma (i.e., acidotic, alkalotic, or unchanged) in the following mixed disturbances: respiratory acidosis plus metabolic acidosis; respiratory acidosis plus metabolic alkalosis; respiratory alkalosis plus metabolic acidosis; and respiratory alkalosis plus metabolic alkalosis?

SUGGESTED READINGS

Cohen, J. J., and Kassirer, J. P. *Acid-Base.* Boston: Little, Brown, 1982.

Davenport, H. W. *The ABC of Acid-Base Chemistry: The Elements of Physiological Blood-Gas Chemistry for Medical Students and Physicians* (6th ed.). Chicago: University of Chicago Press, 1974.

Flessner, M. F., and Knepper, M. A. Renal acid-base transport. In R. W. Schrier and C. W. Gottschalk (Eds.), *Diseases of the Kidney* (5th ed.). Boston: Little, Brown, 1993. Chap. 6.

Gennari, F. J., and Maddox, D. A. Renal regulation of acid-base homeostasis: Integrated response. In D. W. Seldin and G. Giebisch (Eds.), *The Kidney: Physiology and Pathophysiology* (2nd ed.). New York: Raven, 1992. Chap. 43.

Henderson, L. J. *Blood: A Study in General Physiology.* New Haven: Yale University Press, 1928.

Pitts, R. F. Mechanisms for stabilizing the alkaline reserves of the body. *Harvey Lect.* 48:172, 1953.

Tannen, R. L. Renal ammonia production and excretion. In E. E. Windhager (Ed.), *Handbook of Physiology*, section 8: *Renal Physiology,* vol. II. New York: Oxford University Press, 1992. Chap. 23.

Valtin, H., and Gennari, F. J. *Acid-Base Disorders. Basic Concepts and Clinical Management.* Boston: Little, Brown, 1987.

Role of Kidneys in Acid-Base Balance: Renal Excretion of H⁺ and Conservation of HCO₃⁻

10

■ ■ ■ ■ ■

ROLE OF KIDNEYS IN H⁺ BALANCE

REABSORPTION OF FILTERED HCO₃⁻
Mechanism for Reabsorption of Filtered HCO₃⁻
Factors Influencing the Rate at Which Filtered HCO₃⁻
Is Reabsorbed

REPLENISHMENT OF DEPLETED HCO₃⁻ STORES
Excretion of Titratable Acid (T.A.)
Factors Affecting the Rate of T.A. Excretion
Excretion of Ammonium
Proximal Production and Excretion of NH₄⁺
Corticopapillary Interstitial Gradient for NH₄⁺/NH₃
Secretion of NH₃ into Collecting Ducts
Nonionic Diffusion
Control of Renal NH₄⁺ Production and Excretion

**RELATIVE EXCRETION RATES OF TITRATABLE ACID
AND AMMONIUM**

SUMMARY

ROLE OF KIDNEYS IN H$^+$ BALANCE

It is clear from Chapter 9 that the maintenance of a normal plasma pH depends on the preservation of a normal *ratio* between the weak acid and conjugate base components of each of the body buffers. According to the isohydric principle (Eq. 9-12) these ratios can be determined precisely for all plasma buffers, from knowledge of the same ratio for the bicarbonate buffer system in plasma. Except for the slight correction necessitated by the Gibbs-Donnan effect (see Chap. 9, under Isohydric Principle, p. 195), the plasma bicarbonate system will also reflect the ratio of all interstitial buffers; and, as stated previously, in the steady state of most acid-base disturbances, any change in the plasma bicarbonate system will be accompanied by qualitatively similar changes of the intracellular buffers. It thus follows that regulating the ratio of the concentration of HCO$_3^-$ to that of Pco$_2$ in plasma (Eq. 9-8) will tend to regulate the ratio of all other buffer pairs.

The weak acid component of the plasma bicarbonate buffer system is regulated as Pco$_2$ through alveolar ventilation (Eq. 9-8). Preservation of the conjugate base, HCO$_3^-$, is accomplished by the kidneys. This task involves two processes: (1) the reabsorption of virtually all the HCO$_3^-$ that was filtered, and (2) the reclamation of the HCO$_3^-$ that was consumed in buffering fixed acids (Eq. 9-11). The latter process is accomplished through the excretion of an equivalent amount of H$^+$ into the urine. The renal replenishment of HCO$_3^-$ stores through excretion of H$^+$ was mentioned in Chapter 9, under Third Line of Defense, p. 188.

REABSORPTION OF FILTERED HCO$_3^-$

Like Na$^+$ and other small solutes, HCO$_3^-$ is freely filtered by the glomeruli. As is shown in Table 1-1, the daily filtered load of HCO$_3^-$ in an adult human amounts to approximately 4,500 mmol. If even a small portion of this quantity were to be excreted in the urine, the normal stores of this important buffer would quickly be exhausted. This eventuality is prevented by avid tubular reabsorption of HCO$_3^-$, which normally exceeds 99.9% of the filtered load (Table 1-1); that is, normally only about 2 mmol of HCO$_3^-$ are excreted in the urine each day.

Mechanism for Reabsorption of Filtered HCO_3^-

In a series of classic studies conducted in the 1940s, R. F. Pitts and his colleagues showed conclusively that much of the acid that is excreted gets into the urine not by glomerular filtration but by tubular secretion. They reasoned that the source of this acid must be largely or exclusively carbon dioxide (Eq. 9-1), and they strengthened their thesis by demonstrating that inhibition of the enzyme carbonic anhydrase (C.A.; Eq. 9-2) greatly reduces or abolishes the amount of acid that can be secreted. They suggested, furthermore, that acid is secreted in the form of H^+ ion rather than as molecular acid. A tremendous amount of subsequent experimental work by numerous investigators has proved those suggestions to be largely correct; the schema is shown in Figure 10-1.

Within tubular cells, water is in equilibrium with H^+ and OH^- (Fig. 10-1). [As stated in conjunction with Fig. 9-2, this reaction, rather than Eq. 9-1, is chosen for the generation of H^+ because the hydroxylation of CO_2 (Eq. 9-2) is thought to be the reaction that is catalyzed by carbonic anhydrase.] The H^+ is secreted into the tubular lumen mainly by two mechanisms: (1) through a process that is linked to the passive entry of Na^+ into the cell (Na^+/H^+ exchange), and (2) through an active transport pump (H-ATPase). [The presence or absence of each mechanism and its quantitative importance in secreting H^+ varies with the different tubular segments, and a third mode, H-K-ATPase, is present in collecting ducts (Figs. 10-7C and 11-4D). But the first two account for the vast majority of H^+ secretion.] In the tubular lumen the secreted H^+ combines with filtered HCO_3^- to form H_2CO_3, which is converted to CO_2 and water. In the proximal tubule and thick ascending limb of Henle, but not in more distal segments, this conversion occurs within milliseconds under the influence of carbonic anhydrase. The arrow for this step is deflected toward the cell to indicate that the carbonic anhydrase resides in the luminal cell membrane; tubular fluid is thus exposed to the enzyme even though carbonic anhydrase is not found in tubular fluid as such. The CO_2 that is formed within the lumen diffuses into the cell, where it combines with the OH^- that results from the dissociation of water, to form HCO_3^-—again, under the influence of carbonic anhydrase. This HCO_3^- then diffuses passively into the peritubular fluid and blood. As mentioned in conjunction with Figure 7-1A, in most parts of the nephron the HCO_3^- crosses the basolateral membrane by facilitated diffusion. Most of this HCO_3^- is accompanied by Na^+ (on a cotransporter, as shown in Fig. 10-1), and some of the HCO_3^- crosses the basolateral membrane in exchange for Cl^- (not shown). Although some of the

■ **Reabsorption of** ■
Filtered HCO₃⁻

Normally >99.9%
Reabsorbed
Up to 85% in proximal
  tubules

H⁺ Secretion by:
Na⁺/H⁺
  exchange   most
H-ATPase   important
H-K-ATPase; in
  collecting ducts

Na^+ that accompanies the HCO_3^- thus crosses the cell passively, most of it enters the peritubular fluid and blood via the active pump, Na-K-ATPase.

Note the net effects of the processes illustrated in Figure 10-1. For every H^+ that is secreted, a HCO_3^- is returned to peritubular fluid and blood. The mechanism shown in Figure 10-1 thus accomplishes the important task of *reclaiming virtually all the filtered HCO_3^-*. Note that it is not a mechanism for excreting H^+; to the extent that the CO_2 formed within the tubular lumen from secreted H^+ returns to the cell, ultimately to form more H^+ through hydroxylation, no net secretion of H^+ takes place.

The proportion of the total filtered HCO_3^- that disappears from tubular fluid in each of the major parts of the nephron is shown at

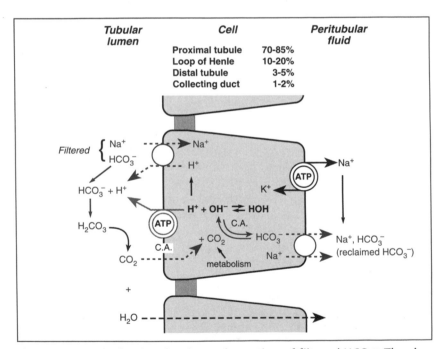

Proximal tubule	70-85%	
Loop of Henle	10-20%	
Distal tubule	3-5%	
Collecting duct	1-2%	

Figure 10-1. Mechanism for the reabsorption of filtered HCO_3^-. The circles containing ATP (adenosine triphosphate) denote specialized membrane proteins, which act as active pumps that require a direct input of energy: Na-K-ATPase in the basolateral membrane and H-ATPase in the apical membrane. C.A. = carbonic anhydrase; in the proximal tubule and loop of Henle, but not in the distal tubule and collecting duct, tubular fluid is exposed to this enzyme, which is located in the apical membrane. The percentages (derived from measurements in rats) indicate the proportion of filtered HCO_3^- that is reabsorbed in each part of the nephron.

the top of Figure 10-1. These values were derived in experimental animals by means of clearance ratios (see Answer to Problem 6-1, part 3), i.e., from knowledge of the concentrations of HCO_3^- and inulin in arterial plasma and tubular fluid. The results show that, by far, the filtered HCO_3^- is reabsorbed largely in the proximal tubule, mainly in its early part (Fig. 7-2A).

Factors Influencing the Rate at Which Filtered HCO₃⁻ Is Reabsorbed

The rate at which filtered HCO_3^- is returned to the blood can be affected by a number of factors, which often interact. Among these influences are the following: (a) the amount of HCO_3^- presented to the tubules; (b) the size of the extracellular fluid compartment; and (c) the arterial P_{CO_2}. It is possible that HCO_3^- reabsorption is altered under some of these circumstances mainly by varying the activation or number of Na/H exchangers and of H-ATPases (Fig. 10-1). Other factors also can be shown to affect HCO_3^- reabsorption, but for many of them (e.g., a host of hormones—parathyroid hormone, adrenal steroids, angiotensin II, catecholamines, dopamine), their possible role in maintaining HCO_3^- homeostasis is not yet defined; and yet others (e.g., K^+ and Cl^- deficiency) exert important influences only in disease states. We shall discuss only the first three.

1. Figure 10-2A shows a 'renal titration curve' for HCO_3^-, obtained by producing stepwise increments in plasma HCO_3^- concentration. As the plasma HCO_3^- concentration is varied, so is the filtered load of this ion (GFR $\times$ $P_{HCO_3^-}$) and hence the amount of HCO_3^- that is presented to the tubules for reabsorption. Provided that other variables, such as the volume of extracellular fluid (see below), are held constant, the amount of HCO_3^- that is reabsorbed is almost the same as the load that is filtered into the tubules. The mechanism for this effect has not been clarified, save that the rate of HCO_3^- reabsorption appears to be closely linked to that of Na^+ reabsorption, especially in the early proximal tubule (Fig. 7-2A). It may thus be in part a consequence of the need to conserve Na^+ and maintain the extracellular fluid volume. The relationship shown in Figure 10-2A for minimal volume expansion protects H^+ balance and is reminiscent of the conservation of Na^+ (as discussed in Chap. 7, under Challenges to Na^+ Balance: 1. Spontaneous Changes in GFR, p. 139), in that an increase in the filtered load of HCO_3^- (which could entail wastage of this important buffer) is followed immediately by increased reabsorption.

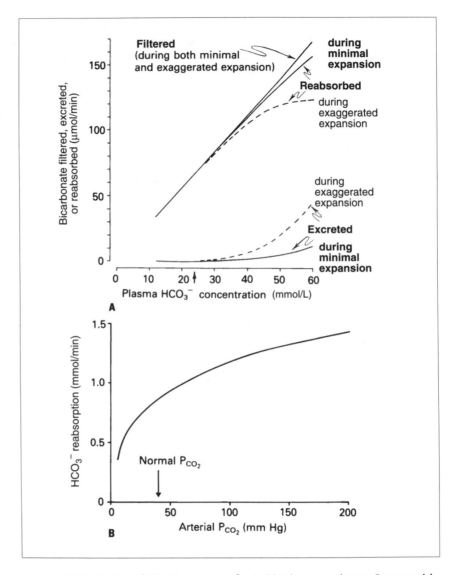

Figure 10-2. A. Renal titration curves for HCO_3^- in normal rats. Over a wide range of filtered loads, virtually all of the filtered HCO_3^- is reabsorbed unless the extracellular fluid volume is markedly expanded, in which case the reabsorptive rate is reduced despite a similar increase in the filtered load. The arrow indicates a normal arterial plasma HCO_3^- concentration (see Table A-1 in Appendix). Adapted from Purkerson, M. L., et al., *J. Clin. Invest.* 48:1754, 1969.

  B. Changes in the rate of HCO_3^- reabsorption in dogs during prolonged alterations of the arterial P_{CO_2}. P_{CO_2} was lowered through chronic hyperventilation or raised through protracted breathing of gas mixtures containing increased concentrations of CO_2. Adapted from Rector, F. C., Jr., et al., *J. Clin. Invest.* 39:1706, 1960.

2. Also shown in Figure 10-2A is the effect of the extracellular fluid volume. When that volume is expanded markedly—as by infusing either $NaHCO_3$ or NaCl—the reabsorption of filtered HCO_3^- is decreased, and the converse holds when the extracellular fluid volume is contracted. Although there appears to be a plateau for HCO_3^- reabsorption during exaggerated volume expansion, the true maximal reabsorptive rate for HCO_3^- (Tm; see Chap. 4, p. 66) is much higher. Again, the mechanisms by which extracellular fluid volume influences HCO_3^- reabsorption have not been fully clarified. Given the close linkage between Na^+ and HCO_3^- reabsorption in the proximal tubule (Fig. 7-2A), the effect may involve reduction in proximal Na^+ reabsorption, which is known to occur during volme expansion and for which some of the mechanisms are known (see Fig. 7-11).

3. The influence of a *prolonged* change in arterial P_{CO_2} is shown in Figure 10-2B. As P_{CO_2} is lowered (as by chronic hyperventilation), the reabsorption of filtered HCO_3^- is decreased, and as P_{CO_2} is raised (as by chronic alveolar hypoventilation), HCO_3^- reabsorption is increased. By and large, these effects are seen only in chronic, not acute, alterations of P_{CO_2}. At least two mechanisms appear to be involved in driving this response: (1) a change in the filtered load of HCO_3^- and hence in the delivery of HCO_3^- to the tubules (point 1 above), and (2) a possible direct influence of P_{CO_2} on H-ATPase and H-K-ATPase (Figs. 10-1, 10-7C, and 11-4D). The first mechanism probably explains why the effect shown in Figure 10-2B is limited to chronic disturbances, since the plasma HCO_3^- concentration (and hence the filtered load of HCO_3^-) changes only minimally during acute respiratory disturbances (see Chap. 9, under Acute and Chronic Respiratory Disturbances). Whatever the mechanisms, it is clear from Equation 9-8 that the response will tend to correct the blood pH during a chronic primary respiratory disturbance (see Chap. 9, under Compensatory Responses).

REPLENISHMENT OF DEPLETED HCO_3^- STORES

It was pointed out at the beginning of Chapter 9 that in persons whose diet is fairly high in protein there is a net daily production of nonvolatile (fixed) acids. These include sulfuric acid, resulting from protein catabolism; phosphoric acid, which is produced chiefly during the catabolism of phospholipids; and organic acids. These acids are buffered by the following types of reactions:

$$2H^+ + SO_4^{2-} + 2Na^+ + 2HCO_3^- \rightleftharpoons 2Na^+ + SO_4^{2-} + 2H_2O + 2CO_2 \nearrow \quad (10\text{-}1)$$

$$2H^+ + HPO_4^{2-} + 2Na^+ + 2HCO_3^- \rightleftharpoons 2Na^+ + HPO_4^{2-} + 2H_2O + 2CO_2 \nearrow \quad (10\text{-}2)$$

The CO_2 is eliminated via the lungs, as indicated by the diagonal arrows, and the two neutral salts, Na_2SO_4 and Na_2HPO_4, are filtered into Bowman's space. If these neutral salts were excreted in the urine, the body would soon become depleted of $NaHCO_3$, the main extracellular buffer that is utilized in neutralizing the fixed acids. The kidneys prevent such depletion of $NaHCO_3$ by two means: (1) the excretion of NH_4^+, and (2) the excretion of titratable acid (T.A.). In both operations HCO_3^-, newly formed within renal tubular cells, is absorbed into the peritubular blood along with Na^+ that was filtered.

Excretion of Titratable Acid (T.A.)

As urine is acidified—by the reabsorption of HCO_3^- and consequent decline of its concentration in tubular fluid (Eq. 9-8; note that the Henderson-Hasselbalch equation can be applied also to urine)—secreted H^+ ions combine with other filtered buffers in the tubular fluid. As part of the latter process, the neutral salt Na_2HPO_4 is converted to the acid salt NaH_2PO_4 (for a depiction of this process, see Fig. 10-3). The amount of strong base required to titrate the acid urine back to a pH of 7.40 (which is the approximate pH of the glomerular filtrate in health) is *equal to the amount of titratable acid that was excreted in the urine.* (Other filtered buffers, such as creatinine and the organic anions, citrate, acetate, and 3-hydroxybutyrate, are also titrated, but they normally contribute only a trivial amount to T.A. because of their low concentration and low pKs.)

The probable schema for the formation of urinary T.A. is shown in Figure 10-3. Note the similarities with Figure 10-1: The major reaction that generates the secreted H^+ is thought to be the dissociation of water, and the OH^- that is simultaneously liberated combines with intracellular CO_2, under the catalysis of carbonic anhydrase, to form the HCO_3^- that is added to peritubular fluid and blood. Within the tubular lumen the secreted H^+ combines with filtered 2 Na^+, HPO_4^{2-} (*monohydrogen phosphate*) to form Na^+, $H_2PO_4^-$ (*dihydrogen phosphate*), which is excreted as T.A. in the urine. The second filtered Na^+ that is liberated in this reaction is reabsorbed to combine with HCO_3^- that was newly formed within the cell. These reactions occur in the parts of the nephron that are listed at the top of Figure 10-3; in fact, they take place in the same cells as the schema depicted in Figure 10-1. But note that, whereas the net effect in Figure 10-1 is to recapture virtually all the filtered HCO_3^-, the net effect in Figure 10-3 is to *replenish the blood with*

■   **Excretion of**   ■
Titratable Acid (T.A.)

Definition
Amount of strong base required to titrate acid urine back to pH of plasma

Mechanism
Conversion of filtered disodium-monohydrogen-phosphate (Na_2HPO_4) to monosodium-dihydrogen-phosphate (NaH_2PO_4). For every H^+ excreted, one HCO_3^- is returned to the blood

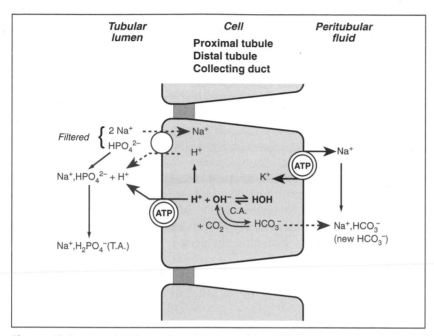

Figure 10-3. Mechanism whereby titratable acid (T.A.) is created, and newly formed HCO_3^- is added to the blood along with a reabsorbed Na^+. In the proximal tubule the CO_2 comes largely from the tubular lumen whereas in more distal parts of the nephron it may come mainly from cellular metabolism (see Fig. 10-1). C.A. = carbonic anhydrase; ATP = adenosine triphosphate.

one HCO_3^- for every HCO_3^- that was consumed in buffering fixed H^+ (Eq. 10-2).

Factors Affecting the Rate of T.A. Excretion

Three factors influence the rate at which T.A. is excreted: (1) the availability of urinary buffers, (2) the pK of those buffers, and (3) the extent to which tubular pH is lowered.

1. The effect of availability of urinary buffers is illustrated in Figure 10-4A, in which an increased supply of urinary buffer is reflected on the abscissa as increased excretion of phosphate. As more buffer is made available, more T.A. is excreted. The explanation involves a limiting concentration gradient for the transport of H^+ by renal cells, and it can be understood by referring to Figure 10-4B. This figure shows the titration curve for inorganic phosphate, as it was reviewed in connection with Figure 9-4; but

whereas in the latter we discussed phosphate in the context of plasma pH, in Figure 10-4B we consider the titration curve for phosphate in light of the pH of tubular fluid. Ordinarily, inorganic phosphate is the main urinary buffer. At a pH of 7.4, at which it is filtered into Bowman's space, phosphate exists mainly in the monohydrogen form, HPO_4^{2-}. As tubular fluid, and hence the urine, become more acid, the phosphate is converted to the dihydrogen form, $H_2PO_4^-$ (Fig. 10-4B), which is the main urinary T.A. The minimal urinary pH is approximately 4.4, probably because the active H^+-pumps in collecting duct cells (Figs. 10-3 and 11-4D) cannot transport H^+ against a concentration gradient exceeding $1:1,000$. When this minimal pH is attained (as it was in the experiment shown in Fig. 10-4A), virtually all the urinary phosphate is in the Na^+, $H_2PO_4^-$ form, and addition of even minute amounts of H^+ would then lead to a precipitous drop in pH (Fig. 10-4B). Hence, under these conditions more H^+ can be excreted as T.A. only if more phosphate is filtered, i.e., only if the availability of more phosphate buffer in the tubular fluid permits the acceptance of more H^+ without a further drop in pH. This requirement was met by raising the plasma phosphate concentration and is reflected in the steadily increasing phosphate excretion in Figure 10-4A.

This example illustrates the difference between *urinary acidification* and *H^+ excretion*. The ability to reduce the pH of urine, which is acidification, does not necessarily tell us much about the amount of H^+ being excreted. Note that the ordinate in Figure 10-4B shows the amount of H^+ excreted per quantum of HPO_4^{2-} presented for titration. Therefore, if, say, 10 times more HPO_4^{2-} were to traverse the tubular system (as was done in the experiment shown in Fig. 10-4A by increasing the filtered load of phosphate), the amount of H^+ excreted could rise tenfold without any change in urinary pH.

2. Figure 10-5A shows that, for any identical rate of urinary excretion of a buffer, more titratable acid can be excreted when phosphate (pK = 6.8) is the main urinary buffer than when creatinine (with the lower pK of 4.97) is the major buffer. The explanation is apparent in Figure 10-5B. When the tubular fluid (hence, urinary) pH decreases to 5.1 (as happened in the experiment shown in Fig. 10-5A), then considerably more H^+ can be buffered by each unit of phosphate than by an equivalent amount of creatinine.

3. The effect of urinary pH is shown in Figure 10-5C, which is the same as Figure 10-5B except that the tubular fluid (hence, urinary) pH was lowered to 4.4 instead of to 5.1. Under these circum-

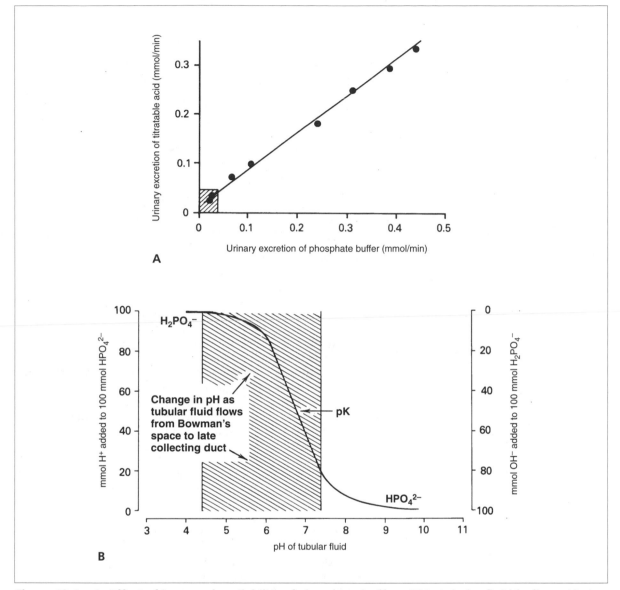

Figure 10-4. A. Effect of increased availability of phosphate buffer within tubular fluid (reflected in increased urinary excretion of phosphate buffer) on urinary excretion of titratable acid (T.A.). In this experiment the person was in mild metabolic acidosis (plasma pH = 7.37; plasma HCO_3^- concentration = 14 mmol/L; urinary pH = 4.5), which was induced by ingestion of NH_4Cl. This salt leads to acidosis through net addition of hydrochloric acid: $2NH_4Cl + CO_2 \leftrightarrow 2HCl + H_2O + CO(NH_2)_2$

The points enclosed in the shaded rectangle represent excretion of endogenous phosphate; all other points were obtained during intravenous infusion of inorganic phosphate at pH 7.40. Slightly modified from Schiess, W. A., Ayer, J. L., Lotspeich, W. D., and Pitts, R. F. *J. Clin. Invest.* 27:57, 1948.

B. Titration curve for HPO_4^{2-} by H^+ as the pH of tubular fluid is decreased from 7.4 in Bowman's space to 4.4 in terminal collecting duct (striped area). Note that, once a pH of 4.4 has been reached and the steep portion of the titration curve has been passed, the addition of the slightest bit of H^+ would lead to a precipitous drop in tubular fluid pH.

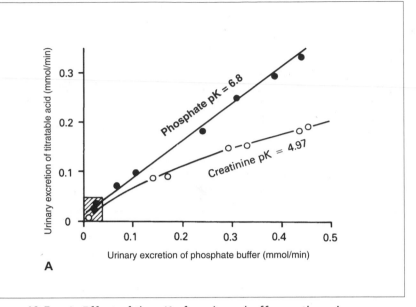

Figure 10-5. A. Effect of the pK of a urinary buffer on the urinary excretion of titratable acid (T.A.). The points for phosphate are those illustrated in Figure 10-4A; those for creatinine (open circles) are data obtained in a separate experiment on the same subject (plasma pH = 7.38; plasma HCO_3^- concentration = 13 mmol/L; urinary pH = 5.1) when creatinine was infused intravenously instead of phosphate. (It is of interest that the subject for this experiment, and for the one shown in Figure 10-4A, was Dr. Robert Pitts, whose work has contributed so much to our understanding of the renal regulation of acid-base balance.) Slightly modified from Schiess, W. A., Ayer, J. L., Lotspeich, W. D., and Pitts, R. F. *J. Clin. Invest.* 27:57, 1948.

B. Titration curves for inorganic phosphate and for creatinine, onto which the fall in tubular fluid pH that occurred in the experiment shown in (A) has been superimposed. Note that under these conditions, nearly twice as much H^+ could be buffered by phosphate as by creatinine. Urinary pH is usually 5.0 or higher (see Table 11-A, p. 284).

C. When the urinary pH drops to the minimal value of 4.4 (as occurs in very severe acidosis), virtually as much H^+ can be buffered by creatinine as by phosphate, despite the lower pK of creatinine.

stances, virtually as much H^+ can be excreted when creatinine is the buffer as when phosphate is the buffer.

Excretion of Ammonium

If the formation of T.A. were the only mechanism for excreting H^+, the amount of H^+ that could be eliminated in the urine would be severely limited by the amount of phosphate and, to a lesser extent, of other buffers that are filtered. This point is clear from Figure 10-4B: The complete titration curve of monosodium-dihydrogen-

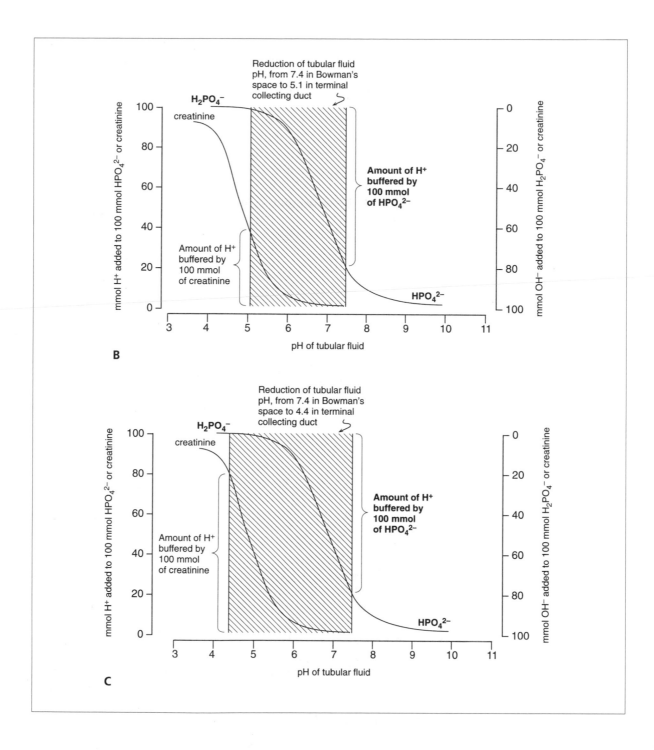

phosphate (NaH_2PO_4) to phosphoric acid (H_3PO_4) cannot be carried out within the range of urinary pH because the pK for that reaction is ~2.0; i.e., at the minimal urinary pH of 4.4 (see point 1 above), less than 0.4% of the total phosphate excreted would be phosphoric acid. Stated differently, as soon as the titration curve for phosphate would shift to the formation of H_3PO_4 from Na^+, $H_2PO_4^-$, urinary pH would fall below 4.4 (Fig. 10-4B) and no more H^+ could be secreted by the renal tubular cells (see point 1 above); yet it can be shown that much more H^+ than that which appears as T.A. can be excreted in the urine, even though the urinary pH does not fall below the minimum value of 4.4. It is therefore apparent that an additional mechanism exists for the excretion of H^+.

The observation that in acidosis there is a rise not only in urinary T.A. but also in urinary NH_4^+ raised the suspicion that NH_4^+ might constitute the additional mechanism. Note that NH_4^+ appears in the urine as neutral salts [e.g., NH_4Cl or $(NH_4)_2SO_4$; see Fig. 11-A, p. 285], which fact satisfies the requirement of excreting H^+ without a further decrease in urinary pH; in other words, with a pK of 9.2 for the NH_3/NH_4^+ system, ammonium salts cannot be titrated within the acid range of tubular fluid (Fig. 10-6).

The probable mechanism for the excretion of NH_4^+ is illustrated in Figure 10-7. Three steps are involved: (a) production and secretion of NH_4^+ in proximal tubules; (b) countercurrent multiplication of NH_4^+ in loops of Henle, resulting in the buildup of a corticopapillary gradient for NH_4^+/NH_3 within the medullary interstitium; and (c) nonionic diffusion of NH_3 into collecting ducts.

Proximal Production and Secretion of NH_4^+

This first step occurs predominantly in proximal tubular cells (Fig. 10-7A), where the deamination of glutamine yields two NH_4^+ ions and one α-ketoglutarate ion. Metabolism of the latter to glucose, or to CO_2 and water, yields two new HCO_3^- ions ('new', since in the reaction shown in Fig. 10-7A, no HCO_3^- was filtered). Thus, in this reaction as in the one for excreting T.A. (Fig. 10-3), *a new HCO_3^- is added to the blood for every H^+ that is excreted*—in this instance, as part of NH_4^+. (That is the important net reaction in Figure 10-7A; the Na^+ that accompanies the HCO_3^- can enter the peritubular fluid via Na-K-ATPase or via the HCO_3^-/Na^+ cotransporter.) The carrier that secretes the NH_4^+ may be the same protein that is responsible for Na^+/H^+ exchange (Fig. 7-1A and B). Under many or most circumstances, the NH_4^+ thus produced in the proximal tubule accounts for virtually all of the NH_4^+ that is excreted in the urine. The process is not as simple, however, as the

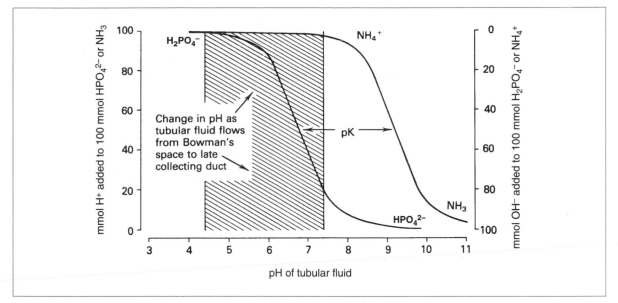

Figure 10-6. Titration of HPO_4^{2-} and NH_3 by H^+ as the pH of tubular fluid is decreased from 7.4 in Bowman's space to 4.4 in late collecting ducts. With a pK of 9.2, the NH_3/NH_4^+ system is a poor buffer in the acid pH range that ordinarily exists in tubular fluid (shaded area). Nevertheless, a great deal of H^+ can be excreted as NH_4^+ because the supply of NH_3 from tubular cells is potentially plentiful (Table 10-1).

secreted NH_4^+ merely traversing the remainder of the tubular system into the collecting ducts.

Corticopapillary Interstitial Gradient for NH_4^+/NH_3

In the loops of Henle (Fig. 10-7B), there is countercurrent multiplication of NH_4^+, which leads to a corticopapillary concentration gradient for NH_4^+/NH_3 within the medullary interstitium. In thick ascending limbs, NH_4^+ is reabsorbed mainly by secondary active transport, 'substituting' for K^+ on the Na:K:2Cl cotransporter that is located in the apical membrane (see Fig. 7-4); in thin ascending limbs, reabsorption of NH_4^+ may be passive. Secretion of NH_4^+ into descending limbs may occur by parallel secretion of H^+ and NH_3 rather than of NH_4^+ as shown. But the net effect is the same, and the important consequence is that the interstitial concentration of total ammonia (i.e., NH_4^+ plus NH_3) rises as the papilla is approached.

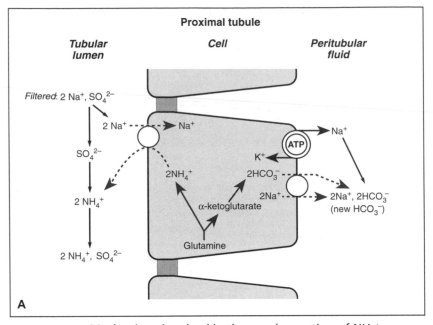

Figure 10-7. Mechanisms involved in the renal excretion of NH_4^+.

A. Events in Proximal Tubules. Production of NH_4^+ and of new HCO_3^- from the catabolism of glutamine, and subsequent secretion of NH_4^+ into the proximal tubular lumen. Details are given in the text. The filtration and excretion of the sulfate salt is shown here to indicate how the Na_2SO_4 (which is derived from buffering of H_2SO_4; Eq. 10-1) is handled; actually, of course, most of the NH_4^+ is excreted as the chloride salt, since Cl^- is the most abundant anion in urine (Fig. 11-A, p. 285).

B. Events in Loops of Henle and Medullary Interstitium. Some of the NH_4^+ that was secreted into proximal tubular fluid is reabsorbed from ascending limbs of Henle. Inasmuch as these limbs are impermeable to water (Table 7-1), the combination of reabsorbing NH_4^+ without water constitutes the 'single effect' for countercurrent multiplication of NH_4^+ and buildup of a corticopapillary interstitial gradient for NH_4^+ (analogous to the system for Na^+—Fig. 8-3). Since the NH_4^+/NH_3 buffer system always exists as two moieties in varying proportions depending on pH (see Fig. 10-6), the interstitial concentration of NH_3 also rises. Modified from Knepper, M. A. *Kidney Int.* 40 (Suppl. 33):S-95, 1991.

C. Events in Intercalated Cells of Collecting Ducts. NH_3 can diffuse across the epithelium, down its concentration gradient from interstitium into collecting duct lumen, where it combines with secreted H^+ to form NH_4^+. Inasmuch as the ionized species, NH_4^+, is relatively lipid-insoluble, NH_4^+ cannot readily diffuse back into the cell; hence, the terms *diffusion trapping* and *nonionic diffusion*. Note that the instantaneous conversion of NH_3 to NH_4^+ keeps the concentration of NH_3 within the luminal fluid very low. Thus, there is a constant sink for the diffusion of NH_3 from medullary interstitium into collecting duct lumen.

225

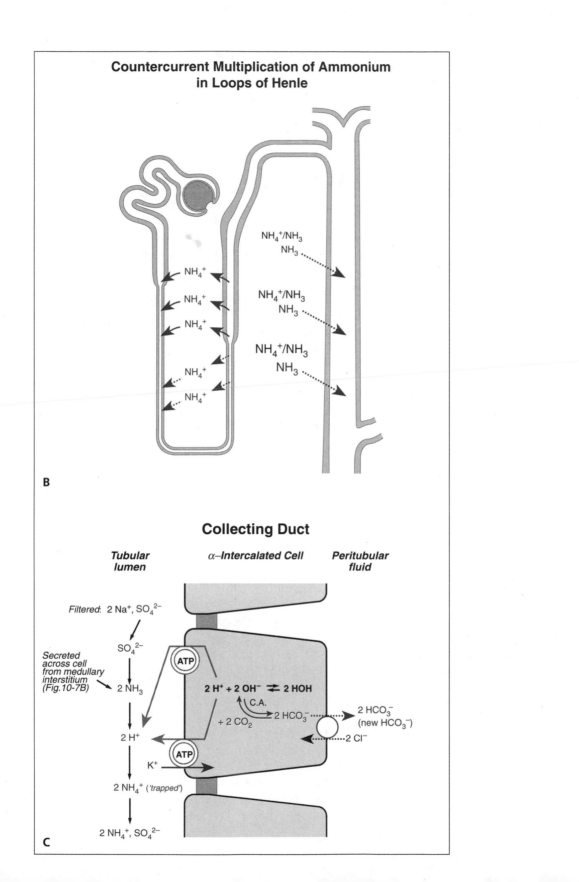

Countercurrent Multiplication of Ammonium in Loops of Henle

B

Collecting Duct

Tubular lumen — *α–Intercalated Cell* — *Peritubular fluid*

C

Secretion of NH₃ into Collecting Ducts

This process is shown in Figure 10-7C. We pointed out in Chapter 7 (under Late Distal Tubule and Collecting Duct , p. 130) that these tubular segments are comprised of at least two major types of cell, one of which, the *α-intercalated cell,* secretes H⁺ but does not reabsorb Na⁺. In this cell, the H⁺ that is derived from the dissociation of water is secreted into the tubular lumen by two active transporters, *H⁺-ATPase* and *H⁺-K⁺-ATPase.* The secreted H⁺ combines with NH₃ to form NH₄⁺, which is then excreted in the form of neutral salts, such as NH₄Cl or (NH₄)₂SO₄. The NH₃ can diffuse passively, from the interstitium where it had been built up by countercurrent multiplication (Fig. 10-7B), across the cell, and into the tubular lumen.

The HCO₃⁻ that was formed during the dissociation of water crosses the basolateral membrane into the peritubular fluid through facilitated diffusion, by way of a HCO₃⁻/Cl⁻ exchanger (Fig. 10-7C). Thus, as was the case with the excretion of T.A. (Fig. 10-3) and with the NH₄⁺ mechanism in proximal tubules (Fig. 10-7A), the net reaction for NH₄⁺ in collecting ducts is the *replenishment of the body stores by one HCO₃⁻ for each H⁺ that is excreted*—i.e., precisely what is needed to restore H⁺ balance after the perturbation of this balance by the addition of fixed H⁺ (Eqs. 10-1 and 10-2). The filtered Na⁺ is reabsorbed by a principal cell, as shown in Figure 7-6.

Nonionic diffusion

This term is used to describe the fact that the lipid-soluble, nonionized moiety of a buffer pair can readily diffuse across a cell membrane, while the lipid-insoluble (or poorly soluble) ionized member cannot. Ammonia (NH₃), because it is a permeable gas, can diffuse easily down its concentration gradient from the medullary interstitium into the tubular lumen. Virtually all of the diffusing NH₃ is immediately converted to NH₄⁺ because the tubular fluid is acid (Figs. 10-6 and 10-7C); thus, a constant 'sink' for the continued diffusion of NH₃ is maintained. This positive feedback, so to speak, is the more effective the lower the urinary pH (Fig. 10-8A) because once NH₄⁺ has been formed it is 'trapped' in the tubular lumen (since it is the ionized moiety), and it cannot diffuse back across the epithelium—i.e., it has to be excreted.

Because the pK of the NH₃/NH₄⁺ buffer system is 9.2 (Table A-3 in the Appendix), more than 98% is in the NH₄⁺ form *as long as the urinary pH is in the range 4.4 to 7.4* (Fig. 10-6); therefore, a reduction in urinary pH will have only a slight effect on the urinary excretion of NH₄⁺. From this quantitative consideration, it appears that the increase in ammonium excretion with decreased urinary

---

■ **Excretion of NH₄⁺** ■

Formation of NH₄⁺ in Proximal Tubular Cells
  secretion of NH₄⁺ into tubular lumen

Countercurrent Multiplication of NH₄⁺
  medullary interstitial gradient for NH₄⁺/NH₃

Diffusion of NH₃ into Collecting Ducts
  diffusion trapping of NH₄⁺

pH (Fig. 10-8A) must be due to increased diffusion of NH_3 into the collecting duct lumen in the presence of an acid urine. The reasons for this increased diffusion remain controversial.

But even though nonionic diffusion may not be quantitatively important to the excretion of NH_4^+, it is a common biological phenomenon that has clinical applications for promoting the urinary excretion of other weak acids and weak bases, *provided that their pK falls within the range of urinary pH.* An example of such application in the treatment of phenobarbital poisoning is given in Problem 10-1.

Control of Renal NH_4^+ Production and Excretion

There are at least two factors that influence the amount of NH_4^+ that is produced by the kidney and excreted in the urine: (1) the pH of the urine, and (2) the chronicity and status of systemic acid-base balance. Both are illustrated in Figure 10-8.

1. During both normal H^+ balance and states of metabolic acidosis, there is an inverse relationship between the urinary pH and the amount of total ammonia (i.e., NH_3 plus NH_4^+) that is excreted in the urine (Fig. 10-8A). As noted above, the mechanisms for this effect remain controversial.

2. The influence of systemic acid-base balance—as it pertains to chronic acidosis—is also illustrated in Figure 10-8A, which shows that, *at any given urinary pH,* the rate of total ammonia excretion is higher in acidosis (especially when acidosis is present for hours or days) than during normal H^+ balance. This effect cannot be accounted for by nonionic diffusion, since the difference can be detected at the same urinary pH. Rather, prolonged systemic acidosis causes a marked increase in the proximal production of NH_4^+ (Fig. 10-8B), while chronic alkalosis causes a decrease. In fact, production of NH_4^+ within proximal tubular cells (Fig. 10-8B) probably is the main regulator that determines the urinary excretion of NH_4^+, even though the rate of tubular transport of NH_4^+ (or of NH_3 plus H^+) is also under regulatory control in some conditions.

RELATIVE EXCRETION RATES OF TITRATABLE ACID AND AMMONIUM

Table 10-1 shows rates of H^+ excretion as NH_4^+ and as T.A., both in the normal situation and in two disease states that are characterized by disturbances of H^+ balance. It was pointed out at the beginning of Chapter 9, p. 184 that in a normal person whose diet is relatively high in protein there is a net daily production of 40 to 60

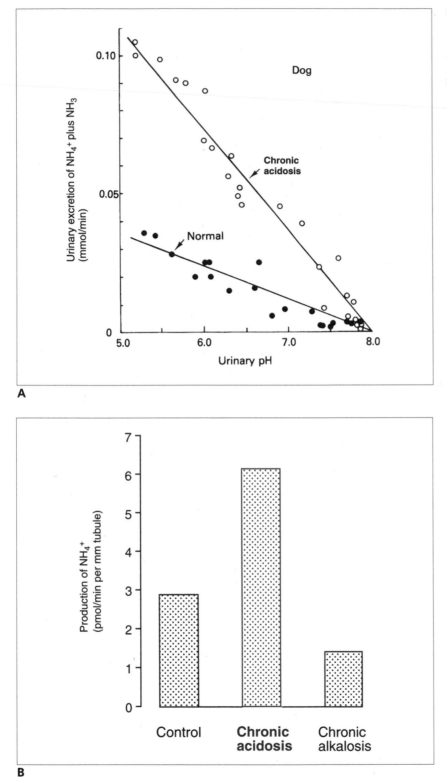

Figure 10-8. Regulators of urinary NH_4^+ excretion.

A. Influence of urinary pH and of chronic systemic acidosis on the urinary excretion of total ammonia (NH_4^+ plus NH_3). All the data were obtained from one dog. At the beginning of each experiment the urinary pH was approximately 5.2, both in normal H^+ balance and after 48 hours of metabolic acidosis. The urinary pH was then gradually increased in each instance by infusing $NaHCO_3$ intravenously. From Pitts, R. F. *Fed. Proc.* 7:418, 1948.

B. In vitro production of NH_4^+ by segments of early proximal convoluted tubules of rats. For 3 to 8 days prior to removal of the kidneys, the animals were treated with NH_4Cl to produce acidosis (for reaction, see legend to Fig. 10-4), and with $NaHCO_3$ to produce alkalosis. Slightly modified from Knepper, M. A., Packer, R., and Good, D. W. *Physiol. Rev.* 69:179, 1989.

Table 10-1. Relative excretion rates of ammonium and titratable acid (T.A.) in healthy persons and in two disease states that are accompanied by primary metabolic acidosis

Condition	mmol of urinary H^+ per day
Health	
H^+ excreted as NH_4^+	30 to 50
H^+ excreted as T.A.	10 to 30
Diabetic acidosis	
H^+ excreted as NH_4^+	300 to 500
H^+ excreted as T.A.	75 to 250
Chronic renal disease	
H^+ excreted as NH_4^+	0.5 to 15
H^+ excreted as T.A.	2 to 20

Slightly modified from Pitts, R. F. *Science* 102:49;81, 1945. Published with permission.

mmol of nonvolatile acids. In the steady (balanced) state, this amount of acid is excreted as NH_4^+ and as T.A.; more H^+ is normally excreted as NH_4^+ than as T.A.

During uncontrolled diabetes mellitus there is an overproduction of nonvolatile acids, mainly 3-OH-butyric acid. This change leads to primary metabolic acidosis, which, as discussed above, increases the urinary excretion of NH_4^+ (Fig. 10-8). The pK of 3-OH butyrate is slightly less than that of creatinine (Table A-3 in the Appendix); hence 3-OH butyrate is ordinarily a less effective urinary buffer than are phosphate and creatinine (Fig. 10-5A and B). During diabetic acidosis, however, the endogenous production and, hence, the filtered load of 3-OH butyrate are so great that in this condition 3-OH butyrate becomes the main urinary buffer, and T.A. appears primarily as 3-OH butyric acid. Nevertheless, the data in Table 10-1 during diabetic acidosis show that the potential supply of NH_4^+ as a means of excreting H^+ is enormous, and considerably greater than that of buffers that form titratable acids.

During chronic renal disease, which is accompanied by a marked decrease in the amount of functioning renal tissue, there may be a reduction in both forms of fixed-acid excretion, depending largely on the protein content of the patient's diet. The reduction, however, is relatively much greater for NH_4^+ than for T.A. This is so because the rate of T.A. excretion depends largely on the urinary

■ **Daily Excretion** ■
of Fixed H^+

In Health: ~*50 mmols*
~⅔ as NH_4^+
~⅓ as titratable acid (T.A.)

In Diabetic Ketoacidosis
~10-fold increase in NH_4^+
~7-fold increase in T.A.

In End-Stage Renal Disease (ESRD)
severe reduction in NH_4^+
lesser reduction in T.A.

excretion of buffer (Fig. 10-4A), which may remain normal until renal disease is far advanced; formation of NH_4^+, however, depends on the renal cellular production of this ion by proximal tubular cells, which is greatly curtailed as the amount of functioning renal tissue is reduced.

SUMMARY

The kidneys play a major role in the regulation of H^+ balance by maintaining the normal body store (and hence concentration) of HCO_3^-, and by excreting the H^+ that is derived from the daily production of nonvolatile (fixed) acids. Preservation of HCO_3^- stores is accomplished through: (1) the reabsorption of virtually all the HCO_3^- that is filtered (Fig. 10-1), and (2) the formation of new HCO_3^- within renal cells and addition of this HCO_3^- to the blood (Figs. 10-3 and 10-7A, C). The second process is accompanied by net excretion of H^+, which also occurs via two mechanisms: (1) the excretion of titratable acid (T.A.; Fig. 10-3), which is defined as the amount of strong base that must be added to acid urine in order to return the pH of that urine to the pH of blood, and (2) the excretion of NH_4^+ salts (Fig. 10-7).

In this chapter each of these processes was described separately, both for the sake of clarity and to account quantitatively for the various aspects of H^+ balance. It must be realized, however, that the major mechanisms take place simultaneously, often in the same cells, that the secreted H^+ comes from a common cellular pool, and that the kidney does not distinguish H^+ that is destined to combine with filtered HCO_3^- from that which will combine with HPO_4^{2-} or NH_3, or is contained in NH_4^+; nor will it distinguish a reabsorbed HCO_3^- that was generated within the cell from one that was initially filtered, or a reabsorbed Na^+ that came from $NaHCO_3$ from one that came from the chloride, phosphate, sulfate, or some other filtered salt.

The rate at which filtered HCO_3^- is reabsorbed is affected mainly by the filtered load of HCO_3^-, by expansion or contraction of the extracellular fluid volume, and by the arterial P_{CO_2}. The rate of T.A. excretion is influenced principally by the availability of buffers within the tubular fluid, the pK of those buffers, and the degree of tubular fluid acidification. The urinary excretion of NH_4^+ is governed most importantly by the rate at which proximal tubular cells synthesize NH_4^+, this rate being increased during systemic acidosis and decreased during systemic alkalosis.

Normally, about two-thirds of the daily endogenous load of nonvolatile acid is excreted as NH_4^+, and the remainder as T.A. The potential supply of NH_4^+ is very large, rising as much as tenfold in states such as diabetic acidosis. Since NH_4^+ is generated within the kidneys, however, this adaptive mechanism may be greatly curtailed in chronic renal disease, when the total amount of functioning renal tissue is reduced.

PROBLEM 10-1

Utilization of the Principle of Nonionic Diffusion in the Treatment of Phenobarbital Poisoning. A 23-year-old man is admitted to the emergency ward in coma and with a history of having ingested a large amount of phenobarbital. His respirations are shallow, and his systemic blood pressure is somewhat low. The patient is several times incontinent of urine, which probably means that urine production is adequate despite the mild hypotension.

After instituting measures to reestablish normal respiration and to support the systemic circulation, the attending physician begins efforts to hasten excretion of the phenobarbital. Although most physicians probably would accomplish this purpose by dialyzing the patient while supporting the patient's ventilation and blood pressure, hastening the urinary excretion of phenobarbital by applying the principle of nonionic diffusion constitutes an alternate or supplementary mode of therapy. While much of the phenobarbital is metabolized in the liver, as much as 30% of the total dose may be excreted unchanged by the kidneys. The compound, having a molecular weight of 232 Daltons, enters the tubular system mainly through filtration, and it is then passively reabsorbed. One can inhibit the second process, reabsorption, by instituting a diuresis and by alkalinizing the urine.

The attending physician therefore begins to infuse mannitol and $NaHCO_3$ intravenously. Mannitol, with a molecular weight of 182 Daltons, is freely filtered but is reabsorbed very poorly or not at all. Hence, by contributing to the osmolality of tubular fluid, mannitol inhibits the passive reabsorption of water and initiates an osmotic diuresis. The consequent dilution of phenobarbital in the tubular fluid decreases its passive reabsorption. The infusion of $NaHCO_3$ will alkalinize the urine, shift the titration of the weak acid phenobarbital (pK of 7.2) toward the ionized form (Fig. 10-6), and thereby diminish the passive reabsorption of the phenobarbital through the process of nonionic diffusion.

It is determined that the concentration of total phenobarbital (i.e., the nonionized plus the ionized form) in this patient is 10 mg per 100 mL of plasma. About 40% of phenobarbital is bound to plasma proteins. On admission, the plasma pH is 7.3 (primary respiratory acidosis due to depression of the respiratory center) and urinary pH is 5.2. After infusion of $NaHCO_3$ and correction of the alveolar hypoventilation through assisted ventilation, the plasma pH is 7.7 and the urinary pH is 8.2. The pK of the phenobarbital system is 7.2. Given these facts, complete the table below.

	Total unbound phenobarbital in plasma (mg/dL)	Ratio of unbound phenobarbital: $\dfrac{[Ionized]}{[Nonionized]}$	Plasma concentration of unbound phenobarbital	
			Ionized	Nonionized (mg/dL)
Plasma, pH 7.3				
Plasma, pH 7.7				
Urine, pH 5.2	—		—	—
Urine, pH 8.2	—		—	—

PROBLEM 10-2

Much H^+ is excreted as NH_4^+ (Table 10-1). Yet, NH_4^+ salts are not titratable acids (T.A.). Utilizing Figure 10-6, explain why NH_4Cl, for example, cannot be titrated within the range of normally acid tubular (i.e., urinary) pH.

PROBLEM 10-3

Theoretically, to what extent could urine be acidified solely by re-absorbing filtered HCO_3^-, without excretion of H^+? *Hint:* Apply the Henderson-Hasselbalch equation (Eq. 9-8, p. 187), using a pK′ of 6.1 and a P_{CO_2} for urine of 40 mm Hg.

SUGGESTED READINGS

Al-Awqati, Q., and Beauwens, R. Cellular mechanisms of H^+ and HCO_3^- transport in tight urinary epithelia. In E. E. Windhager (Ed.), *Handbook*

of Physiology, section 8: *Renal Physiology,* vol. II. New York: Oxford University Press, 1992. Chap. 8.
Chapter 23 of this Handbook, by R. L. Tannen, is entitled Renal Ammonia Production and Excretion.

Alpern, R. J., Stone, D. K., and Rector, F. C., Jr. Renal Acidification Mechanisms. In B. M. Brenner and F. C. Rector, Jr. (Eds.), *The Kidney* (4th ed.). Philadelphia: Saunders, 1991. Chap. 9.

Gennari, F. J., and Maddox, D. A. Renal Regulation of Acid-Base Homeostasis. In D. W. Seldin and G. Giebisch (Eds.), *The Kidney: Physiology and Pathophysiology* (2nd ed.). New York: Raven, 1992. Chap. 78.
Volume 2 of this work contains many other pertinent chapters. Chapters 73–77 deal with Renal Regulation of Acid-Base Balance: Normal, *and Chapters 79–81 cover* Renal Regulation of Acid-Base Balance: Deranged.

Ishikawa, H., Fujimoto, M., and Imai, M. (Guest Eds.). Proton, Bicarbonate and Chloride Transport in the Kidney. *Kidney Int.* 40 (Suppl. 33): S1–S135, 1991.

Kleinman, J. G., and Lemann, J., Jr. Acid Production. In R. G. Narins (Ed.), *Maxwell & Kleeman's Clinical Disorders of Fluid and Electrolyte Metabolism* (5th ed.). New York: McGraw-Hill, 1994. Chap. 9.

Knepper, M. A., Packer, R., and Good, D. W. Ammonium transport in the kidney. *Physiol. Rev.* 69:179, 1989.

Steinmetz, P. R., Levine, D. Z., and Giebisch, G. H. Renal Acid-Base Physiology. In R. L. Tannen, L. G. Fine, C. W. Gottschalk, and G. E. Schreiner (Eds.), *A Quarter Century of Nephrology.* Washington, D.C.: D. F. Gemmill, 1992. Chap. 13.

K+ Balance: Renal Handling of K+

11

Potassium is involved in some very basic processes, such as cell growth and division, the maintenance of cellular volume, the operation of enzymes, excitability and contractility of muscles including those of the heart, and H^+ balance. For this reason, and because the kidney is the major organ that excretes K^+, potassium balance frequently comes into play in the analysis of clinical problems: H^+ balance, nephrogenic defects of urinary concentration, diuretic therapy, acute renal failure, and hypertension, among others.

DISTRIBUTION OF K⁺ IN THE BODY

The status of K^+ in the body and the dynamics of K^+ balance are shown in Figure 11-1. Note the following points: (1) The concentration of K^+ is high within cells (~150 mmol/L) and low in extracellular fluid (~4.5 mmol/L), a fact that was pointed out in Chapter 2 (Fig. 2-2). This difference is maintained by Na-K-ATPase, which actively moves K^+ into cells and Na^+ out of them (e.g., Fig. 7-1). (2) Of the approximately 3,500 mmol of K^+ within the body (Table A-3), only about 2% resides in the extracellular fluid. Maintenance of this low extracellular content, and hence of low extracellular

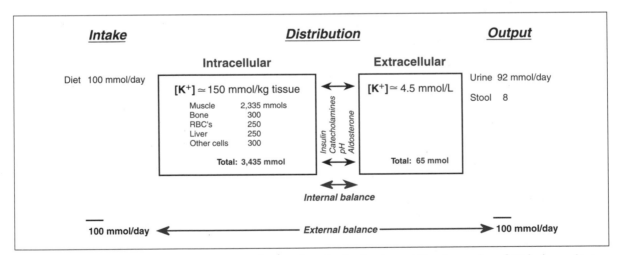

Figure 11-1. Status of potassium in the body and the dynamics of K^+ balance in a healthy adult person. Detailed description in the text. *External balance* refers to the entire body; *internal balance* to shifts between the intracellular and extracellular compartments. [K^+] = concentration of potassium; RBC = red blood cell.

concentration, is crucial; the range of normal is just 3.5 to 5.5 mmol/L (Table A-1), and even just slight deviations from these limits can have serious, even fatal, consequences, such as paralysis and cardiac arrhythmias. (3) From moment to moment, the low extracellular concentration is maintained mainly by *internal balance*, which refers to shifts of substances, in this case K⁺, between the extracellular and intracellular compartments; the major factors that influence internal balance for K⁺ are shown in Figure 11-1, and they are discussed further below. (4) Dietary intake of K⁺ in a healthy adult varies from approximately 50 to 150 mmol per day; all but 5% to 10% of this daily intake is excreted by the kidneys, and the relationship between intake and output is called *external balance*.

INTERNAL BALANCE

Whenever K⁺ is added to the body, whether it be in the diet or by some parenteral route such as an intravenous infusion, there exists the potential for a deleterious rise in the plasma K⁺ concentration (even a rise to 6.5 mmol/L is considered dangerous). Ordinarily, the addition is 'buffered' by a shift of K⁺ into cells. For example, the K⁺ that is contained in a meal is absorbed from the gastrointestinal tract into the interstitial space and thence into the blood. As soon as a slight rise occurs in the plasma K⁺ concentration, there begins a shift of K⁺ into cells so that within 15 to 30 minutes after ingestion, more than 70% of the added K⁺ has been transferred into the intracellular compartments listed in Figure 11-1. Among the regulators of internal balance listed in that figure, insulin probably is the most important. The mechanism by which it causes entry of K⁺ into cells is not clear, but it may involve stimulation of Na-K-ATPase. Catecholamines acting through β_2-receptors, as well as aldosterone, also are stimulated when plasma K⁺ concentration rises, and each can promote the movement of K⁺ into cells; nevertheless, their role in moment-to-moment regulation of internal balance for K⁺ is not yet clear. Acid-base balance also can influence the internal balance of K⁺ under certain circumstances, as discussed further below. The effectiveness and rapidity of three of these factors in influencing internal K⁺ balance is reflected in the standard treatment for dangerous elevation of the plasma K⁺ concentration (*hyperkalemia*): insulin (given with glucose to prevent hypoglycemia), albuterol (a β-agonist), and $NaHCO_3$ are given, and they all shift K⁺ into cells within 5 to 15 minutes after being administered.

Decreases in the plasma concentration of K⁺, called *hypokalemia,* also are buffered mainly by internal balance, through a shift of K⁺ from the large intracellular pool into the extracellular compartment.

Acid-Base Balance. Whether or not deviations of extracellular pH influence internal K⁺ balance depends on how the deviations are brought about, as is illustrated in Figure 11-2. Whenever a change in extracellular H⁺ concentration is caused by a compound that includes an anion that does not readily penetrate cell membranes—e.g., Cl^- in the case of HCl causing a metabolic acidosis, or HCO_3^- in the case of $NaHCO_3$ causing a metabolic alkalosis (Fig. 11-2, left)—the shift of H⁺ into or out of cells, respectively, is linked to movement of K⁺ in the opposite direction. On the other hand, if the compound that causes metabolic acidosis is an organic acid, where the associated anion enters cells readily—e.g., lactic acid in the case of lactic acidosis (Fig. 11-2, upper right), or ketone

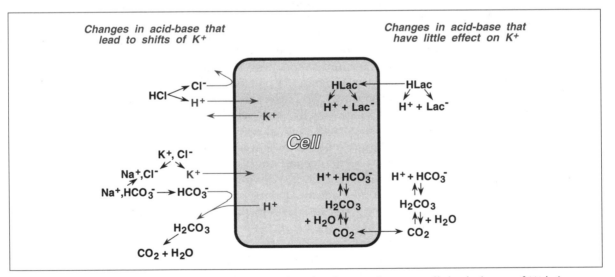

Figure 11-2.   Mechanisms whereby changes in extracellular balance of H⁺ bring about shifts of K⁺ between the intra- and extracellular fluid compartments. Respiratory acid-base disturbances, as well as metabolic acidoses that are caused by organic acids (as opposed to mineral acids), do not cause major changes of K⁺. The explanation for this fact is given in the text. Note that in this instance, *Cell* refers to virtually all cells in the body, not just to the epithelial cells of the kidney.

acids in the case of uncontrolled diabetes mellitus—then there is little or no shift of K⁺ out of cells. Similarly, in a respiratory acidosis or alkalosis, where CO_2 diffuses readily across cell membranes (Fig. 11-2, lower right), little shift of K⁺ occurs because H⁺ as such is not transported in or out of cells in association with K⁺ moving in the opposite direction.

In general, then, metabolic acidoses that are caused by mineral (not organic) acids, as well as metabolic alkaloses, do lead to internal shifts of K⁺, whereas respiratory acid-base disturbances cause lesser shifts.

Other Factors. Many perturbations, mostly pathological, raise the plasma concentration of K⁺ by affecting internal balance. For example, a breaking up of cells (called *hemolysis* when erythrocytes disintegrate, or *rhabdomyolysis* when skeletal muscles break down) can cause a shift of large amounts of K⁺ from the intracellular into the extracellular compartment. Such shifts are seen commonly during chemotherapy for cancer, when malignant cells are destroyed. During moderate to severe dehydration, when the rise in plasma osmolality causes water to shift out of cells, the consequent increase in intracellular K⁺ concentration will lead to a flow of K⁺ out of cells. Muscular exercise can cause hyperkalemia, usually mild, because K⁺ is released from skeletal muscle cells, at least in part due to α-adrenergic stimulation. By and large, the hyperkalemia arising from internal shifts is fleeting unless there are concomitant disorders of external balance or of the endocrine systems that regulate internal balance from moment to moment (Fig. 11-1). Similarly, decreases in the plasma K⁺ concentration arising from internal fluctuations are rare unless there are concurrent disorders of external balance.

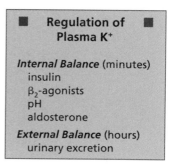

■ **Regulation of** ■
Plasma K⁺

Internal Balance (minutes)
  insulin
  β₂-agonists
  pH
  aldosterone
External Balance (hours)
  urinary excretion

EXTERNAL BALANCE

While internal balance largely protects against major fluctuations in plasma K⁺ concentration (marginal box above), external balance regulates the total amount of K⁺ in the body, which, in an adult human, is equal to approximately 3,500 mmol (Appendix Table A-3 and Fig. 11-1). In a healthy person, external balance is maintained almost entirely by the kidney (Fig. 11-1). Up to 10% of the daily intake of K⁺ is excreted in the stool, and this moiety, unlike urinary excretion, is not under regulatory control. Large amounts of K⁺ can be lost by extrarenal routes—e.g., in gastrointestinal disturbances such as severe diarrhea, with the use of diuretics, and with some endocrine disorders—but not ordinarily. Thus, maintenance of external balance for K^+ depends on the renal handling of this ion, and we shall now consider that topic.

NET TRANSPORT OF K⁺ IN VARIOUS PARTS OF THE NEPHRON

The renal handling of K^+ varies with the dietary intake of the ion: The percentage of the filtered load of K^+ (GFR $\times$ P_K) that is ultimately excreted in the urine (ureteral urine, Fig. 11-3) can range from approximately 1% during a low dietary intake (reflecting avid reabsorption) to as much as 200% during a high intake (reflecting strong secretion). How this wide range of urinary excretion is brought about is shown in Figure 11-3, which summarizes micropuncture data obtained in rats. In sum, virtually all filtered K^+ is first reabsorbed in the proximal tubules and loops of Henle, and then K^+ is secreted selectively in the distal tubules, cortical collecting ducts, and first part of the outer medullary collecting ducts.

Normal K⁺ Intake

Normally (Fig. 11-3A), only 10 to 20% of the filtered K^+ is excreted in the urine. It is clear from the graph, however, that net reabsorption does not occur in all parts of the nephron. Approximately 60% of the filtered load is reabsorbed in proximal tubules (reflected in the steady downward slope to about 40%), and then another 20 to 30% of the filtered load is reabsorbed in the loops of Henle (inferred from the gap between late proximal tubule and early distal tubule), mainly the thick ascending limbs. Consequently, only approximately 10% of the filtered load flows at the beginning of distal tubules. Then, K^+ is secreted in the distal tubules (reflected in the upward slope) and collecting ducts (not shown in Fig. 11-3). Experiments with isolated, perfused tubules (Fig. 7-3) have identified the cortical collecting ducts and early parts of outer medullary collecting ducts (in addition to distal tubules) as the sites of secretion. The amount secreted is attuned precisely to the intake of K^+, so that external balance is maintained.

Low K⁺ Intake

As is shown in Figure 11-3B, net movement of K^+ in distal tubules is not always in a secretory direction. When the intake of K^+ is low, avid conservation of K^+ occurs, so that only 1% to at most 10% of the filtered load is excreted in the urine. Under these circumstances, secretion of K^+ in the distal tubules and collecting ducts is

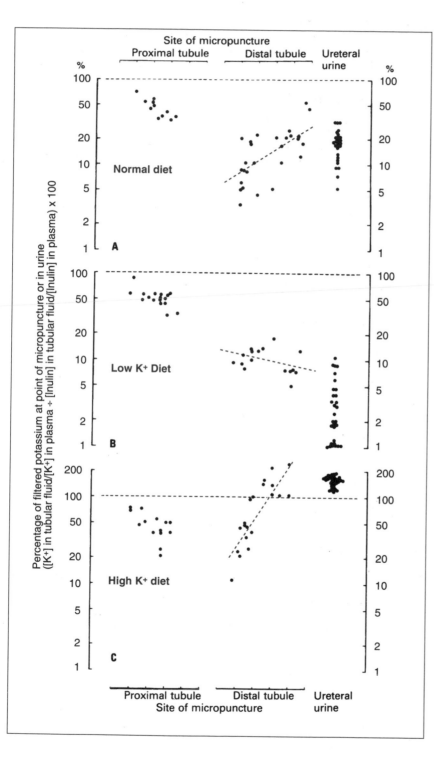

Figure 11-3. Net transport of K+ in various parts of the nephron, as revealed by micropuncture studies in rats on different diets. A negative slope of the points reflects reabsorption; a positive slope, secretion. When the points for ureteral urine lie below the interrupted horizontal lines at 100%, there has been net reabsorption of K+ by the entire kidney; when the urine points lie above this line, net secretion has occurred. The site of micropuncture was determined at the end of each experiment by microdissection of the nephron. Enclosure in brackets denotes concentration. The rationale for using the concentration ratios given on the ordinate, in order to calculate the percentage of the filtered K+ that is found at the various sites, is explained in footnote b to Problem 4-1 (p. 81). Redrawn from Malnic, G., Klose, R. M., and Giebisch, G. *Am. J. Physiol.* 206:674, 1964.

abolished or even converted to moderate reabsorption. Note that net movement in the other parts of the nephron has changed very little, except for more marked reabsorption by the collecting ducts.

High K⁺ Intake

When the intake of K^+ is very high, maintenance of external balance requires that there be net secretion by the entire kidney, so that more than 100% of the filtered load is excreted (Fig. 11-3C). Even under these conditions, there was net reabsorption in the proximal tubules and loops of Henle to nearly the same extent as in the conditions shown in Figure 11-3A and B. This finding emphasizes again that precise tuning to the demands of external balance is achieved mainly in the distal tubules and cortical and outer medullary collecting ducts, which are capable of marked secretion as well as mild reabsorption of K^+.

In summary (see marginal box), urinary excretion of K^+ is governed by the need for external balance. It is brought about by several sequential steps that vary, depending on that need: net reabsorption in the proximal tubules and ascending limbs of Henle; net secretion or net reabsorption in distal tubules, cortical collecting ducts, and first part of outer medullary collecting ducts; and net reabsorption in outer and inner medullary collecting ducts.

MECHANISMS OF K⁺ TRANSPORT

The means by which K^+ is transported in the various segments of the nephron, in both reabsorptive and secretory directions, are illustrated in Figure 11-4. Except when otherwise noted, the cells involved are the same as those that were described in Chapter 7 as transporting Na^+. Therefore, the different parts of Figure 11-4 are adaptations of the corresponding figures in Chapter 7, this time with emphasis on K^+.

Proximal Tubule

Figure 11-4A depicts the known pathways for K^+ transport in the proximal tubule. Micropuncture studies have shown that the K^+ concentration within tubular fluid varies with the parts of this tubular segment, being sometimes slightly above or slightly below that of plasma. When coupled with the fact that in the early proximal tubule the lumen is negative with respect to peritubular fluid (Fig. 7-1A), one might be led to the conclusion that, in this part at least, the reabsorption of K^+ must include an active step

---

■   **Renal Handling**   ■
of K⁺

First
reabsorption of all but 10–20% of filtered K⁺ in proximal tubules and loops of Henle. Then—

Normal K⁺ Intake
secretion in late distal tubules and cortical and outer medullary collecting ducts
reabsorption in outer and inner medullary collecting ducts
net reabsorption by entire kidney

Low K⁺ Intake
reabsorption by rest of nephron
net reabsorption by entire kidney

High K⁺ Intake
secretion in late distal tubules and cortical and outer medullary collecting ducts
net secretion by entire kidney

(i.e., against an electrochemical gradient). Yet, no active transport mechanisms have been identified which could account for this reabsorptive process. Rather, proximal reabsorption of K⁺ can be explained entirely on the basis of passive transport.

The passive transport occurs mainly by the paracellular route (Fig. 11-4A), i.e., by *solvent drag,* where K⁺ is entrained in the water that is reabsorbed via the lateral intercellular spaces (see Chap. 4, under Modes of Transport, p. 65, and Fig. 7-2A, B). The tight junctions between proximal tubular cells are relatively permeable to K⁺. It is thought that, in the early proximal tubule where the tubular lumen is negative, reabsorption of water by the transcellular route raises the K⁺ concentration within tubular fluid sufficiently to overcome the 'unfavorable' electrical gradient; in the late proximal tubule, the lumen-positive transepithelial voltage (Fig. 7-1B) contributes to a favorable electrochemical potential gradient that permits paracellular reabsorption. In addition, there may be some transcellular passive reabsorption of K⁺, which is aided by K⁺-channels in both the apical and basolateral membranes, as well as by a K⁺/Cl⁻ cotransporter in the latter. (Although the channel in the apical membrane can carry K⁺ in either direction, normally entry into the cell along a favorable electrochemical gradient prevails.)

Thick Ascending Limb of Henle

Net reabsorption of K⁺ in thick ascending limbs of Henle is also thought to be mainly (perhaps even solely) by the paracellular route (Fig. 11-4B). Crucial to making that possible are at least two points: (a) the K⁺ channel in the apical membrane, which maintains a favorable K⁺ concentration in the tubular fluid, and (b) the positive luminal electrical potential. These factors enable K⁺ to move passively down its electrochemical gradient through the lateral intercellular spaces and into the peritubular fluid and blood. Recall that there is very limited reabsorption of H_2O from ascending limbs of Henle, which means that solvent drag has very little, if any, influence on the reabsorption of K⁺ in this segment.

The exit steps for K⁺ in the basolateral membrane—via a channel and by cotransport with Cl⁻—when combined with the conductance of the K⁺ channel in the apical membrane, account for the lumen-positive potential in the thick ascending limb. As indicated in Figure 7-4, the 'loop diuretics' inhibit the Na:K:2Cl cotransporter, and thereby the reabsorption of K⁺; this effect is partly the explanation of why these commonly used diuretics tend to cause hypokalemia [the other, more important reason being the increase in

Figure 11-4. Modes of transport of K⁺ by major segments of the nephron. Details are described in the text.

A. Proximal tubule. Circles labeled 'ATP' are specialized membrane proteins, or 'carriers', for active transport. The other circle is a specialized protein, or carrier, for passive transport. Two shaded parallel bars indicate proteins that serve as membrane channels. The broad, open arrow denotes solvent drag. Solid arrows = active transport, requiring a direct input of energy; broken arrows = passive transport. For definitions of the various modes of transport, see Chapter 4, under Modes of Transport, p. 64. Although the K⁺ channel in the apical membrane can carry K⁺ in either direction, normally entry into the cell prevails.

B. Thick Ascending Limb of the Loop of Henle. The open circle with three arrows is called the *Na:K:2Cl cotransporter or symporter* (see Chap. 7, under Na⁺ and H₂O Reabsorption in Other Parts of Nephron, Thick Ascending Limb, p. 127). Other definitions are the same as in legend for (A).

C, D. Principal Cells and α-Intercalated Cells, respectively, in Late Distal Tubule, Cortical Collecting Duct, and Early Part of Outer Medullary Collecting Duct. Symbols same as explained in legend for (A).

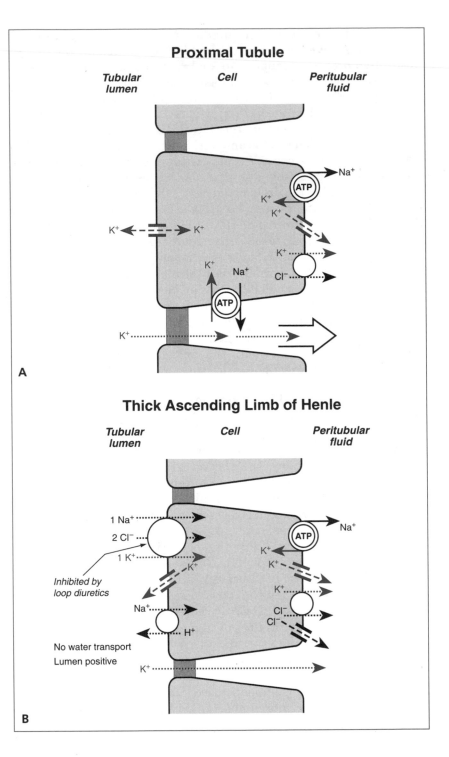

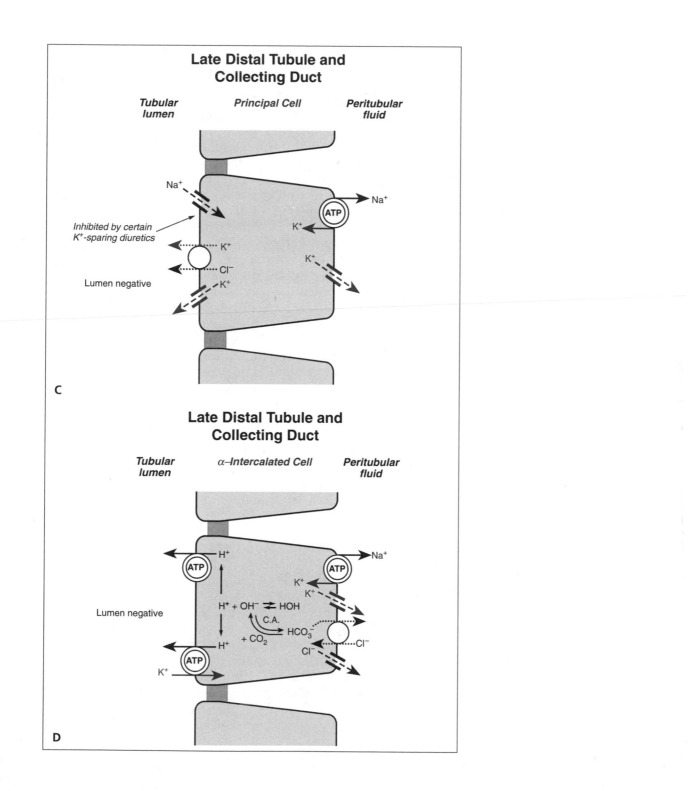

tubular flow rate, and hence stimulated secretion of K+ (Table 11-1, under Diuretics)].

Late Distal Tubule and Collecting Duct

We pointed out in Chapter 7 (under Late Distal Tubule and Collecting Duct, p. 130) that these segments contain two types of cells: (a) the principal cell, and (b) the intercalated cell. The first is responsible for secreting K+, which is the predominant mode in these segments (Fig. 11-3A and C); the second is responsible for the moderate reabsorption of K+ that can occur in these segments under conditions of K+-depletion (Fig. 11-3B).

Secretion by Principal Cells

Net secretion of K+ by principal cells is shown in Figure 11-4C. [The K+-secreting cells extend into the early part of the outer medullary collecting duct, the part that lies in the outer stripe of the outer medulla (see Fig. 1-2A).] By actively transporting K+ into cells, Na-K-ATPase raises the intracellular concentration of K+. This high concentration of K+, when coupled with a lumen negative potential (which results from Na+ diffusing into the cell via its channel in the apical membrane), means that K+ can diffuse passively across the apical membrane and into the tubular lumen. Secretion across the apical membrane may occur by two routes, a K+-Cl− symporter and a K+ channel. Even though there is a K+ channel also in the basolateral membrane, transport is preferentially across the apical membrane because (a) the electrical potential difference favors movement in the secretory direction, (b) the conductance of the apical channel exceeds that of the basolateral channel, and (c) the K+-Cl− symporter can transport K+ across the apical membrane.

Reabsorption by α-Intercalated Cells

These are the same cells that secrete H+ (Fig. 10-7C); the mechanism by which they reabsorb K+ is illustrated in Figure 11-4D. [Like the principal cells that secrete K+ (see above), the intercalated cells that reabsorb K+ extend into the early part of the outer medullary collecting duct, and even beyond.] It is thought that K+ crosses the apical membrane into the cell via an active pump that simultaneously carries H+ out of the cell, called the *H-K-ATPase*. This pump is quite similar in amino acid sequence to the H-K-ATPase in parietal cells of the gastric mucosa, which is responsible for gastric acidification. Once inside the cell, K+ can cross into peritubular fluid passively via a channel, despite the relative negativity of the cell interior. Thus, K^+ reabsorption in this part of the nephron probably involves an active step, a suspicion that is supported by morphological changes that not only are limited to intercalated cells but also are specific for their apical membranes.

Medullary Collecting Duct

Ordinarily, the last portion of the outer medullary collecting duct (the part that runs through the inner stripe of the outer medulla—Fig. 1-2A), as well as the entire inner medullary collecting duct, are thought to reabsorb K^+. The exact mechanisms are not yet known fully. It appears likely, however, that K^+ is reabsorbed passively, via the paracellular pathway in outer and inner medullary collecting ducts, and possibly via a somewhat nonselective cation channel in the apical membranes of inner medullary collecting duct cells. Passive transport by the paracellular route is possible despite the luminal negativity (Table 7-1) because reabsorption of water has raised the concentration of K^+ in the luminal fluid sufficiently to overcome the 'unfavorable' electrical potential gradient.

As indicated by the marginal box, renal transport of K^+ is a fairly complicated story, and it varies not only in different parts of the nephron but also among different cells. Although thorough knowledge of each process is likely to be important toward understanding disease processes and hence toward designing new and more specific therapies, the details have been presented here not for their own intrinsic importance but to emphasize once more the necessarily complex nature of renal function. As we stated at the very beginning of this text (see Chap. 1, under Heterogeneity of Nephrons, p. 7, and under Magnitude of Renal Function), almost certainly this complexity is dictated by the need for the kidney to regulate the excretion of a host of substances—simultaneously and yet independently of one another.

> ■ **Major Mechanisms** ■
> **of Renal K+ Transport**
>
> *Proximal Tubules*
> Passive reabsorption
> — paracellular
> — solvent drag
>
> *Thick Ascending Limbs of Henle*
> Passive reabsorption
> — paracellular
>
> *Late Distal Tubules, Cortical and Early Outer Medullary Collecting Ducts*
> Passive secretion across apical membrane of principal cells
> — K+ channel
> — K+-Cl−-symporter
>
> Active reabsorption across apical membrane of α-intercalated cells
> — H-K-ATPase
>
> *Late Outer Medullary and Inner Medullary Collecting Ducts*
> Passive reabsorption
> — paracellular
> — cation channel

DETERMINANTS OF RATE OF K+ SECRETION

Under most circumstances, external balance for K^+ is determined mainly by altering the rate at which K^+ is secreted by principal cells in the late distal tubules and in the cortical and early outer medullary collecting ducts (Fig. 11-4C). The rate of this secretion is governed mainly by three factors: (a) the difference between the K^+ concentration within the tubular cell and that within the tubular lumen, which difference is regulated principally by the activity of Na-K-ATPase in the basolateral membrane (Fig. 11-4C); (b) the flow rate of tubular fluid, which, acting as a sink, ultimately operates through (a) above by keeping the K^+ concentration within tubular fluid low; and (c) the magnitude of the electrical potential difference between the tubular lumen and the cell. That is, other influences being equal, the rate of K^+ secretion will be greater: the higher the intracellular K^+ concentration, the higher the flow rate of tubular fluid, and the smaller the electrical potential difference.

FACTORS INFLUENCING RATE OF K⁺ EXCRETION

Many physiological or pathological conditions are associated with characteristic changes in the urinary excretion of K^+—i.e., in external balance for K^+. The major conditions are listed in Table 11-1. As shown in the third column of that table, most of the changes in the urinary *excretion* of K^+ (i.e., in the elimination of K^+ from the body) can be explained through alterations in one or more of the determinants of K^+ *secretion* listed in the preceding section.

Intake of K⁺

It was shown in Figure 11-3 that lowering or raising the dietary intake of K^+ leads to enhancement of net reabsorption or to net secretion, respectively, by the entire kidney (see also marginal box on p. 242). This maintenance of external balance is brought about by adaptive changes that alter the secretion of K^+ in the distal nephron (i.e., the nephron beyond the thick ascending limb of Henle, in this instance, the late distal tubule and the cortical and early outer medullary collecting duct).

When intake of K^+ is high (Table 11-1), there is an increase in both the amount and the activity of Na-K-ATPase, as well as amplification of the basolateral membrane of principal cells (Fig. 11-4C). Consequently, increased amounts of K^+ enter the cells from the peritubular (blood) side. Simultaneously, a high plasma K^+ concentration leads to increased aldosterone in the plasma, which increases K^+ secretion by mechanisms outlined in the next section.

The converse chain of events occurs when K^+ intake is reduced. Secretion of K^+ by principal cells probably is abolished and there is now net reabsorption by α-intercalated cells in the distal segments, especially in inner medullary collecting ducts.

Mineralocorticoids

The sites and modes of action of aldosterone were reviewed in Chapter 7 (under Challenges to Na^+ Balance: 2. Changes in Na^+

■ **Physiological** ■
Determinants of
K⁺ Secretion

Chemical concentration gradient between cell and tubular lumen

Tubular flow rate

Electrical potential difference across apical membrane

Intake, p. 142). Its influence on K^+ handling is exerted on principal cells in the late distal tubules and cortical collecting ducts.

Increased aldosterone and similar mineralocorticoids (but not glucocorticoids except at very high dosages) enhance the secretion of K^+ by several means (Fig. 11-4C): (a) acutely, by stimulating existing Na-K-ATPase through an increase in apical Na^+ channels, thereby supplying more Na^+ to the basolateral pump; more chronically, (b) by increasing the number of these pumps; (c) by increasing the number of apical K^+ channels; and (d) by decreasing the back-leakage of K^+ via the basolateral K^+ channel through increased electrical negativity (hyperpolarization) within the cell.

When the plasma concentration of aldosterone is decreased, K^+ excretion is decreased, and the mechanisms responsible for this change are thought to be those listed above, except that they go in the opposite direction.

Intake of Na⁺

In most instances, there is a direct correlation between the increased urinary excretion of Na^+ that follows a high intake of Na^+ (Fig. 7-11) and the urinary excretion of K^+. The relationship also holds when urinary excretion of Na^+ is increased by other means, such as expanding the extracellular fluid volume and especially while using diuretics. The converse holds when the intake of Na^+, and hence the urinary excretion of this ion, are reduced. There are exceptions, however, when the urinary excretion of Na^+ and K^+ do not run in parallel. One example is what is called the *escape phenomenon* from mineralocorticoids: When these hormones are elevated for a prolonged period, Na^+ excretion returns to control values while K^+ excretion remains elevated.

With a high intake of Na^+, the increased excretion of K^+ is due mainly to increased secretion in late distal tubules and cortical collecting ducts. Several factors are responsible for this effect: (1) One critical element is increased delivery of Na^+ to the tubular sites mentioned above, which leads to increased passive entry of Na^+ into the cell via apical Na^+ channels, consequent stimulation of Na-K-ATPase, and increased basolateral uptake of K^+ (Fig. 11-4C). (2) Another important element is increased flow rate of tubular fluid past these sites, which has been shown to stimulate K^+ secretion independently of the tubular Na^+ concentration. This factor may work through the 'sink effect', i.e., partly by sweeping the secreted K^+ more rapidly downstream and partly by keeping the tubular concentration of K^+ low. [Note that even though the K^+ *concentration* may be decreased in collecting ducts and hence in urine, the *excretion* of K^+—which is the product of the urinary K^+

Table 11-1. Conditions that adjust external balance for K+ by altering the rate of urinary K+ excretion, and possible mechanisms through which each condition mainly exerts its influence

Condition	K+ excretion	Possible mechanisms
K+ intake		
High	Increased	Increased distal secretion* resulting from: Increased peritubular uptake of K+ by Na-K-ATPase Increased aldosterone
Low	Decreased	Decrease in distal secretion* by principal cells and shift to net reabsorption by intercalated cells, probably resulting from changes opposite to those listed above Increased reabsorption by inner medullary collecting ducts
Mineralocorticoids		
Excess	Increased	Increased secretion by late distal tubules and cortical collecting ducts, resulting from: Increased peritubular uptake of K+ Increased apical permeability to K+ Increased electrical potential difference across basolateral membrane
Deficiency	Decreased	Decreased secretion by late distal tubules and cortical collecting ducts, due to opposite changes
Na+ intake		
High	High	Increased secretion by late distal tubules and cortical collecting ducts due to: Increased delivery of Na+ to distal sites, increased entry of Na+ into cells, and therefore augmented peritubular uptake of K+ Increased flow rate of tubular fluid Decreased electrical potential difference across apical membrane
Low	Decreased	Increased reabsorption of K+ in outer and inner medullary collecting ducts Decreased secretion by late distal tubules and cortical collecting ducts due to changes opposite to those listed above

H+ balance		
Alkalosis	Increased	Increased secretion by late distal tubules and cortical collecting ducts due to: Increased peritubular uptake of K+ via stimulated Na-K-ATPase Increased permeability of apical membrane to K+ via channels Shift of K+ into cells in some cases (Fig. 11-2) Increased flow rate of tubular fluid in metabolic alkalosis Increased K-Cl symporter in metabolic alkalosis Decreased reabsorption by intercalated cells via decreased H-K countertransport (Fig. 11-4D)
Acidosis	Decreased	Decreased secretion due to changes opposite to those listed above for alkalosis, plus increased excretion of NH_4^+, but: No decreased flow rate No decreased K-Cl symporter Not in chronic metabolic acidosis In chronic metabolic acidosis, K+ excretion may be increased due to: Increased flow rate of tubular fluid Increased aldosterone
Diuretics		
Loop diuretics Furosemide Bumetanide	Increased	Increased distal secretion* due to: Inhibition of Na:K:2Cl symporter in thick ascending limbs of Henle Increased delivery of Na+ to distal sites Increased flow rate of tubular fluid
Osmotic diuretics Mannitol	Increased	Increased secretion due to: Increased delivery of Na+ to distal sites Increased flow rate of tubular fluid
Thiazide diuretics Hydrochlorothiazide	Increased	Increased secretion due to: Inhibition of carbonic anhydrase, consequent decreased distal delivery of Cl⁻, and stimulation of apical K-Cl symporter in principal cells (Fig. 11-4C)
K+-Sparing diuretics Spironolactone Triamterene Amiloride	Decreased	Competitive binding to aldosterone receptors (see above, this Table) Decreased K+ secretion in principal cells due to: Inhibition of apical Na+ channel and consequent reduction in electrical potential difference, with lumen less negative

*The term *distal secretion* refers to secretion in late distal tubules, as well as in cortical and early outer medullary collecting ducts.

concentration and the rate of urinary flow ($U_K \times \dot{V}$)—will be increased because $\dot{V}$ is high.] Finally, (3) a decrease in the magnitude of the electrical potential difference across the apical membrane promotes secretion of K⁺ through a lesser tendency to 'hold' K⁺ within the electrically negative cell.

Perhaps surprisingly, the influences that decrease urinary excretion of K⁺ during a low Na⁺ intake are not simply the reverse of those listed in the preceding paragraph. Although decreased secretion of K⁺ by principal cells probably occurs, the most important element is enhanced reabsorption of K⁺ by intercalated cells, certainly in the inner medullary collecting ducts and probably in those of the outer medulla as well.

H⁺ Balance

As a general rule, alkalosis increases the excretion of K⁺ while acidosis reduces it (Table 11-1). This statement, however, needs to be qualified to the extent that only acute metabolic acidosis decreases K⁺ excretion, while chronic metabolic acidosis may not, or may even increase it.

Alkalosis raises the secretion of K⁺ in late distal tubules and cortical collecting ducts by two direct effects on principal cells (Fig. 11-4C): (1) It stimulates Na-K-ATPase and thereby increases the uptake of K⁺ across the basolateral membrane, and (2) it increases the permeability of the apical membrane to K⁺ by increasing both the number of K⁺ channels and the duration for which these channels remain open. These effects may be abetted by shifts of K⁺ into cells, which occur in some forms of alkalosis—i.e., by effects on internal balance (Fig. 11-2). Metabolic alkalosis further enhances secretion of K⁺ especially by two indirect effects: (a) It increases tubular flow rate, and (b) it reduces tubular fluid concentration of Cl⁻, which raises the activity of the K-Cl symporter in the apical membrane (Fig. 11-4C). Finally, decreased reabsorption by intercalated cells (Fig. 11-4D) also contributes to increased K⁺ excretion during alkalosis. This effect is brought about by decreased H⁺ secretion and hence a decrease in H-K countertransport.

During acute metabolic acidosis, as well as during respiratory acidosis, secretion of K⁺ is reduced largely by changes opposite to those listed above for alkalosis, except for the two indirect effects (a and b), which are not seen. In addition, increased excretion of NH_4^+ inhibits excretion of K⁺, by as yet unknown mechanisms. During chronic metabolic acidosis, two factors may increase K⁺ secretion and excretion rather than decrease them: (a) distal tubular flow rate increases, and (b) plasma concentration of aldosterone may rise secondary to contraction of the extracellular fluid volume.

Diuretics

The diuretics constitute a group of pharmacological agents that increase the urinary excretion of NaCl and water by inhibiting the reabsorption of Na^+ or of Cl^-, or both. The site of inhibition in the nephron and the mode of action vary with the particular diuretic (Table 11-1).

Loop Diuretics. Examples commonly used are furosemide and bumetanide, diuretics that are secreted by proximal tubules (Table 5-1). They block the *Na:K:2Cl symporter* in thick ascending limbs of Henle (Fig. 11-4B), and because approximately 25% of the filtered load of Na^+ is normally reabsorbed in the loops of Henle (Fig. 7-7), the loop diuretics can cause a marked natriuresis and diuresis. These agents increase the urinary excretion of K^+ by two means: (a) by inhibiting the cotransporter in the apical membrane of thick ascending limb cells, they leave secretion of K^+ through the apical channel unopposed (Fig. 11-4B); and (b) by increasing the delivery of Na^+ to sites distal to the loops of Henle, they increase K^+ secretion by principal cells, as described above for a high intake of Na^+.

Osmotic Diuretics. When an increase in urine flow is desired, as in certain types of poisoning (see Problem 10-1, p. 231), the diuretic most commonly given is mannitol. It is a small sugar that is freely filtered and very poorly or not at all reabsorbed, and it inhibits the reabsorption of water and Na^+ all along the nephron. It therefore increases the secretion of K^+ by principal cells through increased flow rate and increased delivery of Na^+ (see above and Table 11-1).

Thiazide Diuretics. These agents are used more as antihypertensives than for the mobilization of edema fluid. They decrease Na^+ and Cl^- reabsorption by inhibiting the Na-Cl symporter in early distal tubular cells (Fig. 7-5). That, however, is not the major means by which they increase K^+ secretion, for that action decreases the entry of Cl^- into the cell and hence slows down an apical K-Cl symporter, which secretes K^+. Rather, the thiazides stimulate K^+ secretion by an additional action, namely, the inhibition of carbonic anhydrase. Through this action, they inhibit HCO_3^- reabsorption, mainly in the proximal tubules (see Figs. 7-1A and 10-1), so that more Cl^- than normally is reabsorbed in this segment. Consequently, there is decreased delivery of Cl^- past principal cells, which stimulates the apical K-Cl symporter in those cells.

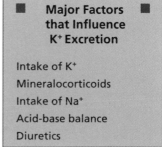

■   **Major Factors**   ■
that Influence
K⁺ Excretion

Intake of K⁺

Mineralocorticoids

Intake of Na⁺

Acid-base balance

Diuretics

K⁺-Sparing Diuretics. Several, less frequently used, diuretics decrease K^+ excretion. They are rarely prescribed by themselves, but more commonly are given as adjuvants with the more effective diuretics listed above. They are classified into two groups: (a) those, like spironolactone, that inhibit aldosterone, and (b) those, like triamterene and amiloride, that do not. The first act through competitive binding to the nuclear receptor for aldosterone, and hence by curtailing the actions listed above under Mineralocorticoids. The second block the apical Na^+ channels in principal cells (Fig. 11-4C). This action renders the tubular lumen less negative and thereby decreases the electrical driving force for K^+ secretion.

EFFECT OF VASOPRESSIN: AN EXAMPLE OF EVOLVED HOMEOSTASIS

The antidiuretic hormone (ADH, or vasopressin; see Chap. 8) stimulates K^+ secretion by principal cells. It does so by increasing the apical permeability of these cells to Na^+ via channels (Fig. 11-4C) and thereby both stimulating Na-K-ATPase and basolateral uptake of K^+, and enhancing the electrical driving force for apical K^+ exit by making the tubular lumen more negative. Yet, ADH does not increase K^+ *excretion.* This fact may represent a beautiful evolutionary adaptation that enables the kidneys to regulate external balance for two important substances, H_2O and K^+, simultaneously and independently of one another. The effects that make this 'balancing act' possible are illustrated in Figure 11-5.

It is possible that the major determinant for the evolution of the kidney was the preservation of water balance (Fig. 1-4). In the case of mammals, this problem was solved by the evolutionary development of the countercurrent systems (multiplier and exchanger) and the influence of ADH on these systems—not only the alteration of water permeability by ADH, but also a number of other effects of this hormone, as on the medullary circulation (Chap. 6), on urea transport (Fig. 8-5), and on Na^+ transport. When the mammalian kidney needs to conserve water, the plasma concentration of ADH increases, which leads to antidiuresis and decreased tubular flow rate past principal cells (Fig. 11-5). The last effect *would* lead to decreased secretion, and hence excretion, of K^+ were it not for the fact that ADH simultaneously stimulates secretion of K^+ (paragraph above). The opposite chain of events occurs during water diuresis, with decreased ADH. Hence, external balance for K^+

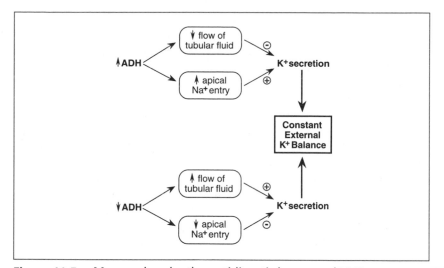

Figure 11-5. Means whereby the antidiuretic hormone (ADH, or vaso-pressin) can regulate external balance for water without perturbing the external balance for K⁺. Explanation is given in the text. The designations 'flow of tubular fluid', 'apical Na⁺ entry', and 'K⁺ secretion' all refer to principal cells in late distal tubules and cortical and early outer medullary collecting ducts. The encircled plus and minus signs designate an increase and a decrease, respectively, in K⁺ secretion. Adapted from Field, M. J., et al. *Kidney Int.* 25:502, 1984.

is preserved while large fluctuations in the renal excretion of water are permitted.

SUMMARY

Maintenance of extracellular and intracellular concentrations of K⁺ at normal levels is essential to many vital functions. Extracellular K⁺ concentration is low (~4.5 mmol/L); by and large, it is protected at this level through *internal balance,* i.e., by rapid shifts of K⁺ between the intracellular and extracellular compartments. In contrast, intracellular K⁺ concentration is high (~150 mmol/L), and this value is regulated primarily by *external balance,* i.e., by equality between the amount of K⁺ that comes into the body, by diet or parenterally, and the amount of K⁺ that leaves the body, mainly via urine. In health, external balance is regulated by the kidneys, and it requires hours or days.

From minute to minute, internal balance for K^+ is regulated mainly by insulin, which promotes the entry of K^+ into cells by stimulating Na-K-ATPase. This specialized protein, which pumps Na^+ out of cells and K^+ into them, is situated in membranes of all cells, specifically in the basolateral membrane of epithelial cells. Other factors that control the migration of K^+ in and out of cells include catecholamines, acid-base status, and aldosterone (Fig. 11-1).

External balance controls the total amount of K^+ in the body. It is regulated by altering the way in which K^+ is handled by the nephron segments beyond the loops of Henle, i.e., by the late distal tubules and collecting ducts (Fig. 11-3 and marginal box on p. 242). At first, virtually all of the filtered K^+ ($\sim$90%) is reabsorbed in the proximal tubules and loops of Henle under all circumstances. When the intake of K^+ is normal or high, the rate of urinary K^+ excretion that is appropriate for external balance is governed by the amount of K^+ that is secreted by principal cells in the late distal tubules, cortical collecting ducts, and first part of outer medullary collecting ducts. This rate of secretion can vary enormously, so that as little as 5 to 10% of the filtered load to as much as 200% of that load can be excreted in the urine under conditions of normal and high K^+ intake, respectively. When the intake of K^+ is very low, then tubular secretion of K^+ is abolished and there is reabsorption throughout the nephron; fine-tuning of K^+ reabsorption involves α-intercalated cells. Under this circumstance, the urinary excretion of K^+ can be as low as 1 to 2% of the filtered load.

Major factors that determine the rate of urinary K^+ excretion include: (a) intake of K^+, (b) mineralocorticoids, (c) intake of Na^+, (d) acid-base balance, and (e) diuretics. As indicated in the preceding paragraph, these factors regulate *excretion* mainly or solely by altering the rate of *secretion,* and that rate, in turn, depends primarily on three factors involving principal cells: (1) the difference in K^+ concentration between the inside of the cell and the tubular lumen, (2) the flow rate of tubular fluid past the principal cells, and (3) the electrical potential difference, mainly across the apical membrane of these cells (see marginal box, p. 248).

The cellular mechanisms by which K^+ is either reabsorbed or secreted vary in different parts of the nephron (see marginal box, p. 247). They have been illustrated in the four parts of Figure 11-4. The modes of transport can be passive, active, secondary active, or solvent drag; utilize specialized channels and carriers; and involve the transcellular or paracellular routes. Normal function of Na-K-ATPase is crucial to all of the mechanisms.

PROBLEM 11-1

Now that you have become an expert on renal function, you can answer these questions:

1. What are the urinary pH and osmolality of a healthy adult human whose diet is normal and contains protein?
2. What are the major solutes in such urine, and what is the approximate concentration of each solute?

SUGGESTED READINGS

Berliner, R. W. Renal mechanisms for potassium excretion. *Harvey Lect.* 55:141, 1961.

Field, M. J., Berliner, R. W., and Giebisch, G. H. Regulation of Renal Potassium Metabolism. In R. G. Narins (Ed.), *Maxwell & Kleeman's Clinical Disorders of Fluid and Electrolyte Metabolism* (5th ed.). New York: McGraw-Hill, 1994. Chap. 7.

Giebisch, G., Malnic, G., and Berliner, R. W. Renal Transport and Control of Potassium Excretion. In B. M. Brenner and F. C. Rector, Jr. (Eds.), *The Kidney* (4th ed.). Philadelphia: Saunders, 1991. Chap. 7.

Malnic, G., Klose, R. M., and Giebisch, G. Micropuncture study of renal potassium excretion in the rat. *Am. J. Physiol.* 206:674, 1964.

Stanton, B. A., and Giebisch, G. H. Renal Potassium Transport. In E. E. Windhager (Ed.), *Handbook of Physiology,* section 8: *Renal Physiology,* vol. I. New York: Oxford University Press, 1992. Chap. 19.

Velázquez, H., and Wright, F. S. Tubular Potassium Transport. In R. W. Schrier and C. W. Gottschalk (Eds.), *Diseases of the Kidney* (5th ed.). Boston: Little, Brown, 1992. Chap. 5.

Wright, F. S., and Giebisch, G. Regulation of Potassium Excretion. In D. W. Seldin and G. Giebisch (Eds.), *The Kidney: Physiology and Pathophysiology* (2nd ed.), vol. 2. New York: Raven, 1991. Chap. 61.
Chapters 59–61 in Volume 2 of this work are grouped under Renal Regulation of Potassium: Normal. *The section is followed by another, entitled* Renal Regulation of Potassium: Deranged.

Answers to Problems

■   ■   ■   ■   ■

PROBLEM 1-1

Except for some minor differences (see Chap. 4, under Quantifying Reabsorption, p. 66), the concentration of Na^+ is the same in the plasma that is filtered into Bowman's space as it is in the plasma before it is filtered. Furthermore, since 93% of plasma is made up of water, we equate the amount of water filtered with the amount of plasma that is filtered. Hence, the so-called filtered load of Na^+—i.e., the rate at which Na^+ is filtered through the glomerular capillaries into Bowman's space—is 180 L/day × 139 mmol/L, or 25,020 mmol per day.

If the urine flow is 1.1 mL per minute and the concentration of Na^+ in that urine is 95 mmol/L (i.e., 0.095 mmol/mL), then the rate of urinary excretion of Na^+ is 1.1 mL/min × 0.095 mmol/mL, or 0.1045 mmol per minute. There are 60 × 24, or 1,440, minutes in each day; hence the urinary excretion of Na^+ in this example is 0.1045 mmol/min × 1,440 min, or 150 mmol per day.

Since 25,020 mmol per day was filtered into the tubules, and only 150 mmol per day was excreted, 24,870 mmol per day must have been reabsorbed; that is, 24,870/25,020 × 100, or 99.4% of the filtered load of Na^+ was reabsorbed.

PROBLEM 1-2

A solution of 0.9% NaCl contains 0.9 g of NaCl per 100 mL, or 9 g of NaCl per liter. Since the atomic weight of Na^+ is 23 and that of Cl^- is 35, 1 mol (or gram molecule) of NaCl weighs 58 g and 1 mmol of NaCl weighs 58 mg. Therefore, 9,000 mg of NaCl (which is contained in 1 liter of the solution) represents 155 mmol of NaCl. At this concentration, the 155 mmol of NaCl is completely dissociated into the ionic constituents of Na^+ and Cl^-; the solution therefore contains 155 mmol (or 155 meq) of Na^+ and 155 mmol (or 155 meq) of Cl^-, and these are the values that one obtains when analyzing a solution of 0.9% NaCl.

The osmolality of a solution, like all colligative properties of solutions, is a function solely of the *number of discrete particles* that it contains. Because NaCl is a strong electrolyte that dissociates completely into Na^+ and Cl^- ions in solution, each mol of NaCl dissociates into two mols of discrete ions. Thus the osmolality of a solution of 155 mmol/L NaCl is *approximately* 310 mOsm/kg. (Strictly speaking, it should be written 'per kg of H_2O,' but for the sake of brevity and in order to conform to the expression 'per L' for other solutions in this text, we will use the abbreviated form.) However, because of the interactions between solutes as well as between solutes and solvent, the osmolality of a solution of 155 mmol/L NaCl, as *measured* in an osmometer (e.g., by freezing point depression), is actually 287 mOsm/kg. Dividing the measured osmolality by the millimols in solution yields the *osmotic coefficient* (in this case, 287/310, or 0.93). The osmotic coefficient of a solution is a function not only of the interaction among all the solutes within that solution but also of the concentration of each solute. Thus, it is too complex to be predicted accurately and it is determined empirically in an osmometer. The osmolalities of many common solutions over a range of concentrations may be found in standard reference works such as the *CRC Handbook of Chemistry and Physics*. Boca Raton: CRC Press, 1992.

A 5% solution of glucose contains 50 g of glucose per liter. Since the molecular weight of glucose is 180, 50 g of glucose represents 278 mmol of glucose. Nonelectrolytes also have colligative properties, and for a 278 mmol/L solution of glucose, the osmotic coefficient is approximately 0.99; hence, the addition of 5 g of glucose to each 100 mL of 0.9% NaCl adds about 275 mmol to each liter, and the new solution would have an osmolality of approximately 562 mOsm/kg.

One molecule of $CaCl_2$ contains one ion of calcium with a valence of two, and two ions of chloride, each with a valence of one. Therefore, 1 mmol of $CaCl_2$ contains 2 meq of calcium and 2 meq of chloride.

Since 1 mmol of $CaCl_2$ contains 1 mmol of calcium and 2 mmol of chloride, it would contribute 3 mOsm/kg to a solution if the osmotic coefficient were 1.0.

PROBLEM 2-1

Plasma Volume

Equation 2-2:

Volume of compartment =

$$\frac{\text{Amount of substance given} - \text{Amount of substance lost}}{\text{Concentration of substance in the compartment}}$$

$$= \frac{10 \text{ mg} - 0}{0.4 \text{ mg/100 mL}}$$

$$= \frac{10 \text{ mg}}{1} \times \frac{100 \text{ mL}}{0.4 \text{ mg}}$$

$$= \frac{1,000}{0.4}, \text{ or } 2,500 \text{ mL, or } 2.5 \text{ L}$$

Whole Blood Volume

$$\frac{\text{Plasma volume}}{55\%} = \frac{\text{Whole blood volume}}{100\%}$$

$$\frac{2,500 \text{ mL}}{55} = \frac{\text{Whole blood volume}}{100}$$

$$\text{Whole blood volume} = \frac{2,500 \times 100}{55} = 4,545 \text{ mL, or } 4.5 \text{ L}$$

PROBLEM 2-2

The answers are shown in Figure 2-A. In clinical parlance, the new steady state following a loss of fluid is known as *volume contraction* and a gain of fluid as *volume expansion.* The change in volume, as well as the adjectives *isosmotic, hyperosmotic,* and *hyposmotic,* refers to the *extracellular* fluid in the new steady state.

(a) *Loss of isosmotic fluid.* Initially the fluid is lost from the plasma, and this loss is largely replenished from the interstitial space because of a change in Starling forces. Therefore, the entire extracellular compartment contracts, but since the loss is isosmotic, there will be no major change in the osmolality of extracellular fluid, and hence no shift of H_2O in or out of the intracellular space. The final result will be a reduction in the volume of the extracellular fluid, but no change in its osmolality; that is, isosmotic contraction will have occurred.

(b) *Loss of 'pure' H_2O.* In persons lost in the desert or patients with fever (as well as in normal individuals—Appendix Table A-4), much H_2O is lost even when they are not sweating. This loss, which occurs by evaporation from the skin and breath, is called *insensible H_2O loss* because it is not perceived, as is sweat. This evaporative H_2O comes first from the plasma, which thereby becomes hyperosmotic with respect to the other body fluids, and this change in turn causes a shift of H_2O from the interstitial into the plasma compartment. The consequent rise in the osmolality of the interstitial fluid causes H_2O to flow out of the intracellular compartment. That is, in hyperosmotic contraction, the volume of all the major fluid compartments is decreased.

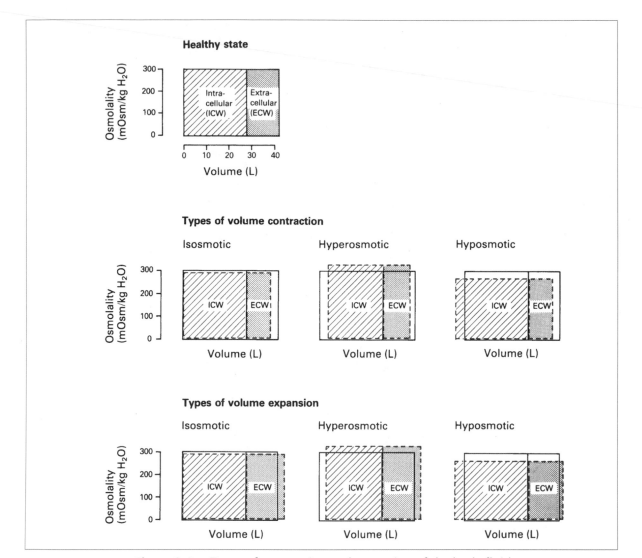

Figure 2-A. Types of contraction and expansion of the body fluid compartments. The plasma and the interstitial fluid are here portrayed as a single extracellular compartment. In each diagram, the healthy state is drawn in solid lines (white background) and the new steady state in dashed lines (red). This type of portrayal, known as a *Darrow-Yannet diagram,* was introduced by these two workers in a classic contribution on this subject (*J. Clin. Invest.* 14:266, 1935). From H. Valtin, *Renal Dysfunction: Mechanisms Involved in Fluid and Solute Imbalance.* Boston: Little, Brown, 1979.

(c) *Loss of NaCl.* Patients with adrenal insufficiency actually lose some H_2O initially, but then they retain H_2O even though loss of NaCl continues. The net result is, therefore, loss of NaCl in excess of H_2O, and this decrement results in decreased osmolality of extracellular fluid. Consequently, H_2O will shift from the extracellular into the intracellular space, and the new steady state will show contraction of the extracellular compartment and expansion of the intracellular space, with both having an osmolality that is less than normal.

(d) *Gain of isosmotic fluid.* Edema fluid is essentially a solution of NaCl that has the same osmolality as plasma. The analysis of this situation is therefore similar to the one given for Figure 2-4, except that in generalized edema the fluid is added to the body through failure of the kidneys to excrete it, not through intravenous infusion. Generalized edema is the classic example of isosmotic expansion, which represents a selective enlargement of the extracellular compartment, without change in osmolality.

(e) *Gain of NaCl.* As with loss of NaCl, so with a gain thereof the subject initially retains H_2O; but thereafter, the net result is addition of NaCl in excess of H_2O. Consequently, the osmolality of plasma rises, and there is then a shift of H_2O from the intracellular into the extracellular compartment until the two equilibrate at a higher osmolality. Therefore, in the new steady state of hyperosmotic expansion, the extracellular compartment is expanded, the intracellular is contracted, and the osmolality of both is greater than normal.

(f) *Gain of 'pure' H_2O.* In the syndrome of inappropriate ADH secretion (SIADH), a sustained normal or high plasma concentration of the antidiuretic hormone (ADH, or vasopressin) causes the kidneys to retain H_2O (see Chap. 8). This H_2O at first enters the plasma, causing its osmolality to decline. This change, in turn, causes a shift of H_2O into the interstitial space, and as the osmolality of that space decreases, there is a further shift of H_2O into the intracellular compartment. Thus, a gain of 'pure' H_2O is shared by all the major body fluid compartments, which equilibrate at an osmolality that is below the normal value.

PROBLEM 2-3

The volumes of the patient's body fluid compartments can be estimated by using the '20, 40, 60' rule:

Extracellular volume $\approx 0.2 \times$ body weight ≈ 14.4 L
Intracellular volume $\approx 0.4 \times$ body weight ≈ 28.8 L
Total body water $\approx 0.6 \times$ body weight ≈ 43.2 L

The first impulse might be to reason that, because exchangeable Na$^+$ resides almost exclusively in extracellular fluid (ECF; Fig. 2-2), the amount needed to correct the hyponatremia might be calculated as the difference between the present amount of Na$^+$ in the ECF and the desired amount. The present amount is the ECF volume multiplied by the present Na$^+$ concentration (14.4 L $\times$ 125 mmol/L = 1,800 mmol); and the desired amount would be the ECF volume multiplied by the desired Na$^+$ concentration (14.4 L $\times$ 135 mmol/L = 1,944 mmol). The Na$^+$ deficit, based on these assumptions, would be 1,944 − 1,800 = 144 mmol.

That answer, of 144 mmol, *would be a gross underestimate of the amount of Na$^+$ needed*. The reason is that, as the patient is given Na$^+$ (presumably as an intravenous infusion of NaCl), the osmolality of the ECF will rise, and water will shift out of the intracellular space until osmotic equilibrium between the two compartments is reestablished. In this way, the Na$^+$ that is being added to the extracellular compartment is continuously being 'diluted', and therefore much more Na$^+$ must be added than was calculated above.

When the new steady-state value of 135 mmol/L is reached, the intracellular fluid will have the same higher osmolality as the extracellular fluid. That is, the intracellular compartment will have participated fully in the change but without the addition of intracellular solute. Hence, Na$^+$(Cl$^-$) must be added *as if it were distributed throughout the intracellular as well as the extracellular space*, and the amount that needs to be added is therefore calculated by multiplying the deficit in Na$^+$ concentration (135 − 125 = 10 mmol/L), by the Total Body Water. Thus, *the correct answer to this problem is:* 10 mmol/L $\times$ 43.2 L = 432 mmol of Na$^+$.

In a sense, this is a theoretical problem in that not enough information is given to identify the cause of the hyponatremia in this patient; depending on what that cause is, giving NaCl is not necessarily the right treatment. The purpose of the problem is to emphasize the point made in the preceding paragraph. In addition, note that the aim was to correct the plasma Na$^+$ concentration only partially, not to raise it to the normal value of about 140 mmol/L. As a general rule, it is best to correct an abnormality of this kind only partly and then, as the patient gets better, to let the patient's kidneys do the final adjustments.

Problem 3-1. Sample calculations illustrating the independence of the inulin clearance from the plasma concentration of inulin (top portion) and from the rate of urine flow (lower portion) in a dog.

| Urine flow (mL/min) | Inulin concentration | | Inulin clearance (mL/min) |
	Plasma (mg/mL)	Urine (mg/mL)	
1.2	0.9	45	60.0
1.3	1.4	68	63.1
1.0	2.3	141	61.3
1.4	3.8	168	61.9
1.2	5.7	294	61.9
1.3	0.5	23	59.8
2.1	0.6	17	59.5
3.1	0.4	8	62.0
5.7	0.5	5	57.0
6.6	0.5	4.6	60.7

Modified from Shannon, J. A. *Am. J. Physiol.* 112:405, 1935.

Problem 3-2. Sample calculations illustrating the identity of the inulin and creatinine clearances in a dog.

| Urine flow (mL/min) | Inulin | | | Creatinine | | |
	Plasma (mg/dL)	Urine (mg/dL)	Clearance (mL/min)	Plasma (mg/dL)	Urine (mg/dL)	Clearance (mL/min)
1.0	104	5,076	48.8	13.7	673	49.1
1.1	106	4,601	47.7	14.7	630	47.1
0.9	108	6,017	50.1	16.0	890	50.1
1.0	109	5,137	47.1	16.6	792	47.7

Modified from Shannon, J. A. *Am. J. Physiol.* 112:405, 1935.

PROBLEM 3-3

1. The urinary excretion of inulin at each time interval is given in Table 3-A. The values were derived by calculating the filtered load of inulin ($P_{In} \times GFR$), which is equal to the urinary excretion of inulin, since this compound is neither reabsorbed nor metabolized, nor secreted by the tubules.

There is danger of a circular argument here: Inulin was given in order to measure the GFR, yet we have utilized the GFR in order to calculate the urinary excretion of inulin. In practice, one measures the urinary excretion as $U_{In} \times \dot{V}$ and determines the GFR as $U_{In} \times \dot{V}/P_{In}$ (just as in Fig. 3-4), *once a steady state is reached.* What we are doing here is utilizing, retrospectively, that steady-state value of GFR in order to illustrate how the steady state is at-

Table 3-A.   Attainment of a steady state for inulin during a stable intravenous infusion of inulin in a healthy adult human.

Elapsed time (min)	Rate of inulin infusion (mg/min)	GFR (mL/min)	P_{In} (mg/mL)	Urinary excretion of inulin (mg/min)
1	72	120	0.005	0.6
5	72	120	0.02	2.4
10	72	120	0.05	6.0
50	72	120	0.24	28.8
100	72	120	0.47	56.4
110	72	120	0.6	72.0
120	72	120	0.6	72.0

tained and to reemphasize some points about the renal handling of inulin.

2. So long as the rate of inulin infusion exceeds its urinary excretion, inulin will continue to accumulate in the body, and the plasma concentration of inulin will rise; this is known as a *positive balance* for inulin. It will stop rising once the input of inulin by infusion equals its output via the urine, for at that point inulin will stop accumulating in the body.

3. By definition, the steady state is reached when input equals output (at 110 minutes in Table 3-A). Note another feature of the steady state: The plasma concentration of inulin is stable during this state, and it levels out at that point where the product of the plasma concentration and the GFR (i.e., the rate at which inulin is filtered into Bowman's space) is equal to the rate of infusion of inulin.

4. The value of 120 mL per minute for a normal GFR in this problem was chosen to be different from the value in Figure 3-4 in order to emphasize that there is a wide range of normality: 85 to 125 mL per minute for women, and 97 to 140 mL per minute for men.

Problem 4-1. Renal handling of inorganic phosphate in dogs.

Urine flow (mL/min)	Phosphate phosphorus*			Creatinine			Phosphate phosphorus*			Clearance ratio: Phosphate clearance/ Creatinine clearance
	Plasma (mg/dL)	Urine (mg/dL)	Clearance (mL/min)	Plasma (mg/dL)	Urine (mg/dL)	Clearance (mL/min)	Filtered (mg/min)	Excreted (mg/min)	Reabsorbed (mg/min)	
6.8	1.25	0.07	0.4	33.9	427	85.7	1.07	0.005	1.07	0.005
9.2	2.75	0.46	1.5	31.2	283	83.4	2.29	0.04	2.25	0.018
9.7	3.70	2.95	7.7	32.5	274	81.8	3.03	0.29	2.74	0.094
8.7	4.64	9.10	17.1	33.3	321	83.9	3.89	0.79	3.10	0.203
6.7	9.34	69.0	49.5	34.5	423	82.1	7.67	4.62	3.05	0.603
8.2	13.0	95.7	60.4	34.5	352	83.7	10.88	7.85	3.03	0.722
10.0	31.7	208	65.6	38.7	293	75.7	24.00	20.80	3.20	0.867

*The values were measured as the phosphorus in phosphate; they have been converted from milligrams to millimols of inorganic phosphate in Table 4-1 and Figure 4-2.

Slightly modified from Pitts, R. F., and Alexander, R. S. Am. J. Physiol. 142:648, 1944. Used with permission of the American Physiological Society.

These calculations emphasize that the concept of clearance is by no means restricted to inulin or creatinine. As explained in footnote b to this problem (p. 81), the clearance ratio is a useful calculation in renal physiology. In this instance, it tells us that at a plasma phosphate phosphorus concentration of 1.25 mg per dL, 0.005 or 0.5% of the phosphate that was filtered was excreted; i.e., 99.5% of the filtered phosphate was reabsorbed. In contrast, at a plasma phosphate phosphorus concentration of 31.7 mg per dL, 86.7% of the filtered phosphate was excreted, and 13.3% was reabsorbed.

Problem 4-2.　Handling of urea by the kidneys of an adult human at varying rates of urine flow.

V̇ (mL/min)	Urine concentration		Plasma concentration		GFR (mL/min)	Urea			Urea	
	Inulin (mg/mL)	Urea (mmol/L)	Inulin (mg/mL)	Urea (mmol/L)		Filtered (mmol/min)	Excreted (mmol/min)	Reabsorbed (mmol/min)	Excreted* (% of filtered load)	Reabsorbed* (% of filtered load)
0.4	144	300	0.5	5	115	0.58	0.12	0.46	21	79
0.8	75	263	0.5	5	120	0.60	0.21	0.39	35	65
1.0	60	240	0.5	5	120	0.60	0.24	0.36	40	60
3.1	20	119	0.5	5	124	0.62	0.37	0.25	60	40
10.2	5.8	37	0.5	5	118	0.59	0.38	0.21	64	36

*Note that these values can be calculated in two ways. (1) From line 1, the % of filtered urea excreted equals (0.12/0.58) × 100 or 20.7%, and the % of filtered urea reabsorbed equals (0.46/0.58) × 100 or 79.3%. (2) Alternatively, as explained in footnote b to Problem 4-1 (p. 81), one can utilize the clearance ratio to derive the same answers without having to measure urine flow and without first calculating the actual amounts filtered, excreted, and reabsorbed. Using this ratio (U/P urea ÷ U/P inulin), the fraction of filtered urea excreted equals 300/5 ÷ 144/0.5 or 0.208 (20.8%), and the fraction reabsorbed equals 1.000 − 0.208 or 0.792 (79.2%).

Lesson: The answer to this problem emphasizes the dependence of passive urea reabsorption upon the renal handling of water (see Fig. 4-5). The chemical concentration gradient favoring urea reabsorption in the terminal portions of the collecting ducts is reflected by the U/P ratio for urea (i.e., the ratio of the urinary concentration of urea to the plasma concentration of urea); note that the higher this ratio, the greater the rate of urea reabsorption.

Problem 5-1. Determination of renal plasma flow (RPF), renal blood flow (RBF), and filtration fraction (FF), using PAH and inulin in dogs. The extraction of PAH changes during the postnatal period, when these data were obtained.

Age (days)	Urine flow (μL per min per g of kidney)[c]	U_{PAH} (mg/dL)	Pa_{PAH}[a] (mg/dL)	Pv_{PAH}[a] (mg/dL)	RPF (μL per min per g of kidney)[c]	RBF[b] (μL per min per g of kidney)[c]	C_{In} (μL per min per g of kidney)[c]	FF
2	3.8	104	2.60	2.16	898	1,633	130	0.14
21	2.7	283	1.70	1.08	1,232	2,240	270	0.22
40	5.2	664	3.00	1.23	1,951	3,547	630	0.32
60	3.2	672	1.20	0.34	2,501	4,547	790	0.32
74	2.3	3,516	3.10	0.52	3,134	5,698	1,200	0.38

[a]Pa_{PAH} and Pv_{PAH} = concentration of PAH in arterial and renal venous plasma, respectively.

[b]Assume that the hematocrit = 0.45.

[c]Values have been expressed per gram of kidney in order to correct for any changes that might be due to growth of the kidney during the postnatal period.

Abstracted from Horster, M., and Valtin, H. *J. Clin. Invest.* 50:779, 1971.

Lessons: (1) Since the renal extraction of PAH is so low at the early postnatal stages, there is a large difference between the effective renal plasma flow (ERPF; given by the clearance of PAH) and the true renal plasma flow (RPF), which utilizes the Fick principle (p. 89 and 104). (2) The filtration fraction (FF) must be calculated using RPF; it cannot be determined accurately using ERPF. (3) In dogs, the mature value for GFR (C_{In}) and RPF, when expressed per unit of time and per gram of kidney, is reached by approximately 3 to 3½ months of age.

PROBLEM 6-1

1. The principle of measuring the filtration rate of a single glomerulus (snGFR) by micropuncture is identical to that used for measuring the GFR of all nephrons combined. Through the inulin clearance (see pp. 50–52), one determines the amount of plasma cleared of inulin by the single glomerulus; the variables TF_{In}, $\dot{v}$, and P_{In} are analogous to U_{In}, $\dot{V}$, and P_{In} of the usual formula for inulin clearance, $U_{In} \times \dot{V}/P_{In}$. Thus,

$$snGFR = \frac{TF_{In} \times \dot{v}}{P_{In}}$$

For the micropunctures of the proximal tubules (Table 6-A):

$$snGFR = \frac{209\ mg}{100\ mL} \times \frac{11.21\ nL}{min} \div \frac{98\ mg}{100\ mL}$$

$$= \frac{209\ mg}{100\ mL} \times \frac{11.21\ nL}{min} \times \frac{100\ mL}{98\ mg}$$

$$= 23.9\ nL/min$$

For the micropunctures of the bends of loops of Henle:

$$snGFR = \frac{583\ mg}{100\ mL} \times \frac{9.14\ nL}{min} \div \frac{93\ mg}{100\ mL}$$

$$= 57.3\ nL/min$$

The difference between the two values reflects the fact that juxtamedullary nephrons have a higher snGFR than do superficial (outer cortical) nephrons (Fig. 6-2). The latter nephrons can be micropunctured at the surface of the kidney (Fig. 1-2A) whereas jux-

Table 6-A.　Results obtained on micropuncture samples.

Flow rate of tubular fluid ($\dot{v}$) (nL/min)	Concentrations in tubular fluid (TF)		Concentrations in arterial plasma (P)	
	Na^+ (mmol/L)	Inulin (mg/dL)	Na^+ (mmol/L)	Inulin (mg/dL)
Micropunctures of proximal tubules				
11.21	140	209	137	98
Micropunctures of bends of loops of Henle				
9.14	283	583	138	93

tamedullary nephrons, arising deep within the cortex and being surrounded by cortical and medullary tissue, are accessible to micropuncture only at the bend of the loop of Henle. [In this experiment flow of tubular fluid to the juxtaglomerular apparatus was blocked by oil droplets and tubuloglomerular feedback (Fig. 6-5) was therefore interrupted. Although this fact yields a value for snGFR that is somewhat higher than during punctures of the distal tubule when the feedback loop is intact, differences of the above magnitude have also been demonstrated by other techniques when the feedback was not abolished.]

2. The fraction is most easily computed by utilizing Equation 3-2. For the proximal tubules:

$$\text{Fraction of filtered water reabsorbed} = 1 - \frac{1}{\text{TF/P inulin}}$$

$$= 1 - \frac{1}{209/98}$$

$$= 1 - 0.47$$

$$= 0.53 \quad \text{or} \quad 53\%$$

This value is lower than that of approximately two-thirds (or 67%) usually cited for reabsorption in the proximal tubule because the very end of that tubule is located beneath the surface of the kidney and is therefore not available for micropuncture.

By the time that tubular fluid reached the bend of the loop of Henle, 1 − 0.16, or 84% of the filtered water had been reabsorbed (see also Answer to Problem 8-2).

One could also calculate the fractions by knowing the amount of tubular fluid flowing at the point of micropuncture (e.g., 11.21 nL per minute for the proximal tubule) and the snGFR of 23.9 nL per minute for that nephron; that is, 11.21/23.9 or 0.47 was flowing at this point so that 1 − 0.47, or 53%, must have been reabsorbed. That method, however, involves the rather cumbersome quantitative collection of tubular fluid. It is far easier to obtain the same information by simply measuring the concentration of inulin in simultaneous samples of tubular fluid and plasma.

3. The answer to this question illustrates the utility of the *clearance ratio*. The derivation of that ratio and its reduction to the expression $U_x/P_x \div U_{In}/P_{In}$ are explained in footnote b to Problem 4-1 (p. 81). That expression, which yields the fraction of the filtered load of substance X that is excreted by both kidneys, can be adapted to samples obtained by micropuncture by substituting the concentration of X and inulin in tubular fluid (TF_x and TF_{In}) for

those in urine (U_x, and U_{In}). Thus the fraction of filtered Na^+ flowing at the point of micropuncture in the proximal tubule is equal to TF/P for Na^+ divided by TF/P for inulin, i.e., 140/137 ÷ 209/98 or 0.48; the fraction of filtered Na^+ reabsorbed up to this point is therefore 0.52 or 52%. For the bend of the loop of Henle 283/138 ÷ 583/93, or 0.33, was still present, and therefore 0.67, or 67%, had been reabsorbed. Note that this experiment does not tell you where the extra 15% (67% − 52%) of Na^+ was reabsorbed. That could have occurred anywhere between the end of the proximal tubule at the surface of the kidney (belonging to a superficial nephron) and the bend of the long loop of Henle (belonging to a juxtamedullary nephron). It is probable that the extra 15% was taken up from the proximal tubule, including its pars recta, as it dips beneath the surface of the kidney (Fig. 1-2A), not from the thin descending limb of Henle.

PROBLEM 7-1

The dietary allotment of Na^+ is commonly quoted as so many grams per day without specifying whether the amount refers to sodium or to sodium chloride. The purpose of this question is two-fold: (a) to emphasize the importance of specifying whether the amount quoted refers to Na^+ or to NaCl, and (b) to give some ball-park values.

A normal intake for an adult is 6 to 15 g of salt (i.e., NaCl) per day. One millimol of NaCl is equivalent to 58 mg (see Answer to Problem 1-2); therefore:

$$\frac{58 \text{ mg}}{1 \text{ mmol}} = \frac{6{,}000 \text{ mg}}{X}$$

$$X = 103 \text{ mmol}$$

Each millimol of NaCl contains 1 mmol of Na^+ and 1 mmol of Cl^-. Thus, the normal daily intake of sodium should be quoted as follows: 6 to 15 g of NaCl (or table salt), or 103 to 259 mmol of NaCl, or 103 to 259 mmol of Na^+ (Fig. 7-7, lower left).

If the use of salt at the table is omitted, the daily intake can be reduced to 4 to 7 g of NaCl, which is 69 to 120 mmol per day or 69 to 120 mmol of Na^+ per day. If, besides eliminating salt at the table, added salt during cooking is also omitted, the daily intake is reduced to 3 to 4 g of table salt (52 to 69 mmol of NaCl or 52 to 69 mmol of Na^+ per day).

A therapeutic low-salt diet (e.g., as prescribed for congestive heart failure) contains about 2 g of table salt per day, that is, 34 mmol of NaCl or 34 mmol of Na⁺. If the intake is reduced below this value, the variety of foods that may be eaten is very limited, and the food becomes unappealing. Furthermore, the concurrent use of diuretic agents makes such severe restriction unnecessary.

Ballpark values: It is useful to memorize the following average values, realizing that the range of normality is great.

Normal daily intake: 10 g NaCl; 150 to 250 mmol Na⁺
Low-salt diet: 2 g NaCl; 35 mmol Na⁺
One level teaspoon contains: 6 g NaCl; 100 mmol Na⁺

The term *normal* is possibly more ambiguous in this context than in most, for it is likely that the intake of sodium by a healthy human is set much more by custom than by need. In fact, there is evidence that the amount of salt we eat may be harmful—at least to individuals who are susceptible to certain disorders, such as hypertension.

PROBLEM 7-2

The essence of this question has been posed twice in this book (earlier, as part of Problem 2-3) in order to express an important concept, namely, that *when calculating the amount of Na⁺ needed to raise the plasma concentration, one must base the calculation on Total Body Water,* not on the volume of plasma nor even on the volume of extracellular fluid—even though Na⁺ is predominantly an extracellular ion. Thus, in the present case, the desired increment in plasma Na⁺ concentration (20 mmol/L) must be multiplied by the total body water (31.8 L; i.e., 60% of the body weight), yielding 636 mmol of Na⁺ needed. (For a more detailed discussion, see the Answer to Problem 2-3.)

A solution of 5% NaCl contains 856 mmol of Na⁺ per liter (see Answer to Problem 1-2). Therefore, the patient should be given 743 mL of this solution; in practice, one would write an order for 750 mL of 5% saline. Because it is wise to correct imbalances slowly, most physicians might aim to err on the low side by initially prescribing 500 mL of 5% saline.

Problem 8-1. Renal handling of salt, water, and urea in varying states of water intake. The following data were obtained on a healthy medical student, under three conditions: (a) while drinking ad libitum; (b) after 12 hours of thirsting; and (c) within 90 minutes after drinking 1 liter of tap water.

	$\dot{V}$ (mL/min)	U_{In} (mg/mL)	P_{In} (mg/mL)	GFR (mL/min)	U/P inulin	Proportion of filtered water (i.e., of GFR) reabsorbed (%)
While drinking ad libitum	1.2	15.8	0.151	126	105	99.1
After 12 hours of thirsting	0.75	25.2	0.155	122	163	99.4
Within 90 minutes after drinking 1 liter water	15.0	1.23	0.154	120*	8	87.5*

*Lessons: (1) Water diuresis is due to decreased tubular reabsorption of water, not to increased filtration. Yet, even during very marked water diuresis (15 mL/min), nearly 90% of the filtered water is reabsorbed. (2) Note the typical values for U/P inulin in various states of diuresis.

Problem 8-1. (Continued)

	P_{Na} (mmol/L)	U_{Na} (mmol/L)	Filtered load of Na (mmol/min)	Urinary Na excretion (mmol/min)	Proportion of filtered Na reabsorbed (%)
While drinking ad libitum	136	128	17.1	0.154	99.1
After 12 hours of thirsting	144	192	17.6	0.144	99.2
Within 90 minutes after drinking 1 liter water	134	10.2	16.1	0.153	99.1*

*Lesson: Water diuresis decreases the fraction of filtered water that is reabsorbed (i.e., % GFR reabsorbed; see above), but not the fraction of filtered sodium that is reabsorbed. That is, by and large, sodium balance and water balance can be regulated independently of each other.

Problem 8-1. (Continued)

	U_{Osm} (mOsm/kg)	P_{Osm} (mOsm/kg)	C_{H_2O} (mL/min)	$U_{Urea\,N}$ [a] (mg/dL)	$P_{Urea\,N}$ [a] (mg/dL)	C_{Urea} (mL/min)	Proportion of filtered urea reabsorbed (%)
While drinking ad libitum	663	290	−1.54	480	12	48	62
After 12 hours of thirsting	1,000	300*	−1.75*	720	15	36	71*
Within 90 minutes after drinking 1 liter water	100	287*	+9.77*	48	10	72	40*

[a] Concentrations of urea are usually determined by measuring the amount of nitrogen in urea; hence, the expression *urea nitrogen*. The two nitrogen atoms constitute 28/60 of the urea molecule: $CO(NH_2)_2$. The clearance of urea (C_{Urea}) can be calculated without converting 'Urea N' to 'Urea', since the conversion factors for $U_{Urea\,N}$ and $P_{Urea\,N}$ cancel out.

*Lessons: (1) C_{H_2O} has a positive value when the urine is hyposmotic to plasma; it has a negative value when the urine is hyperosmotic to plasma; and C_{H_2O} is zero when the urine has the same osmolality as plasma. (2) There is an inverse relationship between the rate of urine flow and the rate at which urea is reabsorbed (see also Fig. 4-5 and Answer to Problem 4-2). (3) A change in plasma osmolality of just 1 to 3% suffices to fully inhibit secretion of ADH, or to stimulate it maximally.

Answer to Problem 8-1 continued on next page.

275

How to compute the fraction of a filtered substance that is reabsorbed. The handling of urea can serve as an example. An inulin clearance of 126 mL per minute means, of course, that 126 mL of plasma were filtered each minute. Hence, the urea contained in 126 mL of plasma was filtered each minute. The fact that the urea clearance was simultaneously 48 mL per minute means that the equivalent of 48 mL of plasma was completely cleared of urea each minute. In other words, the urea contained in 78 mL of plasma (126 − 48) must have been reabsorbed each minute. This amounts to 78/126 = 0.62, or 62%; and the equation for this intuitive fact is:

$$\text{Fraction of filtered urea that is reabsorbed} = \frac{C_{In} - C_{Urea}}{C_{In}}$$

$$= \frac{C_{In}}{C_{In}} - \frac{C_{Urea}}{C_{In}}$$

$$= 1 - \frac{C_{Urea}}{C_{In}}$$

$$= 1 - \left(\frac{U_{Urea} \times \dot{V}}{P_{Urea}} \times \frac{P_{In}}{U_{In} \times \dot{V}} \right)$$

$$= 1 - \left(\frac{U_{Urea}}{P_{Urea}} \times \frac{P_{In}}{U_{In}} \right)$$

$$\text{Fraction of filtered urea that is reabsorbed} = 1 - \left(\frac{U_{Urea}}{P_{Urea}} \div \frac{U_{In}}{P_{In}} \right) \qquad \text{(Answers 8-1)}$$

There is another intuitive way of arriving at the same mathematical expression, through knowledge of the filtered load of urea ($C_{In} \times P_{Urea}$) and of the amount of urea excreted ($\dot{V} \times U_{Urea}$). The fraction of filtered urea that is excreted, X, can be calculated through the proportionality:

$$\frac{C_{In} \times P_{Urea}}{1.00} = \frac{\dot{V} \times U_{Urea}}{X}$$

$$\therefore \text{Fraction of filtered urea that is excreted} = \frac{\dot{V} \times U_{Urea}}{C_{In} \times P_{Urea}}$$

$$= \frac{\dot{V} \times U_{Urea}}{\dfrac{U_{In} \times \dot{V}}{P_{In}} \times P_{Urea}}$$

$$= \frac{\dot{V} \times U_{Urea}}{1} \times \frac{P_{In}}{U_{In} \times \dot{V} \times P_{Urea}}$$

$$= \frac{U_{Urea}}{P_{Urea}} \times \frac{P_{In}}{U_{In}}$$

Fraction of filtered
urea that is excreted
$$= \frac{U_{Urea}}{P_{Urea}} \div \frac{U_{In}}{P_{In}}$$

∴ Fraction of filtered
urea that is reabsorbed
$$= 1 - \left(\frac{U_{Urea}}{P_{Urea}} \div \frac{U_{In}}{P_{In}} \right)$$
(Answers 8-1)

For the example cited in the table (while drinking water ad libitum):

Fraction of filtered
urea that is reabsorbed
$$= 1 - \left(\frac{480}{12} \div \frac{15.8}{0.151} \right)$$

$$= 1 - (40 \div 105)$$

$$= 1 - 0.38$$

$$= 0.62$$

Answers Equation 8-1 is useful because one can compute the fraction without needing accurate urine collections; all that is required is the simultaneous determination of urea and inulin concentrations in urine and plasma. Similarly, one can determine the fraction of the filtered load of a given substance flowing at a point of micropuncture (e.g., see Fig. 11-3) without measuring the flow rate of tubular fluid; all one needs is the concentrations of inulin and of the given substance in the micropuncture sample and in the plasma.

PROBLEM 8-2

(a) Water is probably reabsorbed in appreciable amounts from all parts of the nephron except the ascending limbs of Henle and the early distal tubules (Table 7-1, p. 132). During the formation of hyperosmotic urine, about 70% of the filtered H_2O is reabsorbed in the proximal tubules, 10 to 20% in the loops of Henle, 10 to 15% in the late distal tubules, and—perhaps surprisingly—only about 1% in the collecting ducts. These figures are based on TF/P and U/P ratios for inulin, obtained through micropuncture (Chap. 3, p. 55). They illustrate at least two important points: (1) that the vast majority of filtered H_2O is reabsorbed in the renal cortex, i.e., in the proximal and late distal tubules; and (2) that although the H_2O that is reabsorbed from the collecting ducts is critical to raising the urine osmolality from isosmolality to hyperosmolality (Fig. 8-2A), this process entails the reabsorption of relatively small amounts of H_2O.

(b) The reabsorbed H_2O must be immediately returned to the systemic circulation, lest the kidneys swell and burst. Almost all the reabsorbed H_2O enters the capillary beds, which are found in the cortex and the outer and inner medulla (Fig. 1-2B). Eventually, the reabsorbed H_2O leaves the kidneys via the renal veins. An unknown but probably minimal amount of the H_2O that is reabsorbed from tubules is returned to the systemic circulation through the renal lymphatics.

(c) The answer to this question is based on mass balance for solute: The input of solute to the kidneys must equal the output of solute from them. Solute entering the kidneys is equal to 660 mL/min $\times$ 290 mOsm/1,000 mL, or 191.4 mOsmol per minute. Solute that leaves the kidneys via the urine is equal to 1 mL/min $\times$ 700 mOsm/1,000 mL, or 0.7 mOsmol per minute. Therefore, 191.4 − 0.7, or 190.7 mOsmol per minute must leave the kidneys via the renal veins (ignoring the very small quantity that leaves through the lymphatics); since this amount will be contained in 659 mL of plasma, the osmolality of renal venous plasma will be 190.7 ÷ 659, or 0.2894 mOsm/mL, which is 289.4 mOsm/kg. This tiny difference from the osmolality of normal plasma is too small to be detected. Furthermore, the net removal of solute by the kidneys does not result in progressive dilution of plasma because there is net loss of water through other organs. Normally this net loss, known as *insensible water loss* (Table A-4), occurs from the skin (approximately 500 mL per day in an adult) and through the breath (about 400 mL per day).

Problem 9-1.   The data below were obtained on each of four patients. Normal arterial values from Appendix Table A-1: pH = 7.38 to 7.42; $[HCO_3^-]$ = 22 to 26 mmol/L; Pco_2 = 37 to 43 mm Hg.

Cause of the disturbance	pH	Pco_2 (mm Hg)	$[HCO_3^-]$ (mmol/L)	Type of disturbance
		Arterial plasma		
Prolonged vomiting	7.50	49	37	Metabolic alkalosis
Ingestion of NH_4Cl[a]	7.28	22	10	Metabolic acidosis
Anxiety-hyperventilation syndrome	7.57	24	21	Respiratory alkalosis (acute)[b]
Emphysema	7.33	68	35	Respiratory acidosis (chronic)[b]

[a]The net effect of ingesting NH_4Cl is the addition of hydrochloric acid, by the following reaction:

$2\ NH_4Cl + CO_2 \rightarrow 2\ H^+ + 2\ Cl^- + H_2O + CO(NH_2)_2$ (last compound is urea)

[b]For an explanation of the difference between acute and chronic respiratory disturbances, see Chapter 9 (under Acute and Chronic Respiratory Disturbances p.194).

PROBLEM 9-2

Respiratory acidosis. When CO_2 is retained, as during alveolar hypoventilation due to barbiturate intoxication, the Pco_2 rises. As the CO_2 is hydrated (Eq. 9-1), or hydroxylated (Eq. 9-2), H^+ and HCO_3^- are produced; this H^+ must be buffered by nonbicarbonate buffers (mainly hemoglobin, other proteins, and organic phosphates; Fig. 9-3), and in the process, HCO_3^- rises (Fig. 9-6). Since the primary disturbance is respiratory, the compensatory response will be renal, and it takes days to come to completion. The compensation involves increased reabsorption of HCO_3^- occasioned by the elevated Pco_2 (Fig. 10-2B).

Note that here is an instance in which the plasma HCO_3^- concentration rises during acidosis. Inasmuch as HCO_3^- is a major buffer, there is a reflex tendency for the neophyte in acid-base balance to predict a decrease in plasma HCO_3^- during acidosis. The key to understanding why it increases during respiratory acidosis (but decreases during metabolic acidosis) is to remember that the H^+ derived from the processing of CO_2 (Eqs. 9-1 and 9-2) cannot be buffered by the HCO_3^-/CO_2 system.

Metabolic alkalosis. A net loss of H^+ from the body, as occasioned by the loss of gastric HCl during prolonged vomiting, is accompanied by an increase in the plasma HCO_3^- concentration; this fact is evident from Equation 9-10, which will be driven to the left as HCl is withdrawn. The respiratory compensation for this primary metabolic disturbance is a diminution in alveolar ventilation due to the alkalosis and a consequent rise in P_{CO_2}.

Respiratory alkalosis. The primary event in this disturbance of H^+ balance is alveolar hyperventilation and a decline in P_{CO_2}. This change will drive the reactions shown at the top of Figure 9-6 to the left and the plasma HCO_3^- concentration therefore will decrease. The compensatory response by the kidneys—which will begin within hours of the onset of the disturbance but will take days to take full effect—is to decrease the reabsorption of HCO_3^- as a consequence of the lowered P_{CO_2} (Fig. 10-2B).

Arterial pH in mixed disturbances. The reason for this question is to point out that the plasma pH can be predicted only if the two components shift the pH in the same direction. Thus, a mixture of two acidoses will certainly result in an acidotic pH and two alkaloses in an alkalotic pH. When, however, the two components shift the pH in opposite directions (i.e., a mixture of an acidosis and an alkalosis), the plasma pH might be alkalotic, normal, or acidotic, depending on which component predominates.

PROBLEM 10-1

The Henderson-Hasselbalch equation, being an expression of the ionization or dissociation properties of acids and bases, can be utilized to solve this problem.

$$pH = pK + \log \frac{[\text{base; i.e., } H^+ \text{ acceptor}]}{[\text{acid; i.e., } H^+ \text{ donor}]}$$

For phenobarbital,

$$pH = 7.2 + \log \frac{[\text{Ionized form}]}{[\text{Nonionized form}]}$$

Plasma, pH 7.3

$$7.3 = 7.2 + \log \frac{[\text{Ionized form}]}{[\text{Nonionized form}]}$$

$$0.1 = \log \frac{[\text{Ionized form}]}{[\text{Nonionized form}]}$$

$$\therefore \frac{[\text{Ionized form}]}{[\text{Nonionized form}]} = \frac{1.26}{1}$$

The concentration of total unbound phenobarbital is 6.0 mg/dL plasma; $\frac{1.26}{2.26}$ of this total exists in the ionized form, and $\frac{1.00}{2.26}$ of the total exists in the nonionized form. Hence:

[Ionized form] $= \frac{1.26}{2.26} \times 6.0 = 3.3$ mg/dL

[Nonionized form] $= \frac{1.00}{2.26} \times 6.0 = 2.7$ mg/dL

Plasma, pH 7.7

$7.7 = 7.2 + \log \frac{[\text{Ionized form}]}{[\text{Nonionized form}]}$

$0.5 = \log \frac{[\text{Ionized form}]}{[\text{Nonionized form}]}$

$\therefore \frac{[\text{Ionized form}]}{[\text{Nonionized form}]} = \frac{3.16}{1}$

$\therefore$ [Ionized form] $= \frac{3.16}{4.16} \times 6.0 = 4.6$ mg/dL plasma

[Nonionized form] $= \frac{1.00}{4.16} \times 6.0 = 1.4$ mg/dL plasma

Urine, pH 5.2

$5.2 = 7.2 + \log \frac{[\text{Ionized form}]}{[\text{Nonionized form}]}$

$-2.0 = \log \frac{[\text{Ionized form}]}{[\text{Nonionized form}]}$

$2.0 = \log \frac{[\text{Nonionized form}]}{[\text{Ionized form}]}$

$\therefore \frac{[\text{Nonionized form}]}{[\text{Ionized form}]} = \frac{100}{1}$

i.e., when the reaction of the urine is acid, most of the phenobarbital exists in the nonionized form, which can diffuse across the membranes of tubular cells and hence can be passively reabsorbed.

Urine, pH 8.2

$8.2 = 7.2 + \log \frac{[\text{Ionized form}]}{[\text{Nonionized form}]}$

$$1.0 = \log \frac{[\text{Ionized form}]}{[\text{Nonionized form}]}$$

$$\therefore \frac{[\text{Ionized form}]}{[\text{Nonionized form}]} = \frac{10}{1}$$

i.e., when the reaction of the urine is alkaline, most of the phenobarbital exists in the ionized form, to which renal tubular cells are relatively impermeable. Hence, alkalinization of the urine can markedly diminish the reabsorption and thus enhance the renal excretion of a weak acid, such as phenobarbital.

	Total unbound phenobarbital in plasma (mg/dL)	Ratio of unbound phenobarbital: [Ionized]/[Nonionized]	Plasma concentration of unbound phenobarbital Ionized	Nonionized (mg/dL)
Plasma, pH 7.3	6.0	$\frac{1.26}{1}$	3.3	2.7
Plasma, pH 7.7	6.0	$\frac{3.16}{1}$	4.6	1.4
Urine, pH 5.2	—	$\frac{1}{100}$	—	—
Urine, pH 8.2	—	$\frac{10}{1}$	—	—

Note that alkalinization may have a further advantage: Giving $NaHCO_3$ alkalinizes not only the urine but also the plasma (Eq. 9-8). This change reduces the concentration of the nonionized form in plasma. Since this is the form that passes most readily across cell membranes, including those of the brain, alkalinization probably reduces the concentration of phenobarbital in cerebral cells, and thereby hastens recovery from coma.

The beneficial effects of increased urine flow and alkalinization during experimental phenobarbital intoxication were presented in the following paper: Waddell, W. J., and Butler, T. C. The distribution and excretion of phenobarbital. *J. Clin. Invest.* 36:1217, 1957. Two clinical examples, in which the principle of nonionic diffusion was applied to salicylate therapy and intoxication, appear in: Levy, G., et al. *N. Engl. J. Med.* 293:323, 1975; and Hill, J. B. *N. Engl. J. Med.* 288:1110, 1973.

PROBLEM 10-2

It is clear from Figure 10-A that, because the NH_3/NH_4^+ buffer system has a pK of 9.2 (Table A-3), NH_4Cl cannot be titrated within the pH range of urine. Recall that titratable acid (T.A.) is defined as the amount of strong base that must be added to acid urine in order to return the pH of that urine to 7.40. If urine is thus titrated from a minimal pH of 4.4 (the shaded area in Fig. 10-A), very little NH_4^+ will be converted to NH_3—a consequence of the fact that a buffer is most effective within ± 1 pH unit of its pK.

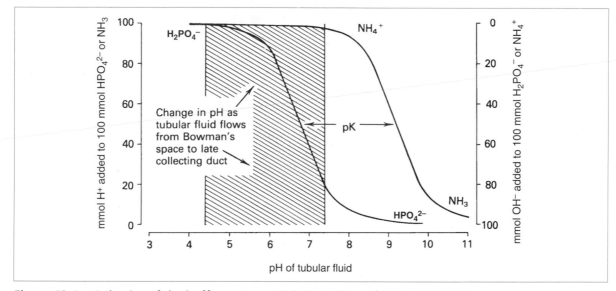

Figure 10-A. Behavior of the buffer systems, $HPO_4^{2-}/H_2PO_4^-$ and NH_3/NH_4^+, in tubular fluid. Note that, as OH^- is added to acid urine (ordinate on right), most of the phosphate is converted to the HPO_4^{2-} form, whereas the vast majority of the ammonia system remains in the NH_4^+ form. In other words, NH_4^+ salts cannot be titrated appreciably from an acid pH to 7.4, and therefore they are not titratable acids.

PROBLEM 10-3

Ordinarily, virtually all of the filtered HCO_3^- is reabsorbed (Table 1-1). Suppose that the urinary concentration of HCO_3^- is 1.0 mmol/L (again, from Table 1-1, a reasonable value, given the numbers for H_2O and HCO_3^- excreted). Then, applying this value and a P_{CO_2} for urine of 40 mm Hg to the Henderson-Hasselbalch equation (Eq. 9-8) yields a urinary pH of approximately 6; and if the urinary HCO_3^- concentration is reduced to 0.1 mmol/L, the urinary pH will be approximately 5. These calculations show that the urinary pH could be lowered almost to the minimal value merely by reabsorbing virtually all of the filtered HCO_3^-. Even though that happens normally (note that no HCO_3^- is listed for the composition of urine in the Answer to Problem 11-1), the situation is theoretical because titratable acids (mainly NaH_2PO_4) are formed simultaneously.

PROBLEM 11-1

These questions were asked because it is a rather remarkable (though understandable) fact that students can be very sophisticated about renal function, and yet not know the composition of normal urine!

The variation in the normal values is so great that it is almost meaningless to give averages; hence only the ranges are given in Table 11-A. When an individual is in balance (the steady state),

Table 11-A. Composition of the urine of a normal adult human whose diet includes protein.

pH	5.0 to 7.0
Osmolality	500 to 800 mOsm/kg H_2O
Na^+	50 to 130 mmol/L
K^+	20 to 70 mmol/L
NH_4^+	30 to 50 mmol/L
Ca^{2+}	2.5 to 6.0 mmol/L
Mg^{2+}	1 to 9 mmol/L
Cl^-	50 to 130 mmol/L
$H_2PO_4^-$	20 to 40 mmol/L
SO_4^{2-}	15 to 23 mmol/L
Organic acids	10 to 25 mmol/L*
Urea	200 to 400 mmol/L
Creatinine	6 to 20 mmol/L

*At an acid urinary pH of 6 or lower, nearly all of the urinary inorganic phosphate exists in the monovalent form (Fig. 10-A). Urinary organic acids (e.g., lactic, uric, citric, pyruvic acids) have different valences; the molar concentration listed assumes an average valence of minus two.

the daily output of various substances (both renal and extrarenal) equals the daily production of those substances (both exogenous and endogenous). For a solute such as Na^+, which normally is excreted almost exclusively by the kidneys, the urinary *concentration* therefore depends not only on the intake of Na^+ but also on the intake of water. It is because the intakes of both solute and solvent can vary greatly from day to day that normal urinary concentrations have such wide ranges.

Note that healthy individuals whose diet contains proteins (i.e., a diet that yields fixed acids) excrete urine with an acid pH. Note also that they normally excrete urine which is hyperosmotic to plasma.

Figure 11-A. Solute concentrations of normal urine. Note that the concentrations have been expressed as mmol per liter. Since urine contains more divalent anions than cations, the column for the anions is lower than that for cations. If the concentrations were given as milliequivalents per liter, the two columns would of course be of equal height.

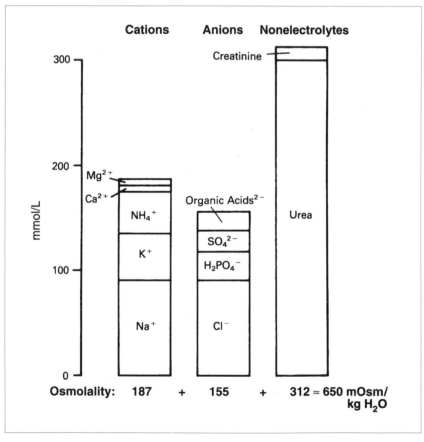

The major solutes that contribute to the osmolality of normal urine are depicted in Figure 11-A. Quantitatively, the most important electrolytes are Na^+, K^+, NH_4^+, and Cl^- (HCO_3^- is normally 'absent'). Urea is the most abundant nonelectrolyte, and it ordinarily constitutes 40 to 50% of the total osmolality. (The reason for the inequality of the columns for cations and anions is given in the legend to Figure 11-A.)

Appendix:
Normal Values

Table A-1. Normal plasma, serum, or blood concentrations in adult humans.

Substance	Range	Average value usually quoted in treating patients	Comments
Bicarbonate (see also Total CO_2)	22 to 26 mmol/L 23 to 29 mmol/L	24 mmol/L	Arterial blood Venous plasma. Measured as 'Total CO_2', which includes HCO_3^-, dissolved CO_2, and H_2CO_3. HCO_3^- constitutes more than 90% of 'Total Venous CO_2', which thus approximates the concentration of HCO_3^-
Calcium	2.1 to 2.6 mmol/L	10 mg/dL (2.4 mmol/L)	Approximately 50% is bound to serum proteins
Carbon dioxide (see Total CO_2)			
Chloride	98 to 106 mmol/L	100 mmol/L	
Creatinine	0.5 to 1.5 mg/dL (44 to 133 μmol/L)	1.2 mg/dL (106 μmol/L)	
Glucose	70 to 100 mg/dL (3.9 to 5.6 mmol/L)	80 mg/dL (4.4 mmol/L)	Determined in the fasting state; so-called *fasting blood sugar* (FBS)
Hematocrit (Hct)	40% to 50%	45%	Also frequently called *packed cell volume* (PCV)
Hydrogen ion [H^+] (arterial)	38 to 43 nmol/L	40 nmol/L	Note small units: nanomol (10^{-9} M)
Lactic acid	0.6 to 1.8 mmol/L	—	
Lipids			
Cholesterol	140 to 250 mg/dL (3.6 to 6.5 mmol/L)	—	
Triglycerides	50 to 150 mg/dL (0.6 to 1.8 mmol/L)	—	

Analyte	Normal range	Representative value	Comments
Magnesium	0.6 to 1.1 mmol/L	0.9 mmol/L	
Osmolality	280 to 295 mOsmol/kg	287 mOsmol/kg	Expressed as milliosmols per kg H_2O. For brevity, we use mOsm/kg in this text
Oxygen saturation (arterial)	96% to 100%	—	
P_{CO_2} (arterial)	37 to 43 mm Hg	40 mm Hg	
P_{O_2} (arterial)	75 to 100 mm Hg	—	While breathing room air. Value varies with age
pH (arterial)	7.38 to 7.42	7.40	
Phosphate	0.9 to 1.5 mmol/L	3.5 mg/dL (1.2 mmol/L)	Measured as phosphorus, inorganic (see Problem 4-1)
Phosphorus, inorganic	0.9 to 1.5 mmol/L	3.5 mg/dL (1.2 mmol/L)	
Potassium	3.5 to 5.5 mmol/L	4.5 mmol/L	
Protein (total)	6 to 8 g/dL	7 g/dL	
Albumin	4 to 5 g/dL	—	
Globulin	2 to 3 g/dL	—	
Sodium	136 to 146 mmol/L	140 mmol/L	
Total CO_2 (venous)	23 to 29 mmol/L	26 mmol/L	See Comment, under Bicarbonate
Urea nitrogen (BUN)	9 to 18 mg/dL (3.2 to 6.4 mmol/L)	12 mg/dL (5 mmol/L)	Measured as the nitrogen contained in urea. Since urea diffuses freely into cells, values for serum, plasma, or whole blood are nearly identical (BUN = blood urea nitrogen). Average value varies with diet; BUN of 18 mg/dL may be normal or may reflect considerable reduction in renal function, depending on intake of protein
Uric acid	3 to 7 mg/dL (0.2 to 0.4 mmol/L)	5 mg/dL (0.3 mmol/L)	

Table A-2.
Normal urinary concentrations in adult humans whose diet includes protein. See also Figure 11-A (under Answers)
Urinary *concentration* depends not only on the rate of excretion of a particular solute but also on the amount of the solvent (i.e., water, or urine) that is excreted. Since the excretion of both solute and solvent can vary greatly depending on their intake, the normal concentrations have wide ranges, and a single average value is almost meaningless. Therefore, the normal rate of urinary *excretion* of a particular substance (e.g., in mmol per day) is normally 1 to 1.5 liters per day. Therefore, the normal rate of urinary *excretion* of a particular substance (e.g., in mmol per day) can be estimated quickly as ranging from the concentration of the substance listed below to about 1.5 times that concentration.

Substance	Range	Comments
Ammonium	30 to 50 mmol/L	Can fall to zero if much bicarbonate is given
Calcium	2.5 to 6 mmol/L (5 to 12 mq/L)	Normal excretion is 150 mg (4 mmol) per day or less For exchangeability of mmol and mq, see last part of Answer to Problem 1-2
Chloride	30 to 130 mmol/L	Can fall to zero in persons ingesting no chloride
Creatinine	6 to 20 mmol/L	Daily production of creatinine depends primarily on skeletal muscle mass. Since this mass varies greatly among individuals, so does the normal urinary excretion of creatinine: children, <8 mg; women, 9 to 27 mg; men, 16 to 32 mg per kg body weight per day
Glucose	~0	About 15 to 130 mg of glucose may be excreted per day by a healthy adult. This amount, however, is not detected by routine tests, which are sensitive to about 400 mg of glucose per liter of urine
Magnesium	1 to 9 mmol/L	
Organic acids (total)	10 to 25 mmol/L	
Citric acid	0.5 to 7 mmol/L	The sum of these three acids does not equal the total because there are other organic acids in urine
Lactic acid	1 to 7 mmol/L	
Uric acid	0.5 to 6 mmol/L	

Osmolality	300 to 800 mOsm/kg	A random sample is likely to have an osmolality in the range indicated. However, a healthy person may show a urine osmolality of <100 mOsm/kg after drinking large amounts of fluid, or up to 1,400 mOsm/kg if dehydrated
pH	5.0 to 7.0	
Phosphate	20 to 40 mmol/L	Measured as phosphorus. Excretion rates are usually expressed in grams per day, and the average normal value is 1 g per day
Potassium	20 to 70 mmol/L	
Protein	~0	Healthy persons excrete small amounts of protein, the normal value being <150 mg per day. This amount sometimes shows up as a 'trace' on routine tests, which are sensitive to about 60 mg per liter
Sodium	30 to 130 mmol/L	Can fall to zero in persons ingesting no sodium
Specific gravity	1.010 to 1.022	See comment regarding osmolality. A healthy person may have a range of urine specific gravity from about 1.001 to 1.030 or slightly higher. In health, urine specific gravity can provide a rough estimate of urine osmolality: 1.010 ~ 300 mOsm/kg; 1.020 ~ 700 mOsm/kg; 1.030 ~ 1,100 mOsm/kg
Sulfate	15 to 23 mmol/L	
Titratable acid (T.A.)	10 to 40 mmol/L	Usually expressed as daily excretion, for which the normal range is 10 to 30 mmol per day
Urea	10 to 20 g/L (165 to 330 mmol/L)	Usually measured as urea nitrogen, for which the range would be about 5 to 10 g per liter

Table A-3. Some useful miscellaneous normal values for adult humans.

	Average value	Comments
Anion gap	12 meq/L	Anion gap = $[Na^+] - ([Cl^-] + [HCO_3^-])$ Normal range: 8 to 16 meq/L
Body surface area	1.73 meter^2	
Body weight	70 kg	
Cerebrospinal fluid (CSF)		
pH	7.30 to 7.38	
$[HCO_3^-]$	22 to 24 mmol/L	
P_{CO_2}	45 to 50 mm Hg	For application of Henderson-Hasselbalch equation to CSF
pK'	6.13	Prime denotes apparent pK for the bicarbonate buffer system
Chloride		
Total body	2,400 mmol	Refers to the total amount of Cl^- in the body
Exchangeable	2,000 mmol	Refers to the amount of Cl^- that is readily miscible with ingested or administered Cl^-
Fluid volumes		
Total body water (TBW)	60% of body weight	
Intracellular water (ICW)	40% of body weight	Often abbreviated as ICF (intracellular fluid)
Extracellular water (ECW)	20% of body weight	Often abbreviated as ECF (extracellular fluid)
Plasma	4% of body weight	Not calculated separately in most clinical problems but usually
Interstitial fluid	16% of body weight	considered as the single space of extracellular fluid
Glomerular filtration rate (GFR)	125 mL/min (180 L/day)	For ranges in women and men, see p. 266

Selected list of some common physiological compounds

pK

Acetic acid	4.7	
Acetoacetic acid	3.8	
Ammonia	9.2	
3-hydroxybutyric acid	4.8	At 25°C
Creatinine	5.0	Also called β-hydroxy butyric acid
Deoxygenated hemoglobin	7.9	
Lactic acid	3.9	
Oxygenated hemoglobin	6.7	
Phosphoric acid	6.8	Refers to $HPO_4^{2-}:H_2PO_4^-$; phosphoric acid has two other pKs

Potassium

Total body	3,500 mmol	Refers to the total amount of K^+ in the body
Exchangeable	3,000 mmol	Refers to the amount of K^+ that is readily miscible with ingested or administered K^+

Sodium

Total body	5,000 mmol	Refers to the total amount of Na^+ in the body
Exchangeable	3,000 mmol	Much of the nonexchangeable Na^+ is in bone

Water content of tissues

Bone	25%
Fat	20%
Muscle	80%
Plasma	93%

Table A-4. Average daily balance (amount per day) for water and some major solutes. Data for an adult human under normal environmental conditions who is eating a normal diet containing protein.

Substance	Input		Output		
	Dietary	Metabolic production	Urinary	Fecal	Insensible
Water (mL)					
As fluid	1,200	300	1,500	100	900
In food	1,000	—	—	—	—
Sodium (mmol)	155	—	150	2.5	2.5
Potassium (mmol)	75	—	70	5	—
Chloride (mmol)	155	—	150	2.5	2.5
Nitrogen (g)	10	—	9	1	—
Acid (mmol)					
Nonvolatile	—	50	50	—	—
Volatile	—	14,000	—	—	14,000

Reproduced from Valtin, H. *Renal Dysfunction: Mechanisms Involved in Fluid and Solute Imbalance.* Boston: Little, Brown, 1979.

Table A-5.   Some useful atomic and molecular weights.

Substance	Symbol	Atomic or molecular weight*
Albumin	—	60,000
Aluminum	Al	27
Bromine	Br	80
Calcium	Ca	40
Carbon	C	12
Chlorine	Cl	35
Chromium	Cr	52
Citric acid	—	192
Copper	Cu	64
Creatinine	—	113
Ethanol	—	46
Glucose	—	180
Hydrogen	H	1
Inulin	—	$\simeq 5,000$
Iodine	I	127
Iron	Fe	56
Lactic acid	—	90
Lithium	Li	7
Magnesium	Mg	24
Manganese	Mn	55
Mannitol	—	182
Mercury	Hg	201
Nitrogen	N	14
Oxygen	O	16
p-Aminohippuric acid (PAH)	—	194
Phosphorus	P	31
Potassium	K	39
Sodium	Na	23
Sulfur	S	32
Urea	—	60
Uric acid	—	158

*Rounded off at least to nearest unit.
Reproduced from Valtin, H. *Renal Dysfunction: Mechanisms Involved in Fluid and Solute Imbalance.* Boston: Little, Brown, 1979.

Index

■   ■   ■   ■   ■

formation of hydrogen and
  bicarbonate from, 184
hydration of, 184, 190
hydroxylation of, 184, 190
partial pressure of
  acid-base status and, 280
  arterial, bicarbonate reabsorption
    and, 212
  arterial value for, normal, 190, 280
  bicarbonate buffer system and,
    186–188
production of, rate of, 184
transport of, in blood, 190–192
as volatile acid, 184, 189–191
Carbonic acid, 186–187
Carbonic anhydrase, 184, 190, 211
Carriers, membrane, 26. *See also*
  Transport, membrane
Catecholamines, 107, 109
  in renin release, 138
Cell(s)
  fluid in. *See* Intracellular fluid
  membranes of. *See* Membrane(s),
    cellular
Cerebrospinal fluid, normal values for,
  294
Channels, membrane, 26. *See also*
  Transport, membrane
Chemical gradient. *See also* Transport
  glucose reabsorption against, 62,
    69–71
  urea transport and, 74, 122
CHIP28. *See* Aquaporins
Chloride
  blood concentration of, 290
  excretion of, 10
    normal, 296
  filtered load of, 10
  in fluid compartments, 23
  intake of, normal, 296
  normal values for, exchangeable and
    total body, 294
  plasma concentration of, bicarbonate
    reabsorption and, 213, 215
  reabsorption of, 62
    active, 126
    in collecting ducts, 130, 131, 132,
      133
    in distal tubules, 120, 131, 132, 133
    in loops of Henle, 127, 128, 129
    passive, 120, 123
    in proximal tubules, 118–126
  renal turnover of, daily, 10
  urine concentration of, 285–286, 292
Chloride-bicarbonate exchanger, 226
Circulation. *See* Blood flow, renal;
  Plasma flow, renal

Clearance
  creatinine, 54. *See also* Creatinine,
    clearance of
  free-water, 176–177
  as general concept, 54
  inulin. *See* Inulin clearance
  of PAH. *See* Para-aminohippuric acid
  ratio. *See* Clearance ratio
  of urea in varying diuretic states,
    276
  of water in varying diuretic states,
    276
  whole body, 54
Clearance ratio, 56, 79, 283
  in calculation of fractional
    reabsorption of filtered sodium,
    272–273
  in calculation of fractional
    reabsorption of phosphate, 268
Collecting ducts, 4, 7, 9, 130–133, 225
  antidiuretic hormone affecting water
    permeability of, 132, 152–156
  reabsorption in
    of chloride, 131–132
    of potassium, 243, 246
    of sodium, 130–131, 133–134
    of urea, 74, 76, 169–170
    of water, 74, 279
  secretion in
    of ammonia, 226, 228
    of hydrogen ion, 216
    of potassium, 240, 242
    sodium balance and, 139
Colligative properties, 260
Colloid osmotic pressure, *see* Oncotic
  pressure
Colloids, 42
Competitive inhibition of active
  transport, 69
Corpuscle, renal. *See also* Bowman's
  capsule
Cortex, renal, 2
  aerobic metabolism in, 106
  blood flow in, 97–98
  structures of, 4, 5
  water reabsorption in, 279
Cortical nephron, outer
  anatomy of, 4, 5
  arterioles of, 96
  functions of, 4
  single nephron glomerular filtration
    rate of, 96–97
Corticomedullary interstitial osmotic
  gradient, 159–163, 166
  washout of, 166
Corticosteroids. *See* Adrenal
  corticosteroids